10-3-66

Use of Digital Computers
for Engineering Applications

Charles M. Haberman

Associate Professor of Engineering
California State College at Los Angeles

CHARLES E. MERRILL BOOKS, INC., COLUMBUS, OHIO

To my nephews and to my niece:

David, Gregory, and *Linda Giese*

C. M. H.

Library of Congress Catalog Card Number: 66-14399

Preface

Because of the ever-growing use of digital and analog computers for solving complex problems that arise in the engineering profession, it is important that the engineering student should learn how to use these computers. Not only should he learn their usage, but he should also learn the changes in problem concept and the mathematical techniques required when these devices are used for problem solution. This book is specially written for engineers with a problem-oriented approach, and for this reason it differs in many respects from similar presentations. This text covers both digital computer programming and elementary numerical techniques, but it does this with an engineering approach and attitude. Its major emphasis is on how engineering problems are set up for solution by the use of a digital computer. This text illustrates these procedures by solving several engineering problems of different elementary types. Included in most engineering examples is a problem description, formulation of the equations that are used, discussion of the numerical solution technique that is chosen, a calculation sequence, and a computer program.

Because of its common usage and because it can be used on many different types of digital computers, the Fortran programming language is used in this text. The first chapter discusses how to use the more elementary Fortran instructions. Chapter 2 uses these elementary Fortran instructions to solve several engineering problems. This is purposely done to allow a student to program engineering problems, check out the program, and solve the problem on a digital computer at a very early stage in the course. The third chapter discusses the use of other types of Fortran instructions, and the fourth chapter uses these instructions to solve more involved types of engineering problems and for numerical-technique subprograms that utilize tabulated data.

This text also covers the use of elementary numerical solution techniques. It introduces them and shows their usefulness by a selection of problems that require their usage in order to obtain a solution. This is often followed by a discussion of better numerical techniques that may be used to solve the previously mentioned problem. Because of the space that it would otherwise take, only elementary numerical methods and methods that an engineer might program are covered in detail. Though this text has many illustrative examples which show how various numerical methods are applied, this text is not a reference for numerical solution techniques. Because it shows their usefulness, this text should help to generate a further interest in numerical methods, and it is hoped that the reader will be stimulated enough to later take a rigorous course on this subject. Because of the necessity of their usage when solving problems on a digital computer, numerical methods should be taught simultaneously with digital computer programming. The approach, however, should be different in a course for engineers than in a course for mathematicians. For this reason and in order to allow this text to be covered in a one-semester course, methods that an engineer would seldom program in professional practice (e.g., matrix inverse, roots of a polynomial equation, curve-fitting and smoothing tabulated data, etc.) are not covered in rigorous fashion. The more advanced numerical methods, whose details may be found in books on numerical analysis or learned in another course, are usually programmed in professional practice as subprograms which can be used by engineers in their programs when they encounter problems that require these methods. Also many of the better numerical techniques are quite sophisticated mathematically and require a good background to be completely understood. The engineer should, however, be educated to know the applicability, limitations, and range of usefulness and validity of all numerical techniques that he may utilize, even those he may never program. An attempt to do this on a minor scale is made whenever a numerical technique is discussed in this text.

The author feels that a textbook of this type (i.e., one that covers the elements of Fortran programming and numerical techniques with an emphasis on how they are used to solve various engineering problems) is worthwhile; because, in professional practice, the author had been exposed to the difficulties that engineers encounter when they try to apply the results of a brief course in Fortran programming to the solutions of actual, large engineering problems. For this reason, the author feels that it is important to emphasize engineering aspects and to include elementary numerical methods when teaching digital computer applications to engineering students. This text is written for the level of junior and senior engineering students. If the reader has had a previous course in Fortran, the first and third chapters may be omitted or be used for reference or review purposes. Many colleges introduce digital computer programming to freshman or sophomore engineering students. There are many versions of Fortran, and this textbook makes reference to the Fortran I and II versions for the IBM 1620 computer. It does not attempt to be a reference for all of the rules for these two versions because the details for these rules can be found elsewhere and because the student will probably use another version in professional practice. Because of the level of this course, this text uses elementary engineering problems that are encountered by junior and senior engineering students, so that they will be familiar with their details when they are discussed. Various types of engineering problems (e.g., electrical circuits, vibration, heat transfer, fluid mechanics, etc.) requiring various solution techniques (e.g., trial and error, solution of an ordinary or partial differential equation, selection of optimum design parameters, etc.) are used as examples. Usually a brief review of the physical background is included.

The last chapter of this text contains brief introductions to both digital machine-language programming and to analog computers, in order to give the reader some idea of how these two types of computers work. To aid the student's learning and so that details may be minimized, the digital machine-language is a typical language and is simpler than most actual languages. The author feels that it is easier to introduce a student to a simple, typical machine-language than an actual one. Also, computer installations have a habit of replacing their digital computers every several years with newer and larger ones that very often have different machine-languages. The brief treatment of analog computers covers several types of analog computers, rather than dealing with just the D.C. electronic differential analyzer, as many textbooks do. This allows a broadening of the student's outlook on analog computers. This very brief treatment of analog computers should be adequate enough to show the reader the difference in concepts applied when analog computers are used to solve problems, as compared to digital computers.

The author wishes to express his gratitude for helpful suggestions from Professors C. L. Sayre of Maryland and G. B. Bouse of California State College at Los Angeles and to Mrs. Alrae Tingley, Mrs. Yolanda Flowers, and Miss Barbara Lockhart who typed the manuscript. He also wishes to thank E. M. Manderfield, Professor C. V. Chelapati, and T. C. Cantwell for proofreading portions of the galley proofs. He especially wishes to express his appreciation to the students he taught in the first four sessions of this computer applications course for their interest, for their suggestions, and for providing the means for presenting and testing this course. The author hopes that the reader will find this text useful and that it achieves the objectives stated herein.

California State College at Los Angeles   C. M. Haberman
March, 1966

Table of Contents

CHAPTER 1

Elementary Fortran Instructions

1.1 Introduction

A digital computer solves problems by executing a series of previously designated *instructions*. The series of instructions (that are to be executed) is called a *program*. The actual instructions that a computer executes must be expressed in a form or language that the computer can understand, and for this reason they are called *machine-language instructions*. Each machine-language instruction is a number (usually consisting of 7 to 10 digits), and it performs only one elementary operation, such as an addition or the shifting of a number. Chapter 5 discusses the details of a typical machine language for a digital computer.

The trend today is to program engineering problems, not in the computer's machine language, but by using a system whose language is oriented to that of the user. **Fortran** is a *programming language* that is very similar to the mathematical language of the scientist and engineer. Two other very popular, user-oriented programming languages are *Algol* and *Cobol*. The computer must translate a Fortran program into its own machine-language before it can perform or execute the various steps of the program. That is, the computer itself first converts a Fortran program into a machine-language program, and then executes the latter program in order to solve the particular problem. In this way, the user does not have to be concerned with the basic language of the computer or its details of operation. The original Fortran program is called a *source program*. The translated, machine-language program is called an *object program*. A Fortran instruction consists of symbols, numbers, etc., that are easily understood by the engineer (instead of being a pure number), and it usually performs several computer operations. Thus, a Fortran program is shorter and easier to interpret than a machine-language program.

The advantages of using Fortran, instead of the computer language itself, are many. Problem solutions can be organized and set up on a digital computer faster and with less effort. Since Fortran is easier to learn than machine language, the training time is shorter and more people can be taught how to solve problems on digital computers. It is also easier to make engineering changes in a Fortran-language program. The Fortran language can be used on many different types of digital computers, which means that a problem that is programmed in Fortran may be solved on various types of computers. This is especially useful when a company purchases a new type of digital computer.

Before we can write a digital computer program, we must first learn the rules for using a programming language. This chapter contains an introduction to the Fortran language and discusses the rules for using the more elementary instructions. Chapter 3 discusses the use of other types of Fortran instructions. There are several versions of Fortran (over 15), so some changes may be necessary when a Fortran program written for one type of computer is used on a different type of computer. The versions vary with the type of digital computer and from installation to installation. This text uses the *Fortran II version* that is designed for the *IBM 1620 computer*. Deviations to be made when *Fortran I* is used for the IBM 1620 computer are also mentioned in this text. This text does not attempt to be a reference for all of the rules for these two versions because the details for these rules can be found elsewhere and because these versions can undergo modification. This also makes it easier for the beginner to learn Fortran programming. The details and a complete set of rules for a specific Fortran version can be found in pamphlets available at the computer center or supplied by the computer manufacturer. The reader will probably use a Fortran version for a larger computer than the IBM 1620 (and therefore use a slightly different set of rules) when he enters professional practice.

1.2 *Example of a Fortran Program*

Figure 1-1 shows a Fortran program for solving a very elementary problem. The beginning reader may not understand all of the details of this program until he goes further in this chapter, but he will get an idea of what a Fortran program looks like. As stated before, a Fortran program consists of a series of statements or instructions that are written in the Fortran language.

C FOR COMMENT

STATEMENT NUMBER (1–5)	Cont. (6)	FORTRAN STATEMENT (7 … 40)
1		READ 4, A, B
4		FØRMAT (F3.2, F5.1)
		C = 6.541 * B
		D = A + B
		E = C - A
		F = E / D
		G = F ** 3.58
		PRINT 5, A, B, C, D, E, F, G
5		FØRMAT (7F10.4)
		GØ TØ 1
		END

Fig. 1-1

This program calculates the terms *C*, *D*, *E*, *F*, and *G* from the equations

$$C = 6.541B \qquad F = E/D$$
$$D = A + B \qquad G = F^{3.58}$$
$$E = C - A$$

for specific values of the algebraic quantities *A* and *B*. The reader can easily recognize where these equations are used in the Fortran program given by Fig. 1-1.

Figure 1-1 shows the Fortran program as it would appear if it were written on a standard Fortran programming sheet. These programming sheets are usually available at the computer installation. Columns 2 to 5 are used for writing the *statement number*, which is a means of identifying a particular Fortran statement. Only statements that are referred to by another Fortran statement need to have a statement number. In Fig. 1-1, the statement numbers (i.e., 1, 4, and 5) were put in column 5, but they could also be put in column 2, 3, or 4. That is, a statement number may be placed anywhere in columns 2 to 5.

The *Fortran statement* itself is written in columns 7 to 72. Thus, a Fortran statement can contain 66 symbolic characters on one line. A Fortran statement is unaffected if it contains blank spaces (i.e., blanks anywhere in columns 7 to 72). Thus, the individual characters in a Fortran statement may be spaced as desired in order to improve the readability of that statement. This was done in the GO TO 1 statement in Fig. 1-1. GOTO1 has the same meaning. Also, the statement does not have to start in column 7. If more than 66 symbolic characters are required for a Fortran statement, then the statement can be continued on the following line of the Fortran programming sheet if a numerical digit (i.e., 1 to 9) is placed in column 6 of the *continued statement*. That is, if a digit appears in column 6, then the contents of that line are a continuation of the statement on the previous line. However, Fortran I does not permit this continuation feature (i.e., each statement must be written on one line). A Fortran II statement must be written within a maximum of five lines, where the first line must contain a blank or zero in column 6, and each of the four continuation lines must contain a numerical digit (i.e., 1 to 9) in column 6. The rules for writing Fortran statements themselves are covered in the rest of this chapter.

The instructions that are written on a Fortran programming sheet are then punched on *Hollerith cards*, which are also called *IBM cards*. One line of information on a Fortran programming sheet is punched on an IBM card, and this information must be punched within the first 72 columns of the IBM card. Columns 73 to 80 on an IBM card are usually used for identification purposes. Figures 1-2 and 1-3 show the first and third Fortran instructions of the Fig. 1-1 program punched on IBM cards. The IBM cards containing the Fortran instructions are called the *source program deck*. The source program deck is loaded into the digital computer, and the Fortran instructions are translated into machine-language instructions. The computer then executes the machine-language instructions.

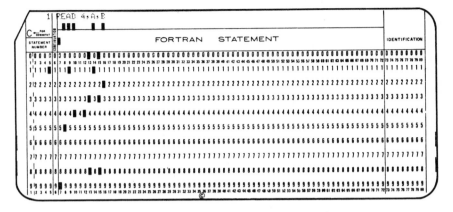

Fig. 1-2

The Fortran program of Fig. 1-1 requires that the numerical values of the quantities A and B be supplied. This is done by punching these numerical values on an IBM card that is placed behind the source program deck. The Fortran statement numbered 1 reads these values from the IBM

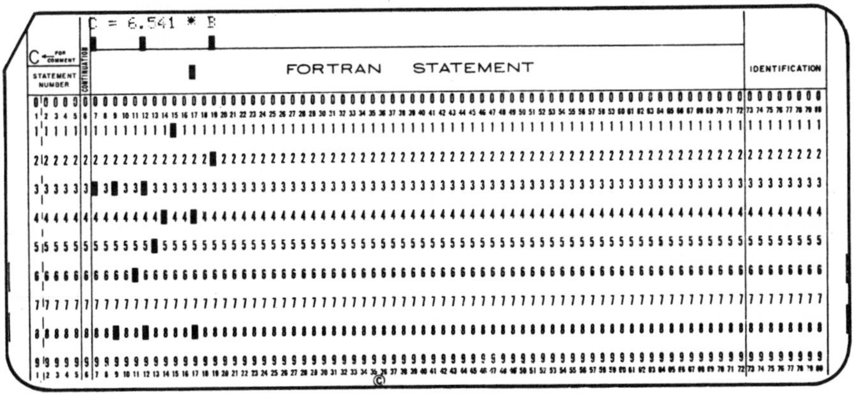

Fig. 1-3

card and loads them in the computer. Figure 1-4 contains an IBM data card for the case where $A = 1.21$ and $B = 321.4$. The statement numbered 4 tells where to locate the decimal points on this IBM input data card. The eighth statement of the program in Fig. 1-1 prints the values of the quantities A, B, C, D, E, F, and G on one line.

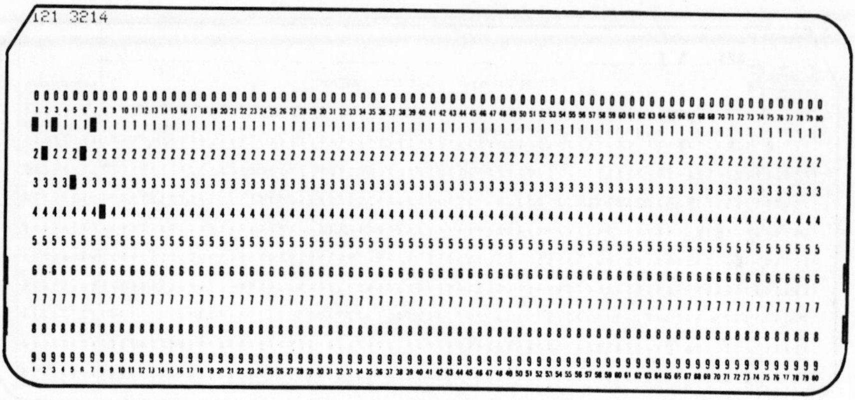

Fig. 1-4

1.3 Fortran Constants

The numbers used by Fortran are classified into 2 types: *fixed point* and *floating point*. A Fortran *constant* is a *particular value* of one of these numbers (i.e., a fixed-point constant or a floating-point constant). A *fixed-point number* is an integer (i.e., whole number) used for specific purposes. A *fixed-point constant* is a *fixed-point number* that has a specific value which will not change in the program, and it is written *without* a decimal point. For positive numbers, a preceding + sign is optional. For the IBM 1620 computer, the maximum value of a fixed-point number is variable (up to 10 digits), but most installations set the maximum value to be 99999 (i.e., a five-digit integer). This maximum will be assumed in this text. The first four of the following numbers are acceptable fixed-point constants. The last three numbers are *not* acceptable because one contains a decimal point, the next one contains more than five digits, and the last one contains a comma.

$$+62$$
$$0$$
$$-1104$$
$$78$$
$$6.89$$
$$184619$$
$$5,148$$

To simplify matters, consider a *floating-point number* to be merely a real decimal number which can be an integer, a fraction, or can have an integral and fractional part. A *floating-point constant* is a floating-point number of specific value, and is always written with a decimal point.

A preceding + sign is optional if the number is positive. Most numbers in a Fortran program are written in floating-point form. The maximum number of significant digits for a floating-point number is variable (up to 28 digits) for the IBM 1620 computer, but most installations set a limit of 8 significant digits. This maximum will be assumed in this text. The first 4 of the following numbers are acceptable floating-point constants. The last number is unacceptable because of the absence of a decimal point.

$$+62.$$
$$0.0$$
$$-81.8$$
$$0.0051$$
$$78$$

For the IBM 1620 computer, the absolute value or magnitude of a floating-point number must lie between 10^{-50} and 10^{49} for Fortran I and between 10^{-100} and 10^{99} for Fortran II. The letter E is used to simplify the writing of very large and very small Fortran constants. For example, the number 516,200 (i.e., 5.162×10^5) may be expressed as a floating-point constant by any of the following 4 forms. The number to the right of the E is the ten's exponent. Note that the exponent must not contain a decimal point, and that the use of a + sign is arbitrary.

$$5.162E5$$
$$5.162E+5$$
$$0.5162E6$$
$$516.2E+3$$

The number -0.00183 (i.e., -1.83×10^{-3}) may be expressed as a floating-point constant by the term

$$-1.83E-3$$

Illustrative Example 1.1.   State whether the following numbers are fixed-point constants or floating-point constants: -72.0, 614, 8.2E7, 611781, 72E-8, and 1.8E210. If any of these numbers fall in neither category, state why.

Solution.   The number 614 is a fixed-point constant, and the numbers -72.0 and 8.2E7 are properly written floating-point constants. The number 611781 is too large to be a fixed-point number and needs a decimal point to be a floating-point number. The number 72E-8 needs a decimal point to be a properly written floating-point number, and the number 1.8E210 exceeds 10^{99}.

1.4   Fortran Variables

A *Fortran variable* is a term or quantity whose magnitude can be varied as the Fortran program is executed, whereas the magnitude of a Fortran constant does not change during program execution. A Fortran variable is referred to in a program by a symbolic name consisting of 1 to 6 uppercase alphabetic and numeric characters. The first character must be alphabetic. For Fortran I, the maximum is 5 alphabetic and numeric characters. A constant, on the other hand, is written as a number. As with Fortran constants, a Fortran variable is in either a fixed-point or a floating-point form.

A *fixed-point variable* is a *fixed-point number* that may assume various magnitude values. Its symbolic name must begin with one of the following letters: I, J, K, L, M, or N. The first four of the following terms are acceptable fixed-point variables. The last two are unacceptable because one starts with an improper letter (i.e., H), and the other contains an improper character (i.e., $).

MIN

J

N2

L4K3

HN

L$P

The most commonly used type of variable is the *floating-point variable*, which is a *floating-point number* that may assume values of different magnitude during program execution. Its symbolic name may begin with any alphabetic letter except I, J, K, L, M, or N. The first four of the following terms are acceptable floating-point variables. The last three are unacceptable because two of them start with improper characters (i.e., M and 2), and the other contains an improper character (i.e., a decimal point).

BMN

C

D3

R4K2

MAX

2A5

C3.8

Illustrative Example 1.2. State whether the following Fortran terms are fixed-point variables or floating-point variables: B5R, T$M, N2R, 3PR, H4.9, and MINIMUM.

Solution. The term B5R is a properly written floating-point variable and the term N2R is a properly written fixed-point variable, but all of the other terms are unacceptable. The terms T$M and H4.9 contain improper characters, the term 3PR does not start with an alphabetic character, and the term MINIMUM contains more than six characters.

1.5 Fortran Operations and Expressions

Five mathematical *operations* are provided by Fortran: *addition, subtraction, multiplication, division,* and *exponentiation.* Addition is represented by the $+$ symbol. Thus, the expression

$$A + B$$

adds the two floating-point variables A and B. Subtraction is represented by the $-$ symbol. The expression

$$C - A$$

subtracts A from C. Multiplication is represented by the $*$ symbol. Thus, the expression

$$6.541 * B$$

multiplies the floating-point variable B by the floating-point constant 6.541. Division is represented by the $/$ symbol. The expression

$$E/D$$

divides E by D. Exponentiation is represented by the symbol $**$. Note that $**$ is considered to be one symbol. This is the only case where two operation symbols may be written side by side (i.e., next to each other). For example, the expression $E + (-F)$ is permissible, but not $E + -F$. The expression

$$F ** 3.58$$

calculates the term $F^{3.58}$. The ambiguous expression $E ** F ** G$ must be written either as $E ** (F ** G)$ or as $(E ** F) ** G$, depending upon which was originally intended. The exponent may be a fixed-point or a floating-point quantity, but only floating-point quantities may have floating-point exponents. Thus, $MAX ** F$ is not permissible.

A *Fortran expression* is a combination of constants, variables, and/or functions separated by *operation symbols, commas,* and/or *parentheses,* for which certain rules must be fulfilled (e.g., no side-by-side operation symbols). A single Fortran constant, variable, or function can also be considered to be a Fortran expression. In Fortran expressions, *parentheses* can be used to indicate *groupings of terms* just as is done in algebra. This has been done previously in this section. As further examples, the expression $X + Y ** 4$ differs from the expression $(X + Y) ** 4$, and the expression $X - Y + Z$ differs from the expression $X - (Y + Z)$. The expression X(Y + Z) is an improper one and does not produce the product of X and (Y + Z). The expression should be written as X * (Y + Z), since the parentheses here are used only to group terms. It may also be mentioned that XY represents only one term and not the product of X and Y.

An expression can consist of all floating-point quantities or all fixed-point quantities, but it must not contain both types of quantities. The only exceptions are that fixed-point quantities may appear in floating-point expressions as exponents and as subscripts (which will be described later). Thus, in the following expressions, the first one is proper, while the rest are improper because they are *mixed expressions* that contain both fixed-point and floating-point quantities in an improper manner.

$$(A + B) ** (I + 2)$$
$$E ** (J + 3.2)$$
$$F + R - K$$
$$E * F * (R + 7)$$

As for the order of performing the mathematical operations in a Fortran expression, the order of the calculations is from left to right if there are no parentheses and if the operations are either all additions and subtractions or all multiplications and divisions. Thus, the order of calculations in the expression X + Y − Z is

$$X + Y$$
$$(X + Y) - Z$$

and the order of calculations in the expression X * Y/Z is

$$X * Y$$
$$(X * Y)/Z$$

Now let us consider any expression without parentheses. The exponentiations are performed first (from left to right), then the multiplications and divisions (from left to right), and finally the additions and subtractions (from left to right). Thus, the order of the calculations in the expression A + B * C ** D is

$$C^D$$
$$B \times (C^D)$$
$$A + (BC^D)$$

Parentheses are used in a Fortran expression to specify the order of the calculations. Operations within the innermost parentheses are performed first. The expressions (X/Y) − (C ** D) and X/Y − C ** D are equivalent expressions, since the exponentiation and the division operations are performed before the subtraction is done in either expression. The order of calculations in the expression

$$(R + (E/D)) * F - E$$

is as follows:

$$\frac{E}{D}$$

$$R + \frac{E}{D}$$

$$\left(R + \frac{E}{D}\right) \times F$$

$$\left(\left(R + \frac{E}{D}\right)F\right) - E$$

The following Fortran expression

$$1.61/(3.7 * B) - C ** 3/(E + 6.1 * D)$$

represents the mathematical expression

$$\frac{1\,61}{3.7B} - \frac{C^3}{E + 6.1D}$$

Illustrative Example 1.3.   Write the corresponding mathematical expressions for the following Fortran expressions: $(F + D/E) * R$, $X * B * (K + 4)$, $E ** 5/A + 1.62$, $5 * B ** A$, and $A * B ** (4 * K)$.

Solution.   The mathematical expressions for the first, third, and fifth Fortran expressions are

$$\left(F + \frac{D}{E}\right) R$$

$$\frac{E^5}{A} + 1.62$$

$$AB^{4K}$$

The second and fourth expressions are improper because they are mixed expressions that contain floating-point and fixed-point quantities in an improper manner.

1.6   Arithmetic Statements

The *arithmetic statement* is generally the most commonly used type of statement in a Fortran program, because it is the statement that performs mathematical calculations. Its general form is $a = b$, where a is a Fortran variable (fixed or floating point) and b is an expression. The expression b must be properly written according to the rules specified in Sec. 1.5. Thus,

$$C = 6.541 * B$$
$$D = A + B$$
$$E = C - A$$
$$F = E/D$$
$$G = F ** 3.58$$

are proper Fortran arithmetic statements. It may be noted that these five statements were used in the program given by Fig. 1-1. The following statements are improper because the left-hand side does not consist only of a single Fortran variable.

$$I - 2 = L * K - N$$
$$-A = E ** F$$
$$R * S = (A + B) ** 1.82$$
$$3.8 = R * T/Y$$

In an arithmetic statement, the equal sign specifies a replacement or substitution, rather than an equivalence (as is done in algebra). An arithmetic statement $a = b$ replaces the value of the variable a with the computed value of the expression b. Thus, in the statement $N = 7$, the value of N is replaced with the fixed-point number 7. If N had a previous value, it is now destroyed. The statement $D = X * Y - R$ first calculates the value of the expression $X * Y - R$, and then sets the new value of D to equal the computed value of the expression. The following Fortran algebraic statement does not state that (DYDT)(DT) equals zero

$$Y = Y + DYDT * DT$$

because it replaces the old value of Y by the sum of its old value plus the product $(DYDT)(DT)$. Effectively, this statement increments the value of Y by this latter product. Similarly, the statement $N = N + 4$ increments the value of N by 4. Since the rules for writing an expression must be fulfilled, a statement such as

$$X = 2 * A + B(E + F)$$

is an incorrect algebraic statement. This is because the expression is mixed (since 2 is a fixed-point constant) and because there is no multiplication symbol (i e., *) between B and (E + F). The statement $Y = I ** 3.4$ is improper, because a fixed-point quantity may not have a floating-point exponent.

Something might be said here about fixed-point arithmetic calculations. If a fixed-point calculation gives a result that is not a whole number, the fraction is dropped (i.e., the result is *truncated* instead of rounded). Thus, the result of the fixed-point operation 11/4 is 2 and not 2.75. Since fixed-point additions, subtractions, and multiplications give correct whole-number results, we have to be cautious only about fixed-point divisions. This truncation feature is often a useful tool for programmers. As another example, the expression $11/4 * 3$ has a value of $(2)(3)$ or 6, while the expression $11 * 3/4$ has a value of $33/4$ or 8. This difference occurs because the operations are performed from left to right.

Usually in an arithmetic statement, $a = b$, the variable a and the expression b are both in floating-point form or are both in fixed-point form. If the expression b is in floating-point form while the variable a is fixed-point, then the computed result of the expression b is truncated (i.e., the fraction is dropped after the complete floating-point calculation is performed). This truncated result is converted to a fixed-point number and becomes the new value of the variable a. Thus, the statement

$$I = 5.007 * 6.2 * 1.0001$$

is equivalent to the statement $I = 31$. This feature can be used to *convert* a floating-point quantity to a fixed-point quantity. For example, the statement $J = A$ truncates A to an integer and converts the result to fixed-point form before this result becomes the new value of J. If the variable a, in the algebraic statement $a = b$, is in floating-point form while the expression b is in fixed-point form, then the result of the fixed-point computation is converted to floating-point form, before it becomes the new value of the variable a. For example, the value of the fixed-point variable I may be obtained in a floating-point form by use of the statement

$$AI = I$$

This statement converts I to floating-point form before it becomes the new value of the variable AI.

Illustrative Example 1.4. Write the corresponding mathematical equations for the following Fortran arithmetic statements. If any of these arithmetic statements are improper, state why.

$$A = P * R ** (5 * M)$$
$$9 = I * J - L$$
$$R = M * K ** (L - 4)$$
$$C + D = R * T - A$$
$$M = A(B + D)$$

Solution. The second and fourth arithmetic statements are improper because 9 and $C + D$ are not Fortran variables. The last arithmetic statement is improper because there is no multiplication symbol (i.e., $*$) between A and $(B + D)$. The mathematical equations for the first and third arithmetic statements are $A = PR^{5M}$ and $R = MK^{L-4}$.

1.7   READ, PRINT, and PUNCH Statements

Punched IBM cards, magnetic tape, and paper tape are the most common means by which input data is received by a digital computer. We shall consider only punched IBM-card inputs. The *card reader* is a device that reads the data from punched cards, by scanning the holes in these cards, and transmits this data to the digital computer, where it is stored. The Fortran statement

READ 9, A, B, C, D, E

causes the computer to take an IBM card containing 5 quantities from the card reader and store these quantities in the storage unit. The first quantity is assigned the symbol A, the second B, the third C, the fourth D, and the fifth E. The number 9 is the statement number of a **FORMAT** *statement* that describes the arrangement of these 5 quantities on the card. FORMAT statements are discussed in Sec. 1.8. Suppose that quantities A, B, and C are on one IBM card and that D and E are punched on another IBM card. The **READ** *statement* will cause the program to read card after card from the card reader until *all* of the quantities *specified in that statement* have been read and stored. Thus, several cards may be read by one READ statement.

Punched IBM cards, magnetic tape, paper tape, and the printed page (by either a typewriter or a line-printer) are the most common means by which data or problem results from a computer are transmitted as output. So that the output data may be viewed by the engineer, data obtained on magnetic tape, paper tape, or punched cards is later taken to a line-printer, where it is printed. Magnetic and paper tape and punched cards are used for output, because the direct use of a printer slows down the operation of a digital computer. That is, the computer can write on magnetic tape or punch an IBM card faster than it can print the data, thus saving expensive computer time.

In this text, the only output means we shall consider are the printing of data by a typewriter during computer operation and the punching of output data on IBM cards. The punched-card output is then later taken to a line-printer, where this output data is printed. The following Fortran statement, which is a **PRINT** *statement*,

PRINT 8, A, B, C, D, E, X, Y, Z, AVG

causes the digital computer to print the specified quantities (i.e., A to AVG) by typewriter on one or several lines. Line after line is printed in an arrangement specified by statement 8 (which must be a FORMAT statement) until all of the specified quantities have been printed. If instead, we desired to punch this same output data on an IBM card for eventual printout, the following Fortran statement, which is a **PUNCH** *statement*, should be used.

PUNCH 8, A, B, C, D, E, X, Y, Z, AVG

Note that the only change was to substitute the word PUNCH for the word PRINT.

Illustrative Example 1.5. Write Fortran statements to read quantities K, X, Y, Z, and R from an IBM card and to print these quantities using an on-line typewriter. Let statement 11 specify the arrangement of the quantities on the IBM card and let statement 12 specify the arrangement of the printed quantities.

Solution. The Fortran statements are as follows

READ 11, K, X, Y, Z, R
PRINT 12, K, X, Y, Z, R

1.8 FORMAT Statements

The **FORMAT** *statement* describes the arrangement of input or output data on an IBM card or the manner in which output data is printed. That is, this statement tells how many card columns should be allocated for each quantity, where to locate the decimal point, whether the number is fixed or floating point, etc. Since FORMAT statements are not executed statements, they may be placed anywhere in a Fortran program, but one should never transfer to a FORMAT statement. The FORMAT statement has many flexibilities, and we shall utilize a simple example before we discuss the details of this type of statement.

Consider the following two statements from the Fortran program of Fig. 1-1

1   READ 4, A, B
4   FORMAT (F3.2, F5.1)

along with the IBM card given in Fig. 1-4. This IBM card contains the values of the input data (i.e., A and B) for the problem given in Sec. 1.2. In this section, it was given that these values were A = 1.21 and B = 321.4. These two statements cause a card reader to read these two values from the IBM card and to transmit them to the computer. In statement 4 (i.e., the FORMAT statement), F3.2 specifies the arrangement for quantity A, and F5.1 specifies the arrangement for quantity B. Also note that these arrangement terms (i.e., F3.2 and F5.1) are separated by a comma. It is a requirement that these arrangement specification terms in a FORMAT statement must be separated by a comma. The field description term

F3.2 specifies that quantity A must occupy three card columns and that the decimal point must be located such that two digits lie to the right of this decimal point. Note in Fig. 1-4 that quantity A occupies three card columns (i.e., columns 1 to 3). The field description F5.1 specifies that quantity B must occupy five card columns and that one digit is to lie to the right of the decimal point. In Fig. 1-4, quantity B occupies five card columns (i.e., columns 4 to 8), where the blank in column 4 is assigned to quantity B. It may be noted that the decimal points can be punched in the IBM cards for the input quantities. If the decimal point location on the IBM card *contradicts* the location specified by the corresponding FORMAT statement, then the Fortran program will use the decimal point location that is punched on the IBM card. This flexibility permits the handling of *special-magnitude inputs*. A maximum of 72 characters may be punched on an IBM card.

Also in the program of Fig. 1-1 were the two statements

$$\text{PRINT 5, A, B, C, D, E, F, G}$$
$$5 \quad \text{FORMAT (7F10.4)}$$

The first of these statements causes a typewriter to print the values of A, B, C, D, E, F, and G on one line in an arrangement specified by statement 5. The FORMAT statement (i.e., statement 5) specifies that each of these seven printed quantities must occupy ten spaces and that each quantity must be printed so that four digits lie to the right of the decimal point. The specification 7F10.4 is valid for Fortran II, but when Fortran I is used, one must write F10.4 seven times in the FORMAT statement. It should be cautioned when writing a FORMAT statement for output terms that one should specify enough spaces for each quantity to allow for the *digits*, a possible *minus sign*, a *decimal point*, and some *blank characters* to separate the output term from the adjacent one. The printed quantities are not rounded by the IBM 1620 Fortran. It may be noted that all seven of these printed quantities were floating-point quantities. A maximum of 87 characters may be printed on one line by the typewriter. Thus, a FORMAT statement for typewritten output should not ask to print more than 87 characters per line (including blank spaces).

Now we shall discuss FORMAT statements in more detail. The printing or reading of a fixed-point quantity is represented in a FORMAT statement by the form Iw, where w is the number of card columns or print spaces to use for this integral quantity.

To print or read a floating-point quantity without expressing it in an exponent form, we represent this quantity in a FORMAT statement by the form F$w.d$, where w is the number of card columns or print spaces used to represent this quantity and d is the number of digits to the right of the decimal point. Thus, the number -15.1687 would print as -15.168 if an F7.3 specification is used; and improperly as 5.1687 if an F6.4 specification is used. This type of specification has been applied previously in this section. If d equals zero, no decimal point is printed. As mentioned before, when F$w.d$ is used for printing purposes, the number w must be large enough to allow room for a sign, decimal point, digits, and blank spaces (which appear at the left) to separate printed quantities.

To print or read a floating-point quantity in an *exponential form*, we represent this quantity by the form E$w.d$ in a FORMAT statement, where w is the number of card columns or print spaces used to represent this quantity and d is the number of digits to the right of the decimal point. When the form E$w.d$ is used on the IBM 1620 for output printing or punching, the number of significant digits printed or punched is often, but not always, equal to $(w - 6)$. This is to allow for the printing of a sign, two-digit exponent, exponent sign, decimal point, etc. If an E10.2 specification is used, the number -8.114 would be printed as follows when the Fortran II version is used

$$-81.14E-01$$

When the E$w.d$ form is used to represent an input quantity, the quantity punched on the IBM card need not have a decimal point. Also, the first digit of the exponent may be omitted if it is a zero. If either the quantity sign or the exponent sign is positive, it may be omitted. Also the term E may be omitted if the exponent sign is included. Thus, for floating-point input the following exponent forms are equivalent: E+04, E04, E4, E+4, +04, and +4.

As a summarizing example for this section, the following two Fortran statements

$$\text{PRINT 4, A, B, J}$$
$$\text{4   FORMAT (E12.4, F10.5,I4)}$$

would print the quantities A $= -86.7211$, B $= 37.13811$, and J $= 31$ as follows

$$-8\,6\,.\,7\,2\,1\,1\,\text{E+}0\,0\,b\,b\,3\,7\,.\,1\,3\,8\,1\,1\,b\,b\,3\,1$$

where the symbol b indicates a blank space in this example.

Illustrative Example 1.6.   Write FORMAT statements for the READ and PRINT statements in Ill. Ex. 1.5. Let each input quantity occupy five card columns, and let each output quantity occupy eight print spaces. Let each floating-point quantity be read and printed in non-exponential form with two decimal places.

Solution.   The two FORMAT statements can be written as follows if Fortran II is used.

11   FORMAT (I5, 4F5.2)
12   FORMAT (I8, 4F8.2)

If Fortran I is used, the two FORMAT statements must be written as follows:

11   FORMAT (I5, F5.2, F5.2, F5.2, F5.2)
12   FORMAT (I8, F8.2, F8.2, F8.2, F8.2)

1.9   Use of FORMAT Statements for Printing Alphameric Information and for Output Spacing

By using the / symbol to indicate the beginning of a new IBM card or a new printed line, one FORMAT statement may be used to read or punch several cards or print several lines when the quantities on each card or line have a different arrangement. For example, the statements

PRINT 10, I, A, B, C
10   FORMAT (I5/F5.1, F5.2, F4.1)

may cause the following printout

b b 5 1 2
$b-1.2b6.81b9.2$

where the symbol b indicates a blank space in this example. Thus, the / symbol is used to *separate* two different one-line or one-card formats. In this example, statement 10 specifies a two-line arrangement where the first line has format I5 and the second line has format F5.1, F5.2, F4.1. Blank lines can be obtained by putting consecutive / symbols in a FORMAT statement. N consecutive / symbols cause $(N-1)$ blank lines. For example, the following FORMAT statement will cause three blank lines to occur between a printed line of format F10.3 and a printed line of format F8.6, F10.1.

12   FORMAT (F10.3////F8.6, F10.1)

It may be mentioned again that *all* of the quantities listed in a READ, PRINT, or PUNCH statement are read, printed, or punched by that statement. The FORMAT statement specifies the arrangement of these quantities on an IBM card or a printed line. The / symbol and the closing parenthesis *each* indicate the termination of an IBM card or a printed line. For example, the FORTRAN statements

PRINT 10, A, B, C
10   FORMAT (F5.1, F5.2)

may cause the following printout

$-16.8b7.41$
3 1 2 . 2

where the value of C is printed on the second line with an F5.1 specification. That is, the first statement causes the printing of three quantities (i.e., *A, B*, and *C*), while statement 10 allows no more than two quantities to be printed per line.

It is also possible to specify one arrangement for the first (or more) cards or lines and a different arrangement for *all* of the cards or lines *that follow*. That is, one FORMAT statement can be used to specify one arrangement for the first card or line and a second arrangement for all of the successive cards or lines. This is done by enclosing the *repeating* specification in *parentheses*. For example, the statements

PRINT 8, K, A, B, C, D
8   FORMAT (I5/(F5.1, F5.2))

may cause the following printout

b b 6 0 1
− 2 1 . 7 *b* 6 . 8 5
4 3 4 . 2 *b* 3 . 0 8

In this example, statement 8 is equivalent to the following statement:

8   FORMAT (I5/F5.1, F5.2/F5.1, F5.2)

In practice, it is often desired to print, read, or punch *n* successive quantities in the same manner on a single line or an IBM card. As was previously stated in Sec. 1.8 and exemplified in Ill. Ex. 1.6, the form of this instruction may be simplified when using Fortran II (but not Fortran I) by putting the number *n* before the letter I, F, or E in the format specification. Statement 5 in the program of Fig. 1-1 used this feature. Thus, 3I5 is equivalent to I5, I5, I5, and 2E11.3 is equivalent to E11.3, E11.3. Also, in Fortran II it is possible to repeat a *group* of specifications. For example, the statement

12   FORMAT (I5, 2(F10.2, F8.4))

is equivalent to the statement

12   FORMAT (I5, F10.2, F8.4, F10.2, F8.4)

The printed output becomes much more readable if we put alphabetic titles above the numerical values. When it is desired to print *alphameric* (i.e., alphabetic and numeric) information, use *n*H followed by the alphameric characters to be printed in the FORMAT statement. The number *n* denotes the *number* of alphameric characters to be printed. *Blanks* are considered to be alphameric characters and must be accounted for by the number *n*. This is the *only* case where a blank space in a FORTRAN statement is not ignored. The following two statements print the two words INPUT DATA, starting at the left-hand margin of the page.

PRINT 15

15   FORMAT (10HINPUT DATA)

As another example, the statements

PRINT 8, A

8   FORMAT (2HA=F5.1)

would result in the following printout if A was equal to -51.8

$$A = -51.8$$

Note that in statement 8, the number 2 includes both the A and the $=$ characters, and that F5.1 specifies the manner in which quantity A should be printed.

A means of providing *successive blank characters* in a printed output is to use nX in the FORMAT statement, where n is the *number* of successive blank characters. Thus, the statements

PRINT 9, C

9   FORMAT (4X1HC/F5.2)

would result in the following printout if $C = -6.45$

C

-6.45

That is, the first line contains 4 blank spaces (that are caused by the 4X in statement 9) followed by the letter C (caused by the 1HC in statement 9). The second line contains the value of C printed according to an F5.2 specification. It may be noted that a field description (e.g., Iw, F$w.d$, etc.) is usually terminated by a comma, but X and H field descriptions do not require a trailing comma because their lengths are denoted in another manner.

On larger computers (e.g., IBM 704, 709, 7090, etc.) the first character after the H is used for a *pre-print spacing feature*. This special pre-print character which follows the H is not printed. If this pre-print character is a 1, then the printer skips to the top of the page before the next output is printed. If the character is a 0, one line is skipped to obtain a blank line; and if the character is a blank, no line is skipped. As an example, the statements

PRINT 7

7   FORMAT (7H1OUTPUT)

will cause the word OUTPUT to be printed at the top of the next page for titling purposes. This very useful feature is mentioned in this text because many IBM 1620 installations provide this feature and because most engineers will use larger computers when they enter professional practice.

Illustrative Example 1.7.   Write Fortran statements to read quantities *C*, *D*, *E*, and *F* from one IBM card and quantities *G* and *H* from a second IBM card. Let 21 be the number of the FORMAT statement, do not use any / symbols in this statement, and read these quantities in non-exponential form. Let each quantity occupy eight card columns with three digits after the decimal point.

Solution.   This can be done using two Fortran statements as follows. Note that data from two IBM cards are read using only one READ and one FORMAT statement, because the closing parenthesis indicates the termination of an IBM card after each set of four quantities is read.

READ 21, C, D, E, F, G, H

21   FORMAT (4F8.3)

Illustrative Example 1.8.   Write Fortran statements to read the quantity *KODE* from one IBM card, quantities *A* and *B* from the second card, quantities *C* and *D* from the third card, and quantities *E* and *F* from the fourth card. Use an I5 format specification for each fixed-point quantity, and use an F8.4 format specification for each floating-point quantity. Use only one READ statement and one FORMAT statement. Choose 17 to be the number of this FORMAT statement, and do not use more than one / symbol in this statement.

Solution.   This can be done using two Fortran statements as follows. Note the use of parentheses within parentheses to specify the format arrangement for the last three IBM cards.

READ 17, KODE, A, B, C, D, E, F

17   FORMAT (I5/(2F8.4))

Illustrative Example 1.9.   Write Fortran statements to print quantity *K* on one line using an I6 specification; skip two lines; print quantities *V*, *X*, and *Y* on the next line using an F9.4 specification for all three quantities; and print quantities *R* and *T* on the last line using an F9.1 and an F9.7 specification respectively. Do not use more than two Fortran statements.

Solution.   This can be done as follows, where three consecutive slash symbols were used to cause the skipping of two lines.

PRINT 51, K, V, X, Y, R, T

51   FORMAT (I6///3F9.4/F9.1, F9.7)

Illustrative Example 1.10.   Suppose that we are writing a program for an IBM 7090 digital computer. Write two Fortran statements that will, upon execution, print the title MISSILE TRAJECTORY at the top of an output page, skip a line, and then print the title PROBLEM INPUTS. Use only one / symbol in the FORMAT statement.

Solution. This can be done as follows. It should be noted that these two Fortran statements will print both titles starting at the left-hand margin. We could use the nX spacing-feature in statement 101 if we wanted to center either or both titles.

PRINT 101
101   FORMAT (19H1MISSILE TRAJECTORY/15H0PROBLEM INPUTS)

1.10   STOP, PAUSE, and END Statements

The **STOP** *statement* tells the computer, during program execution, to stop calculating. This is one of the two ways in which to prevent the digital computer from making any additional calculations during the execution of a given program. The other way is to cycle the program such that it keeps executing a specific READ statement. When there are no more data to read and store (i.e., no more cards in the card reader), the computer will automatically stop the computation for that program.

The **PAUSE** *statement* permits a temporary stop in the execution of a program. When the *start button* on the *computer console* is pressed, the program execution is continued, starting with the first statement *after* this PAUSE statement. This feature allows the engineer to inspect the printed output, stop the program if the results are satisfactory, or put in new input values and do further calculations. Both the PAUSE and STOP statements may be followed by a five-digit number, for which each digit must be less than 8. Since this number will be displayed on the computer console when the computer stops calculating, this feature can be used to tell the programmer which statement caused the halt of computations when several PAUSE or STOP statements are used. Thus, either of the two following statements can cause a temporary halt of computer execution.

PAUSE
PAUSE 17631

The last statement of every Fortran program must be an **END** *statement*. This statement has no effect during program execution. It *separates* the Fortran program from the input data (if there are any), and takes effect when the Fortran source program is converted to machine language. It tells the computer that there are no more Fortran instructions in the program to be translated into the language of the computer.

1.11   GO TO, IF, and Computed GO TO Statements

Fortran statements are executed in the same sequence as they are written on the programming sheet unless a different sequence is specified.

The **GO TO**, **IF**, and **Computed GO TO** *statements* are three types of statements that can cause a *different sequence*, and, hence, are commonly called *control statements*. These three types of statements tell the program to go to a *specific* statement in the program. As stated previously, statements that are referred to by another statement (e.g., by a control statement or an input-output statement) in the program must have a statement number. These are the *only* statements that need to be numbered, and no two statements may have the same number. There is no requirement that the statements must be numbered in sequence. That is, the first statement can be numbered 32, the second statement numbered 4, etc.

The **GO TO** *statement* takes the form GO TO *n*, where *n* is a *statement number*. It causes a transfer of control to the statement whose number is *n*. The program then continues from statement *n*. Thus, the GO TO state· ment provides a means for transferring control to any executable statement in the program. The GO TO statement is utilized in the program of Fig. 1-1, and it is the last executable statement in this program. It causes the program to go to statement 1, thus reading a new set of values for quantities A and B. Since we have now discussed all of the types of statements utilized in this program, we can examine the program more thoroughly. The sequence of operations for this program (which we shall call a *calculation sequence*) is as follows.

(1) Read the values of A and B from the card reader.
(2) Calculate the values of C, D, E, F, and G using the following equations

$$C = 6.541B$$
$$D = A + B$$
$$E = C - A$$
$$F = E/D$$
$$G = F^{3.58}$$

(3) Print the values of A, B, C, D, E, F, and G on a typewriter.
(4) Go to (1) for the next case (or set of calculations), using new values for quantities A and B.

The **IF** *statement* is another statement that allows a transfer of control to some statement other than the next one in sequence. Its form is

$$\text{IF } (d) \, n1, \, n2, \, n3$$

where d is a Fortran *expression* and $n1$, $n2$, and $n3$ are *statement numbers*. This statement transfers control to statement $n1$ if quantity d (which can be algebraic) is negative. If quantity d equals zero, statement $n2$ is the next statement to be executed. This IF statement causes the program to skip to statement $n3$ if expression d is positive (i.e., statement

$n3$ is executed next if $d > 0$). Thus, the IF statement is a *conditional transfer statement* that depends upon the sign of expression d. As an example, suppose that we wished to calculate the quantity F, where

$$F = 0 \qquad \text{if } A < D$$
$$F = A^2 \qquad \text{if } A = D$$
$$F = 5.2D \qquad \text{if } A > D$$

This calculation can be programmed in FORTRAN as follows

```
    IF (A − D) 2, 3, 4
2   F = 0.0
    GO TO 5
3   F = A ** 2
    GO TO 5
4   F = 5.2 * D
5
```

where the expression in the IF statement is $(A - D)$. If $(A - D)$ is negative, then $A < D$ and $F = 0$. If $(A - D) = 0$, then $A = D$ and $F = A^2$. If $(A - D) > 0$, then $A > D$ and $F = 5.2D$. The two GO TO 5 statements are used to prevent a recalculation of the term F when $(A - D) \leq 0$. Statement 5 is the next statement to be executed in the program after quantity F is calculated.

The general form of a **computed GO TO** *statement* is

$$\text{GO TO } (n1, n2, \ldots, nm), i$$

where $n1, n2, \ldots, nm$ are *statement numbers* and i is a *fixed-point variable* in the range 1 to m. For this statement, the next statement to be executed depends on the value of the fixed-point variable i. The next statement to be executed would be statement nk if $i = k$. For example, if we had the statement

$$\text{GO TO } (51, 3, 41, 11), \text{IA}$$

the next statement to be executed would be statement 51 if IA = 1, statement 3 if IA = 2, statement 41 if IA = 3, and statement 11 if IA = 4. Normally the term IA would be an input quantity or it would be calculated in the program itself.

As an example, let the term KR be a program input that states how the term F should be calculated. That is

$$\text{If } KR = 1, F = X$$
$$\text{If } KR = 2, F = 1.8X^3 - 4.1X$$
$$\text{If } KR = 3, F = 3.7X^{1.9}$$

This calculation can be programmed in Fortran as follows

$$\text{GO TO } (13, 14, 15), \text{KR}$$

```
    GO TO (13, 14, 15), KR
13  F = X
    GO TO 18
14  F = 1.8 * X ** 3 − 4.1 * X
    GO TO 18
15  F = 3.7 * X ** 1.9
18
```

Illustrative Example 1.11. Consider the preceding example in this section for the computed GO TO statement. Solve this problem, which calculates quantity F according to the value of KR, using an IF statement instead of a computed GO TO statement.

Solution. This can be done using the following Fortran statements. Note that the quantity $(KR − 2)$ is negative if $KR = 1$, equals zero if $KR = 2$, and is positive if $KR = 3$. Also note that the only difference between these two examples is the replacement of a computed GO TO statement with an IF statement.

```
    IF (KR − 2) 13, 14, 15
13  F = X
    GO TO 18
14  F = 1.8 * X ** 3 − 4.1 * X
    GO TO 18
15  F = 3.7 * X ** 1.9
18
```

1.12   The Comment Card

We shall now discuss the use of column 1 for Fortran statements. If column 1 for a Fortran statement card contains a C, the contents of that card are *not* treated as a Fortran instruction. The contents of the card are printed when the Fortran program is printed (during the machine-language translation process), but the contents of that *comment card* (i.e., the one with a C in column 1) are not translated into machine language. Thus, a comment card does *not* become incorporated into the machine-language program. Comment cards are used to title a Fortran program and to title or identify different parts of a Fortran program. This can help to make a program more readable, especially for other programmers and also to the original programmer when he has not looked at it for a while, since the use of a comment card statement allows a quick identification of a Fortran program or parts of a program.

Illustrative Example 1.12. Use comment cards in the program of Fig. 1-1 to title the program and to warn that the calculation of G will be in error if F is negative (since we cannot obtain a fractional root of a negative number).

Solution. The resulting program is shown in Fig. 1-5. The statements on the 2 comment cards were chosen to be

A PROGRAM TO CALCULATE C, D, E, F, AND G
TERM G WILL BE IN ERROR IF F IS NEGATIVE

```
C FOR COMMENT
STATEMENT NUMBER | Cont. | FORTRAN STATEMENT
C     A PRØGRAM TØ CALCULATE C, D, E, F, AND G
    1 READ 4, A, B
    4 FØRMAT (F3.2, F5.1)
      C = 6.541 * B
      D = A + B
      E = C - A
      F = E / D
      G = F ** 3.58
C     TERM G WILL BE IN ERRØR IF F IS NEGATIVE
      PRINT 5, A, B, C, D, E, F, G
    5 FØRMAT (7F10.4)
      GØ TØ 1
      END
```

Fig. 1-5

1.13 *Solution of Two Elementary Algebraic Problems*

As a first example, suppose that we wanted to solve the following three equations for x, y, and z for several sets of a, b, c, d, and e values.

$$x = a + b(c - d)$$
$$y = c^e$$
$$z = e + b/d$$

The following Fortran program could be used to solve this problem

```
1 READ 2, A, B, C, D, E
2 FORMAT (5F4.2)
  PRINT 3, A, B, C, D, E
3 FORMAT (6HINPUTS/5F6.2/)
  X = A + B * (C - D)
  Y = C ** E
```

$Z = E + B/D$
PRINT 4, X, Y, Z
4   FORMAT (7X1HX, 7X1HY, 7X1HZ/3F8.3///)
GO TO 1
END

In this program, the quantities a, b, c, d, e, x, y, and z are represented by the symbols A, B, C, D, E, X, Y, and Z respectively. This program (i.e., the statement numbered 1) reads the five quantities a, b, c, d, and e from an IBM card and stores these quantities in the digital computer. These five quantities are stored on the IBM card in a format specified by the statement numbered 2, which, in this case, is the second statement in the program. Statement number 2 says that the format for each of the five input quantities (i.e., a, b, c, d, and e) is that each quantity consists of four digits, where two digits follow the decimal point. Thus, if $a = 30$, $b = 12$, $c = 11$, $d = 3$, and $e = 2$, the numbers can be punched in the first 20 columns of the IBM card as follows

3 0 0 0 1 2 0 0 1 1 0 0 b 3 0 0 b 2 0 0

where the first four digits represent the term a (i.e., 30.00), the second four digits represent input quantity b (i.e., 12.00), etc., and the symbol b represents a blank card column. It may be noted that we could also have keypunched the decimal points on the input IBM card as follows. (The punched decimal point locations are now used by the computer, instead of those specified by statement 2.)

30.012.011.03.002.00

The third statement in the program prints the inputs (i.e., a, b, c, d, and e) according to the format specified by the statement numbered 3. The fourth statement (i.e., the statement numbered 3) says to print the six letters, INPUTS, on one line as a title. On the next line the five input quantities are printed, and six print spaces are reserved for each quantity, with two digits after each decimal point. The slash marks state that the next items are to be printed on the following line. For the previously given numerical values for a, b, c, d, and e, this printout would look like the following, where b indicates a blank space.

INPUTS
3 0 . 0 0 b 1 2 . 0 0 b 1 1 . 0 0 b b 3 . 0 0 b b 2 . 0 0

It might be mentioned that it is always *wise* to print the input quantities as a check to see if the proper values were used. After a program is completely checked out, a large percentage of the errors made are due to putting in the inputs improperly.

The next 3 statements perform the algebraic calculations where the quantities x, y, and z are represented by the symbols X, Y, and Z respectively. The statement X = A + B $*$ (C − D) calculates x according to the equation $x = a + b(c − d)$. The symbols +, −, and $*$ represent addition, subtraction, and multiplication, respectively, and parentheses are used to group terms as is done in algebra. The statement Y = C $**$ E calculates $y = c^e$, where the symbol $**$ represents exponentiation. The next statement calculates $z = e + b/d$, where the slash symbol / represents a division operation.

The next statement prints the quantities x, y, and z according to the format specified by the statement numbered 4. The statement numbered 4 says to print the alphabetic titles X, Y, and Z on one line and the values of x, y, and z on the next line, as denoted by the slash symbol. The values of the three quantities x, y, and z are printed so that eight spaces are allowed for each quantity, with three digits after the decimal point. The symbols 7X1HX are used to print the title X. The symbol 1HX prints the single letter X, while the symbol 7X says to skip seven spaces before the letter X is printed. For the previously specified numerical values for a, b, c, d, and e, this printout would look like

X   Y   Z
126.000b121.000bbb6.000

If the statement PUNCH 4, X, Y, Z were used instead of PRINT 4, X, Y, Z, then the output quantities x, y, and z and their titles would be punched on IBM cards, instead of being printed by a typewriter or printer. These output IBM cards would then be taken to a high-speed printer, where the values of x, y, and z would be printed along with their titles. The PUNCH statement is often used in order to minimize the computer operation time. Some installations may require that all of the output be printed on an on-line typewriter. In this case, PRINT statements will always be used, instead of PUNCH statements. Most installations, however, will probably prefer the use of PUNCH statements in order to more efficiently utilize the computer operation time. We shall use both types of statements in the programs of this text, so the reader may wish to change these to his satisfaction when he runs these programs at his computer installation.

The statement GO TO 1 says to go to the statement numbered 1 for the next operation, which is the reading in of another set of five input values for a, b, c, d, and e and is the start of another set of calculations of x, y, and z. The program will stop at statement 1 when there are no more IBM cards containing values of a, b, c, d, and e to be read into the computer. The statement END separates the Fortran program, which eventually becomes punched on IBM cards, from the IBM cards containing the input data.

As a second example, suppose that we wished to calculate

$$y = ax^3 + bx^2 + cx + d$$

for several values of x. A program to do this might be

```
1   READ 2, A, B, C, D
2   FORMAT (4F5.3)
    PUNCH 3, A, B, C, D
3   FORMAT (6HINPUTS/4F6.2//7X1HX, 12X1HY)
5   READ 2, X
    Y = A * X ** 3 + B * X ** 2 + C * X + D
    PUNCH 4, X, Y
4   FORMAT (F8.3, F13.3)
    GO TO 5
    END
```

In the previous program, the symbols A, B, C, D, X, and Y are used to represent the quantities a, b, c, d, x, and y respectively. The output is punched on IBM cards before they are printed on a high-speed printer. No parentheses were needed in the statement that computes y (which is represented by Y) because Fortran performs the exponentiations before it does multiplications and divisions, and it performs the multiplications and divisions before it does additions and subtractions. The statement GO TO 5 shows that y is calculated for several values of x and one set of a, b, c, and d values. Suppose that $a = 1.5$, $b = 3.0$, $c = 2.2$, and $d = 5.8$. If we calculate y for $x = 1.0$, 2.0, and 3.0, using this Fortran program, the printed output would look like

```
        INPUTS
        1.50bb3.00bb2.20bb5.80

            X                   Y
        1.000               12.500
        2.000               34.200
        3.000               79.900
```

For this given set of inputs, the numbers punched on the four input IBM cards could be as follows

```
        150003000022000 5800
        1000
        2000
        3000
```

where the first digit is punched in column 2 of the IBM card. The zeros in the above numbers could be replaced by blanks (i.e., the absence of a punch in that particular column of the IBM card).

As previously mentioned in Sec. 1.3, the variable field length capability of the IBM 1620 computer allows the user to define the precision to which fixed-point values (i.e., 4 to 10 decimal digits) and floating-point values (i.e., 2 to 28 decimal digits) may be carried. This precision can be defined on an IBM *parameter card* that precedes (i.e., is on top of) the source deck. Column 1 of this card contains an * symbol to denote that it is a parameter card, columns 2 and 3 contain the floating-point precision, and columns 4 and 5 contain the fixed-point precision. If the user does not define these, then the fixed-point precision is five significant digits and the floating-point precision is eight significant digits. Most Fortran versions for larger IBM computers have this same fixed- and floating-point precision. Thus, it may be wise to let 5 be the maximum number of card columns allotted for each positive fixed-point input quantity. Similarly, it may be wise to let the maximum value of w in all F$w.d$ input specifications be 8 if no signs or decimal points are to be keypunched on the IBM card. If we wish to keypunch the decimal point, however, and if the quantities are all negative, then it may be wise not to allot more than 10 card columns for each floating-point quantity when an F$w.d$ input specification is used.

1.14   Calculation of Square Roots, Exponentials, Sines, and Other Common Functions

In this section, we shall briefly discuss how sines, square roots, and other common functions may be calculated on a digital computer. We shall not go into a lot of detail because Fortran provides a relatively easy means for calculating the more common functions. Let us first discuss the calculation of a *square root*. We shall use *Newton's method* to calculate $\sqrt{x}$. We shall not go into the theory of this method, which is also called the **Newton-Raphson** method, because it is presumed that the reader has previously studied this in a calculus course. For the purpose of review, Newton's method is an *iterative* process to find the values of y that satisfy the equation $f(y) = 0$. The method is to first assume a value for y (i.e., y_1) and then repeat the following calculation until $y_{n+1} = y_n$.

$$y_{n+1} = y_n - \frac{f(y_n)}{f'(y_n)} \tag{1-1}$$

To use Newton's method to calculate $\sqrt{x}$, we let $f(y) = y^2 - x = 0$, so that $y = \sqrt{x}$. Since $f'(y) = 2y$, the iteration equation for y (i.e., $\sqrt{x}$) is

$$y_{n+1} = y_n - \frac{y_n^2 - x}{2y_n} \tag{1-2}$$

Before we write the Fortran program, we shall first write a *calculation sequence* whose purpose is to specify the sequence of operations to be performed by this program. We shall write a Fortran program based on the following calculation sequence:

(1) Read the input value of x from an IBM card.
(2) Test the value of x:
    (a) If x is negative, $\sqrt{x}$ is imaginary, print a warning message, and go to step (1) for the next value of x (i.e., the next case).
    (b) If $x = 0$, set $\sqrt{x} = 0$, and go to step (7).
    (c) If x is positive, let $y_1 = x$ as a first guess and go to step (3).
(3) $y_{n+1} = y_n - (y_n^2 - x)/2y_n$.
(4) Test $(y_{n+1} - y_n)$: If $\neq 0$, go to step (5)
                    If $= 0$, go to step (6) since we have a solution.
(5) Set $y_n = y_{n+1}$ and go to step (3) to calculate the next value of y_{n+1}.
(6) $\sqrt{x} = y_{n+1}$.
(7) Punch x and $\sqrt{x}$ for eventual printout.
(8) Go to step (1) for the next value of x (i.e., next case).

A Fortran program, based on the previous calculation sequence, is as follows, where the symbols X, YN, YN1, and SQRX are used to represent x, y_n, y_{n+1}, and $\sqrt{x}$ respectively.

```
 1   READ 10, X
10   FORMAT (F8.5)
     IF (X) 2, 3, 4
 2   PRINT 11, X
11   FORMAT (13HNEGATIVE TERM, F10.5)
     GO TO 1
 3   SQRX = 0.0
     GO TO 8
 4   YN = X
 7   YN1 = YN - (YN ** 2 - X)/(2.0 * YN)
     IF (YN1 - YN)5, 6, 5
 5   YN = YN1
     GO TO 7
 6   SQRX = YN1
 8   PUNCH 12, X, SQRX
12   FORMAT (2F10.5)
     GO TO 1
     END
```

Statement 1 reads the value of x from an IBM card into the computer. The third statement uses an IF statement to test the sign of x. If $x < 0$, the square root is an imaginary number and the program goes to statement 2, which prints the warning message "NEGATIVE TERM" on the same line as it prints the value of x. The program then skips to statement 1 for the next case. If $x = 0$, the third statement causes the program to skip to statement 3, which states that $\sqrt{x} = 0$. The program then skips to statement 8, which punches both x and $\sqrt{x}$ on an IBM card. If $x > 0$, the third statement causes the program to skip to statement 4 which sets the first value of y_n to equal x, as a first assumption for $\sqrt{x}$. Statement 7 uses Eq. (1-2) to calculate y_{n+1}. The following statement uses an IF statement to test $(y_{n+1} - y_n)$. If $(y_{n+1} - y_n) \neq 0$ (i.e., >0 or <0), then $y_{n+1} \neq y_n$ and the iteration process has not converged. The program then sets $y_n = y_{n+1}$ (which is done by statement 5), and then skips to statement 7 to go through another cycle of the Newton-Raphson method iteration. If $(y_{n+1} - y_n) = 0$, then $y_{n+1} = y_n$ and the iteration procedure has converged. For this case, the IF statement causes the program to skip to statement 6, which sets $\sqrt{x} = y_{n+1}$. The values of x and $\sqrt{x}$ are punched on an IBM card, for eventual printout, by statement 8, and the next statement causes the program to skip to statement 1 to start another calculation of $\sqrt{x}$, if there is another IBM card containing a value of x. When this program is being checked out, it might be desirable to insert a statement, located just after statement 7, that prints y_{n+1}. This statement would be removed after the program is checked out. It may be noted that Eq. (1-2) can be simplified to the form $y_{n+1} = 0.50(y_n + x/y_n)$, which can be employed in the computer program to shorten the calculation time. That is, this equation requires only one division, one addition, and one multiplication. It may also be noted that it is preferable to use $|y_{n+1} - y_n| < \varepsilon$, where ε is the desired accuracy, rather than $y_{n+1} = y_n$ as a convergence criteria for iterative calculations, in order to insure convergence to a solution when ε is sufficiently larger than the resolution of the computer.

For a program like this, which does a lot of skipping to various statements, instead of generally going through the program statements in a consecutive order, it is helpful to draw a block diagram *before* starting the program. Figure 1-6 is a *block diagram* for this $\sqrt{x}$ program.

Let us next consider the calculation of an *exponential function*. From calculus, we know that the term e^x may be calculated using the following *infinite series*

$$e^x = 1 + x + \frac{x^2}{2!} + \frac{x^3}{3!} + \frac{x^4}{4!} + \ldots = \sum_{n=0}^{\infty} \frac{x^n}{n!} \qquad \textbf{(1-3)}$$

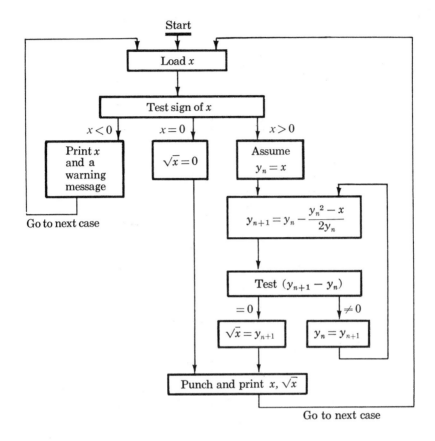

Fig. 1-6

where $0! = 1! = 1$. It may be noted that the $(n + 1)$th term of the series is obtained by multiplying the nth term by $x/(n + 1)$. We may use this fact as a basis to devise a computer program to calculate e^x. The block diagram for this computer program is shown in Fig. 1-7, where P.T. denotes the present term, N.T. denotes the next term of the series, n is the number of the present term in the series minus one, and SUM is the sum of the first $(n + 1)$ terms of the series.

As can be seen from this block diagram, after the inputs are loaded, the program then sets both the first term of the series and the partial sum equal to unity and sets n equal to zero. For the calculation of each successive term of the series, the program multiplies the present term by $x/(n + 1)$ and adds this newly calculated term to the partial sum of the series. We would usually not want to print the individually calculated

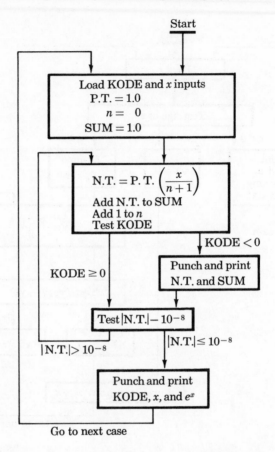

Start

Load KODE and x inputs
P.T. $= 1.0$
$n = 0$
SUM $= 1.0$

N.T. $= $ P. T. $\left(\dfrac{x}{n+1}\right)$
Add N.T. to SUM
Add 1 to n
Test KODE

KODE < 0

KODE ≥ 0

Punch and print
N.T. and SUM

Test $|$N.T.$| - 10^{-8}$

$|$N.T.$| > 10^{-8}$

$|$N.T.$| \leq 10^{-8}$

Punch and print
KODE, x, and e^x

Go to next case

Fig. 1-7

terms and the partial sums of the series, *unless* we were checking out the program. For the purpose of having a *permanent* debugging or checkout feature in the program, we use the term KODE as a program input. If this KODE term is loaded as a *negative* quantity, then the individual terms and partial sums of the series are printed for *checkout* purposes. If the KODE term is positive or zero, as can be seen from the block diagram, these terms are not printed. After testing the KODE term, the program compares the absolute value of the newly calculated term with 10^{-8}. If this term is larger than 10^{-8} in absolute value, another term is calculated. Since this series is a convergent power series, if the absolute value of the term is less than 10^{-8}, the finite series calculation approximates e^x with a sufficient accuracy, and the inputs and the calculated value for e^x are

1398981

printed. It can be seen from Eq. (1-3) that fewer terms are needed to approximate e^x when the absolute value of x is decreased.

The following Fortran program calculates e^x, and is based upon the block diagram of Fig. 1-7. The symbols X, AN, TERM, and SUM represent x, n, the present term and the next term (i.e., P.T. and N.T.), and the partial sum, respectively. In the following program, note that statement 4 causes a transfer to statement 2 when TERM $> 10^{-8}$, and that statement 6 causes a transfer to statement 2 when TERM $< -10^{-8}$. Thus, the program goes to statement 5 only when $|\text{TERM}| \leq 10^{-8}$.

```
 1   READ 10, KODE, X
10   FORMAT (I5, 2F10.5)
     TERM = 1.0
     AN = 0.0
     SUM = 1.0
 2   AN = AN + 1.0
     TERM = TERM * (X/AN)
     SUM = SUM + TERM
     IF (KODE)3, 4, 4
 3   PUNCH 11, TERM, SUM
11   FORMAT (2F10.5)
 4   IF (TERM - 0.00000001)6, 5, 2
 6   IF (TERM + 0.00000001)2, 5, 5
 5   PUNCH 10, KODE, X, SUM
     GO TO 1
     END
```

We may calculate the sine and cosine of x in a manner similar to that previously done for e^x, since we know from calculus that they may be calculated by using the following *infinite series*, where x is in radians.

$$\sin x = x - \frac{x^3}{3!} + \frac{x^5}{5!} - \frac{x^7}{7!} + \dots \qquad \textbf{(1-4)}$$

$$\cos x = 1 - \frac{x^2}{2!} + \frac{x^4}{4!} - \frac{x^6}{6!} + \dots \qquad \textbf{(1-5)}$$

It should be noticed that in either of the above series, each new term is obtained by multiplying the previous term by $-x^2/[(n + 1)(n + 2)]$. The following Fortran program calculates $\sin x$ in a manner similar to that done in calculating e^x. The symbols X, AN, TERM, and SUM represent x, n, the present term and the next term, and the partial sum, respectively.

```
 1   READ 10, KODE, X
10   FORMAT (I5, 2F10.5)
```

```
      TERM = X
      SUM = X
      AN = 1.0
   2  TERM = −TERM * (X ** 2)/((AN + 1.0) * (AN + 2.0))
      SUM = SUM + TERM
      AN = AN + 2.0
      IF (KODE)3, 4, 4
   3  PUNCH 11, TERM, SUM
  11  FORMAT (2F10.5)
   4  IF (TERM−0.00000001)6, 5, 2
   6  IF (TERM+0.00000001)2, 5, 5
   5  PUNCH 10, KODE, X, SUM
      GO TO 1
      END
```

After loading the inputs KODE and x, the previous Fortran program sets the first term of the series and the partial sum both equal to x, and it sets $n = 1$. Statement 2 calculates each successive term of the series by multiplying the previous term by $-x^2/[(n + 1)(n + 2)]$. The program then adds this newly calculated term to the partial sum of the series and adds 2 to n. If the KODE term is negative, then the individual terms and the partial sums of the series are printed by statement 3 for checkout purposes. Statements 4 and 6 test the absolute value of the newly calculated term to determine whether it equals or is less than 10^{-8}. If it is, then the finite series calculation for sin x is accurate to eight decimal places (because Eq. (1-4) is an alternating and convergent power series), and the KODE input, x, and the calculated value for sin x are punched by statement 5 on an IBM card for eventual printout. If the absolute value of the newly calculated term is larger than 10^{-8}, the program goes to statement 2, which calculates the next term of the series.

This program uses x in radians. Alternatively, we could have read in the input angle in degrees and then used a Fortran program statement to convert it to radians. It should be noted that if the input angle is large, Eq. (1-4) is still valid, but the program may require calculations to more than eight significant, floating-point digits in order to get accurate results. We can obtain more than eight significant, floating-point digits for this program by use of a parameter card, as discussed in Sec. 1.13. We can also use the relation $\sin(\bar{x} + n\pi) = (-1)^n \sin \bar{x}$, where n is an integer, in order to keep angle x in Eq. (1-4) from being large (i.e., greater than π). We could insert statements in the previous Fortran program to calculate the value of $\bar{x}$ from the value of the input angle, if desired. In both the e^x and sin x programs, note that statement 10 is a FORMAT statement for both a READ statement and a PUNCH statement. Thus, it should be cautioned that a parameter card, which is discussed in Sec. 1.13, will be required if input x contains more than eight significant digits.

Very fortunately, we do *not* have to program or write a calculation subroutine when we wish to calculate $\sqrt{x}$, sin x, etc., when Fortran is used. To do this, we can use *library functions* which in actuality consist of a set of program statements similar to those previously described for $\sqrt{x}$, e^x, and sin x. This section was written in order to give the reader some idea of how these types of functions are calculated on a digital computer. It shows the reader that they must be numerically calculated or approximated. For the Fortran II system for the IBM 1620 computer, there are seven available library functions. For these seven library functions, use

1. SINF(X)   to compute sin x
2. COSF(X)   to compute cos x
3. EXPF(X)   to compute e^x
4. SQRTF(X)   to compute $\sqrt{x}$
5. ABSF(X)   to compute $|x|$
6. LOGF(X)   to compute $\log_e x$
7. ATANF(X)   to compute $\tan^{-1} x$

The IBM 1620 Fortran I system has all of the previous library functions except ABSF(X). This latter function may be very easily programmed, as is shown in Ill. Ex. 1.13. A library function is handled like any other variable in a Fortran arithmetic statement, and a Fortran expression may be contained within the parentheses. Thus, Fortran provides a very easy means for programming the use of the more common functions. For example, $A\sqrt{BC}$ may be computed by the following Fortran arithmetic statement.

$$Y = A * SQRTF(B * C)$$

Illustrative Example 1.13. Write a Fortran program to calculate the *absolute value* of a number.

Solution. The following Fortran program utilizes an IF statement to calculate $|x|$ (i.e., the absolute value of input quantity x).

```
 1   READ 10, X
10   FORMAT (2F10.5)
     IF (X)2, 3, 3
 2   ABX = −X
     GO TO 4
 3   ABX = X
```

4   PUNCH 10, X, ABX
  GO TO 1
  END

Statement 1 reads quantity x, represented by the symbol X, from an IBM card into the computer. The program uses the symbol ABX to represent $|x|$. The statement IF (X)2, 3, 3 is based on the following

$$|x| = x \quad \text{if } x \geq 0$$
$$|x| = -x \quad \text{if } x < 0$$

That is, if X $<$ 0, the program goes to statement 2 (which says that $|x| = -x$); and if X $\geq$ 0, the program goes to statement 3 (which says that $|x| = x$). Statement 4 punches the values of x and $|x|$ on an IBM card for eventual printout, and the next statement causes the program to skip to statement 1 to start another calculation of $|x|$, if there is another IBM card containing another value of x.

Illustrative Example 1.14.   Write a Fortran program that utilizes Eq. (1-5) to calculate the cosine of x.

Solution.   This can be done by modifying the Fortran program in this section that calculates sin x. That is, if we changed the third, fourth, and fifth statements of this sin x program to be

TERM = 1.0
SUM = 1.0
AN = 0.0

it can be seen from Eq. (1-5) that this program would now calculate cos x, instead of sin x, because it would initially set $n = 0$ and also set both the first term of the series and the partial sum equal to unity. We could also use other means of modifying this sin x program so that it would calculate cos x, instead of sin x. Since cos x = sin $(x + \pi/2)$, we could do this by inserting the following statement after statement 10 in the sin x program: X = X + 1.5708. This will cause the program to now calculate sin $(x + \pi/2)$, instead of sin x. The sin x program can also be modified to calculate both sin x and cos x. Once sin x is calculated, we can use the equation cos $x = \sqrt{1 - \sin^2 x}$ to calculate cos x. This can be done without using a library function by the Fortran statement XCOS = (1.0 − SUM ** 2) ** 0.50.

Illustrative Example 1.15.   Write 2 Fortran statements to calculate $y = xe^{a+b}$ and $t = \sqrt{a + \log_e b}$.

Solution.   This can be done, using the EXPF(X), SQRTF(X), and LOGF(X) library functions, as follows:

Y = X * EXPF(A + B)
T = SQRTF(A + LOGF(B))

Illustrative Example 1.16.   Calculate the functions tan x, $\log_{10} x$, tanh x, sinh x, cosh x, and $\sin^{-1} x$ using only one Fortran statement for each function.

Solution.   Using the following formulae

$$\tan x = \frac{\sin x}{\cos x}$$

$$\log_{10} x = \log_e x / 2.3026$$

$$\tanh x = \frac{e^x - e^{-x}}{e^x + e^{-x}}$$

$$\sinh x = \tfrac{1}{2}(e^x - e^{-x})$$

$$\cosh x = \tfrac{1}{2}(e^x + e^{-x})$$

$$\sin^{-1} x = \tan^{-1}\left(\frac{x}{\sqrt{1 - x^2}}\right)$$

and using Fortran library functions, we can calculate these six functions as follows:

```
XTAN  = SINF(X)/COSF(X)
XLOG  = LOGF(X)/2.3026
XTANH = (EXPF(X) − EXPF(−X))/(EXPF(X) + EXPF(−X))
XSINH = 0.50 * (EXPF(X) − EXPF(−X))
XCOSH = 0.50 * (EXPF(X) + EXPF(−X))
XASIN = ATANF(X/SQRTF(1.0 − X ** 2))
```

It should be mentioned that if any of the previous functions were to be utilized several times in a program, then the *arithmetic statement function*, which is discussed in Sec. 3.5, can be advantageously used to do this. That section illustrates the use of such a statement for calculating the tangent of three different angles. In effect, the arithmetic statement function defines a function, which can be used later in the program in the same manner as a library function. It might also be wise at this time to discuss the differences in calculation for Fortran fixed- and floating-point exponents. We shall use the calculation of A^3 as an example. If A ** 3.0 is used, then the 2 calculations $y = 3 \log_e A$ and $A^3 = e^y$ would result. If A ** 3 is used, then this would be equivalent to A * A * A, since the calculation is performed by successive multiplication. Thus, the use of A ** 3 results in a much faster computation than A ** 3.0. The use of A ** 1121, however, results in 1120 multiplications.

Illustrative Example 1.17.   Discuss how the functions $\log_e x$ and $\tan^{-1} x$ may be calculated.

Solution.   These two functions may be calculated by *infinite series*, whose formulae may be found in math tables and in calculus texts, but these two infinite series converge more slowly than those for sin x, cos x, and e^x. Thus, *polynomial approximation formulae* may be desirable. It should be noted that mathematical forms other than polynomials are also used to approximate specific functions. One easy means for obtaining a polynomial approximation formula is to use a finite number of terms of the Taylor series expansion for that function.

For example, the first four terms of Eq. (1-4) give us the following 7th degree polynomial approximation for sin x:

$$\sin x = \left(-\frac{1}{7!}\right) x^7 + \left(\frac{1}{5!}\right) x^5 + \left(-\frac{1}{3!}\right) x^3 + x$$

Since Eq. (1-4) is a convergent power series that alternates in sign, the error of this approximation is less than the absolute value of the next term (i.e., the fifth term) in Eq. (1-4). Thus, this error is less than $x^9/9!$, so that this error decreases as angle x is decreased. For the $\log_e x$ and $\tan^{-1} x$ functions, we wish to use better polynomial approximation methods. Section 4.11 of this text discusses methods for fitting polynomials of specified degree through tabulated points of a given curve or function. It is possible to approximate $\tan^{-1} x$, with an error of less than 10^{-5}, by an 11th degree polynomial in x, consisting of six terms, where $|x| < 1$. The function $\log_e x$ may be approximated rather accurately for a specified range of x by a 7th degree polynomial in u of the form $a_1 u^7 + a_2 u^5 + a_3 u^3 + a_4 u$, where $u = (x - 1)/(x + 1)$. We could use such a polynomial approximation for values of x above $x_{\max}$, the specified maximum, by use of the equation $\log_e x = a + \log_e y$, where $x = (y)(e^a)$. We could obtain the values of a and y by successive divisions by e until we obtain a remainder y such that $y < x_{\max}$.

Illustrative Example 1.18.   Suppose that we had calculated term A in a Fortran program by an arithmetic statement and that quantity A is usually not a whole number. Another term B is to be calculated from an equation that utilizes the truncated value of A (i.e., the value of A without its decimal fraction). Write Fortran statements to obtain the truncated value of A.

Solution.   This can be done as follows where term AI, the truncated value of term A, can be utilized in the Fortran statement that calculates term B.

$$I = A$$
$$AI = I$$

Illustrative Example 1.19.   Develop a *recursion method* for calculating the following polynomial of degree n

$$P(x) = a_0 x^n + a_1 x^{n-1} + \ldots + a_{n-1} x + a_n$$

Solution.   This polynomial can be rewritten in the following form

$$P(x) = a_n + x(a_{n-1} + \ldots + x(a_1 + x(a_0)) \ldots)$$

Thus, the sequence of calculations start as follows:

$$d_1 = a_0$$
$$d_2 = a_1 + xd_1 \equiv a_1 + a_0 x$$
$$d_3 = a_2 + xd_2 \equiv a_2 + a_1 x + a_0 x^2$$
$$d_4 = a_3 + xd_3 \equiv a_3 + a_2 x + a_1 x^2 + a_0 x^3$$
$$d_5 = a_4 + xd_4 \equiv a_4 + a_3 x + a_2 x^2 + a_1 x^3 + a_0 x^4$$

It can be seen that if $n = 4$, the term d_5 is equivalent to polynomial $P(x)$. Stating this in more general form, $P(x) = d_{n+1}$, since the previous equations show that $P(x) = d_1$ if $n = 0$, $P(x) = d_2$ if $n = 1$, $P(x) = d_3$ if $n = 2$, etc. Thus, to calculate polynomial $P(x)$, we let $d_1 = a_0$, calculate $d_2, d_3, \ldots, d_{n+1}$ using the recursion formula $d_{i+1} = a_i + xd_i$, and then equate $P(x)$ to d_{n+1}. This recursion method for calculating a polynomial is rather easy to program for a digital computer calculation.

Illustrative Example 1.20. The *Chebyshev polynomial* $C_n(x)$ of degree n is defined as follows, where $\theta = \cos^{-1} x$

$$C_n(x) = \cos n\theta$$

Express the equations for $C_0(x)$, $C_1(x)$, $C_2(x)$, and $C_3(x)$ as polynomials in x.

Solution. Since $x = \cos \theta$, it can be shown, using trigonometric formulae, that

$$C_0(x) = \cos 0 = 1$$
$$C_1(x) = \cos \theta = x$$
$$C_2(x) = \cos 2\theta = 2\cos^2 \theta - 1 = 2x^2 - 1$$
$$C_3(x) = \cos 3\theta = 4\cos^3 \theta - 3\cos \theta = 4x^3 - 3x$$

It may be noted that for $n \geq 2$, the Chebyshev polynomial $C_n(x)$ can be calculated from the following recursion formula:

$$C_n(x) = 2xC_{n-1}(x) - C_{n-2}(x)$$

Thus, a set of Chebyshev polynomials may be calculated in a Fortran program for a digital computer by setting $C_0(x) = 1$ and $C_1(x) = x$, and then calculating the other polynomials by this recursion formula. As mentioned later in Sec. 4.11, Chebyshev polynomials have an important use in obtaining polynomial approximations of rather high accuracy, for curves and functions.

PROBLEMS

1.1. Write each of the numbers -731, 231, 2.6×10^{-9}, and 7.8×10^{107} as a fixed-point constant and as a floating-point constant. State which are impossible to do and furnish a reason.

1.2. State why each of the following numbers is not a proper floating-point constant: -718; $815{,}612.8$; $81E7$; $1.8E+105$; and $7E-8$.

1.3. State whether the following numbers are fixed-point constants or floating-point constants: $+85$; 0.0; $6{,}120$; -71; 81.5; $41E5$; 61507; $-5.8E4$; 0; $+4.8E-8$; and $7{,}185.0$. If any of these numbers fall in neither category, state why.

1.4. State which of the following symbols can be used to represent a fixed-point variable and which can represent a floating-point variable: A4, IB, X\$A, KN2, 3PA, N, D, K4A6, X−8, Y3.7, and MAXIMUM. If any of the preceding symbols cannot represent either variable, state why.

1.5. Write a Fortran expression to represent each of the following mathematical expressions:

(a) $\dfrac{C}{D} - \dfrac{4A}{R}$

(b) $7.8(X + Y^3)^{1.81}$

(c) $\dfrac{XY - AB}{4.8E^4}$

(d) $7X + \dfrac{13Y}{Z - 9.81}$

(e) $\dfrac{4X + 9}{C + D^2}$

1.6. For all of the following Fortran expressions (if they are proper), write their corresponding mathematical expressions. Also state the sequence of the calculations, and rewrite any of the Fortran expressions if any of them contain an unnecessary pair of parentheses. If any Fortran expression is improper, state why.

(a) $(X + Y)(A + 6.5)$
(b) $(C + 8.71) * (D/E)$
(c) $(X * Y + Z) ** (T + 9)$
(d) $X - 8.71 * R ** (I + 7)$
(e) $7.85 * X + P - K * T$
(f) $A - P * (R/(F/7.87)) * T ** (KP - 11)$
(g) $(K * IA) - (NPA ** C)$
(h) $S * (P - (T - R))$

1.7. Which of the following Fortran expressions represents the following mathematical expression? Write the mathematical expressions represented by the other Fortran expressions (if they are validly written). State the errors in the invalid Fortran expressions.

$$\frac{6X - 8}{Y + Z} - A^{I+5}$$

(a) $(6 * X - 8)/(Y + Z) - A ** (I + 5)$
(b) $(6. * X - 8.)/Y + Z - A ** (I + 5)$
(c) $(6.0 * X - 8.0)/(Y + Z) - A ** (I + 5)$
(d) $(6.0 * X - 8.0)/(Y + Z) - A ** (I + 5.0)$
(e) $6.0 * (X - 8.0)/(Y + Z) - A ** (I + 5)$
(f) $(6.0X - 8.0)/(Y + Z) - A ** (I + 5)$
(g) $(6.0 * X - 8.0)/(Y + Z) - A ** I + 5$

1.8. Identify the error or errors in each of the following Fortran arithmetic statements.

(a) $Z = 4 * KR ** B$
(b) $R + T = 5 * IN - KS ** N$

(c) $7 = A * B ** 6.8$

(d) $A = R * T ** 2 - 7 * T ** B$

(e) $-D = 8.5 * X + 9.8 * Y ** 2$

(f) $T = 6.8 * Y + (X - A)(Y - B)$

(g) $R = 5.1 * (Y - (A + B))$

1.9. State the value of Y or M stored for each of the following arithmetic statements if $J = 3$, $K = 8$, $L = 5$, $B = 2.0$, and $D = 5.8$.

(a) $Y = K/J - L$

(b) $M = B * D ** (L - J)$

(c) $Y = (K + L)/J$

(d) $M = K/J + L/J$

(e) $Y = D * B ** (K/J)$

(f) $M = K + 5 * (L/J)$

1.10. Write the necessary Fortran statements to read quantities A, B, C, and D from an IBM card and to punch these same quantities on an IBM card for eventual printout. Read and punch these quantities in non-exponential form. For the input card, let each quantity occupy eight card columns with three digits after the decimal point. For the punched output card, let each quantity occupy twelve card columns with three digits after the decimal point. Let 12 be the number of the input FORMAT statement and 13 be the number of the output FORMAT statement.

1.11. Using only one READ statement, write the necessary Fortran statements to read the quantities A, B, and C from one IBM card and the quantities X, Y, and Z from another IBM card. Let each of these six quantities occupy seven card columns with two digits after the decimal point, and use the non-exponential form. Let 87 be the number of the FORMAT statement, and do not use the / symbol in this statement.

1.12. Write the necessary Fortran statements to print the quantities K, L, X, Y, and Z on one line. Let K and L occupy six print spaces, X and Y occupy nine print spaces with two digits after the decimal point, and Z occupy fourteen spaces with three digits after the decimal point. Let Z be the only term printed in exponential form. Let 17 be the number of the FORMAT statement.

1.13. Let quantity D equal -814.7183. State how the output would appear if this quantity were printed by each of the following specifications: F9.4, F11.6, F8.3, F7.2, F8.4, F7.4, F5.3, and F5.0.

1.14. State whether the following forms can be properly used to represent the input quantity A, where $A = 348.5$, if this quantity is punched in exponential form on an IBM card as follows: 3.485E2, 34.85+1, 348.5E+00, 3.485E02, or 3.485+01.

1.15. Same as Prob. 1.12, except print quantities K and L on one line and X, Y, and Z on another line. Also write the FORMAT statement so that there will be two blank lines between these two printed lines.

1.16. Write the necessary Fortran statements to successively print the quantities MA, MB, IA, IB, A, B, C, D, E, F, G, and H on six lines. Print two quantities on each line, and let 31 be the number of the FORMAT statement. Use the specification I6 for each fixed-point quantity and the specification F11.3 for each floating-point quantity.

1.17. Rewrite the following Fortran II FORMAT statements in a form that is suitable when the Fortran I version is used for the IBM 1620 computer.

(a)   11   FORMAT (F6.1, 3(F8.2, F5.3))
(b)   85   FORMAT (4I5, 2F7.2, 3F9.4)
(c)   27   FORMAT (2I6, 2(F5.1, F3.0, F6.2), 2F7.1)

1.18. Write the necessary Fortran statements to print the following words, starting at the left-hand margin: QUANTITY A IS TOO LARGE. Let 32 be the number of the FORMAT statement.

1.19. Same as Prob. 1.12, except print the title OUTPUT DATA above the numerical values. Let this title start at the eleventh space from the left-hand margin.

1.20. Same as Prob. 1.18, except that we are programming for a large computer and we wish to print these words at the top of the next page.

1.21. Keypunch the Fortran program of Fig. 1-1 and the data card in Fig. 1-4. Run this program on the computer. Use a slide rule to check whether your printed results are correct.

1.22. Write the proper IF statement that will cause the program to go to statement 51 if $(A^2 - D) = R^{1.8}$, to statement 54 if $(A^2 - D) > R^{1.8}$, and to statement 47 if $(A^2 - D) < R^{1.8}$.

1.23. Write Fortran statements (including an IF statement) that will calculate the term R as follows:

$R = 5.8X^{3.1}$ if $X < (Y^2 - 7.2Z)$
$R = 3.7X^{1.2}$ if $X = (Y^2 - 7.2Z)$
$R = -7.8X^{-0.7}$ if $X > (Y^2 - 7.2Z)$

1.24. Write Fortran statements (including a computed GO TO statement) that will calculate the term M as follows:

If $K = 1$, then $M = 3K^2$
If $K = 2$, then $M = 0$
If $K = 3$, then $M = 2K - 8$
If $K = 4$, then $M = 4K^2 - 1$

1.25. Write a complete Fortran program to perform the following operations. Title your program using a comment card statement.

(a)   Read quantities A and B using an F8.3 specification for each quantity.
(b)   If $A < B$, print the words A IS LESS THAN B, and go to step (a) for the next case.

(c) If $A \geq B$, calculate quantity D, where $D = 4.8A^B$.

(d) Print quantities A, B, and D using an F12.3 specification for each quantity.

(e) Go to (a) for the next case.

1.26. Keypunch the program and the input data cards for the two programs of Sec. 1.13. Use the inputs that are given in that section. For the first program, also keypunch the inputs for a second case where $a = 14.2$, $b = 3.5$, $c = 1.4$, $d = 7$, and $e = 3$. Run these two programs on the computer, and check the output data to determine whether they are correct.

1.27. Keypunch the $|x|$, $\sqrt{x}$, e^x, sin x, and cos x programs of Sec. 1.14. Also keypunch input data cards for ten input values including $x = -2.00$, 0.500, and 2.00. Run these five programs on the computer, and check the output data to determine whether they are correct.

1.28. Combine the $|x|$, $\sqrt{x}$, e^x, and sin x programs of Sec. 1.14 into one program. Print the results of these four calculations on one line along with the value of input x. Also calculate these same four terms using Fortran library functions. For each of the four terms, subtract the library function value from the previously calculated value, and print these results. For input data, choose ten input values including $x = -2.00$, 0.500, and 2.00.

CHAPTER 2

Setup and Solution
of Engineering Problems
on Digital Computers

2.1 Introduction

The purpose of this chapter is to use various examples to show how different types of engineering problems can be solved by the use of a digital computer. In Chapter 1 of this text, we learned how to use the Fortran arithmetic, READ, PRINT, PUNCH, FORMAT, GO TO, IF, computed GO TO, PAUSE, STOP, and END statements. That is, we learned the rules and details for using these types of statements in a Fortran program. Most of these statements are used in the program examples for this chapter. When the solution of a specific engineering problem is discussed, the engineering aspects (sometimes with a review of necessary physical background and basic fundamentals) and the numerical techniques utilized are covered, in addition to the Fortran program itself. Most of these problems demonstrate the necessity for using a numerical solution technique, and a relatively simple numerical method is usually employed for its initial solution. Usually these sections are followed by sections that discuss better (e.g., more accurate or more versatile) numerical methods that may be utilized to solve the problem.

As an introductory engineering example, this chapter first discusses a Fortran program that calculates the analytical solution of an elementary electrical circuit problem. This chapter then discusses program checkout, classifies numerical solution techniques, and lists the steps utilized for setting up and solving an engineering problem on a digital computer. This chapter later solves a nonlinear electrical circuit using the Euler numerical method, and follows this with a discussion of printout control and of better numerical techniques that may be used to solve this problem and other first-order ordinary differential equations. A nonlinear mechanical vibration problem is used as an example for showing how to numerically solve a second-order differential equation, while a heat transfer problem is used to demonstrate the numerical solution of simultaneous, ordinary differential equations. A direct trial-and-error procedure is used to try to solve a fluid-flow problem, and this is followed by a discussion of better trial-and-error solution methods. The last physical example in this section is a mechanical vibration problem, where the natural frequencies for this system are obtained by solving for the roots of a polynomial equation. This chapter is concluded with a very brief discussion of various methods for finding the roots of polynomial equations.

2.2 Solution of a Single-Loop, Linear Electrical Circuit Problem

Consider a one-loop electrical circuit that is illustrated in Fig. 2-1 and which consists of a voltage source, resistor, and inductor connected in series. We want to find the current variation with time for this circuit.

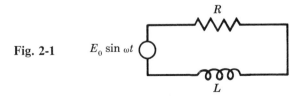

Fig. 2-1 $E_0 \sin \omega t$

Using *Kirchoff's voltage law*, the *loop equation* for this circuit is

$$L \frac{di}{dt} + Ri = E_0 \sin \omega t \tag{2-1}$$

which is a linear, non-homogeneous ordinary differential equation. Let us solve this differential equation by classical means. The *homogeneous equation* is

$$L \frac{di}{dt} + Ri = 0$$

The *homogeneous solution* is of the form

$$i_h = A e^{mt}$$

Substitution of the above equation for i_h in the homogeneous equation gives

$$LAme^{mt} + RAe^{mt} = 0$$

from which we find that $m = -R/L$, so that

$$i_h = A e^{-Rt/L}$$

We shall use the *method of undetermined coefficients* to find the particular solution. Since the forcing function is $E_0 \sin \omega t$, this method states that the *particular solution* must be of the form

$$i_p = C \cos \omega t + D \sin \omega t$$

Substitution of the above equation for i_p in Eq. (2-1) gives

$$L(-C\omega \sin \omega t + D\omega \cos \omega t) + R(C \cos \omega t + D \sin \omega t) = E_0 \sin \omega t$$

Since the previous equation shows that

$$(-LC\omega + RD) \sin \omega t = E_0 \sin \omega t$$
$$(LD\omega + RC) \cos \omega t = 0$$

the previous two equations can be solved simultaneously for C and D to obtain

$$C = -\frac{\omega L E_0}{\omega^2 L^2 + R^2} \tag{2-2}$$

$$D = \frac{R E_0}{\omega^2 L^2 + R^2} \tag{2-3}$$

Thus, the *complete solution* for current i is as follows, where the homogeneous solution i_h dies out with time

$$i = i_h + i_p = A e^{-Rt/L} + C \cos \omega t + D \sin \omega t \tag{2-4}$$

where the values of C and D are given by Eqs. (2-2) and (2-3) respectively. This equation is an exact solution for current i. Let i_0 be the value of the current when time t equals zero. Letting $t = 0$ in Eq. (2-4), we have

$$i_0 = A + C$$

from which we obtain

$$A = i_0 - C \qquad (2\text{-}5)$$

Let us now program a digital computer solution for this electrical circuit using the Fortran language. Though the configuration of the circuit is specified, we shall make the problem somewhat general by allowing any value of R, L, E_0, and ω to be used for this problem, which allows a parameter study. This increase in generality is done by letting R, L, E_0, and ω be inputs to the Fortran program. This program will solve for the current i from $t = 0$ to time t_{max}, and the results will be printed with a time interval Δt. The computer output will contain a table of current i as a function of time t. The basis of this program are Eqs. (2-2), (2-3), (2-4), and (2-5). The calculation sequence for this program is as follows:

(1)   Load inputs: $KODE$, R, L, E_0, ω, i_0, Δt, and t_{max}.
(2)   Punch and print the inputs.
(3) $t = 0$
(4) $F = \dfrac{E_0}{\omega^2 L^2 + R^2}$

(5) $C = -\omega L F$
(6) $D = R F$
(7) $A = i_0 - C$
(8) $i_p = C \cos \omega t + D \sin \omega t$
(9) $i_h = A e^{-Rt/L}$
(10) $i = i_h + i_p$
(11)   Punch and print t and i.
(12)   New value of time $t = $ old $t + \Delta t$
(13)   Test $(t - t_{max})$: If $t > t_{max}$, go to (1) for the next case.
                If $t \le t_{max}$, go to (8) for the next Δt time cycle.

The term KODE is an arbitrary number used for a quick identification of a particular case. The previous calculation sequence is the basis of the following Fortran program, which solves for the variation of current i with time t for the electrical circuit illustrated in Fig. 2-1. Figure 2-2 is a block diagram for both the calculation sequence and the Fortran program. In the calculation sequence or the block diagram, note that all of the inputs were printed. This was done so that the user can determine whether the proper inputs were used for a specific problem, and whether the input keypunch forms were properly filled in. Input errors are sometimes too common due to carelessness. Also note that the constant terms F, C, D, and A are calculated first, so that they will not be recalculated during every Δt time-cycle. Also note that we need initial values for time t and

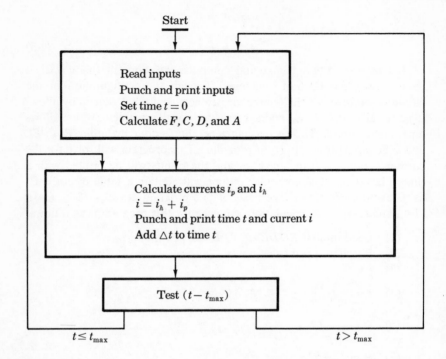

Fig. 2-2

current i and that we need a final value for time t, so that we can end the problem (i.e., not go through an endless number of cycles). The Fortran symbols KODE, R, DUC, E, W, ZCUR, DT, TMAX, T, CUR, A, F, C, D, PART, and HOM are used to represent the physical terms *KODE*, R, L, E_0, ω, i_0, Δt, t_{max}, t, i, A, F, C, D, i_p, and i_h, respectively.

```
 1   READ 10, KODE, R, DUC, E, W, ZCUR, DT, TMAX
10   FORMAT (I5, 7F9.3)
     PUNCH 11, KODE, R, DUC, E, W, ZCUR, DT, TMAX
11   FORMAT (///6HINPUTS/I5/7F10.3//6X4HTIME,
       3X7HCURRENT)
     T = 0.0
     F = E/((W * DUC) ** 2 + R ** 2)
     C = −W * DUC * F
     D = R * F
     A = ZCUR − C
 8   PART = C * COSF(W * T) + D * SINF(W * T)
     HOM = A * EXPF(−R * T/DUC)
```

```
      CUR = HOM + PART
      PUNCH 12, T, CUR
   12 FORMAT (2F10.3)
      T = T + DT
      IF (T − TMAX)8, 8, 1
      END
```

If the inputs for this program were $KODE = 1101$, $R = 20$ ohms, $L = 15$ henries, $E_0 = 180$ volts, $\omega = 5$ rad/sec, $i_0 = 6$ amperes, $\Delta t = 0.100$ sec, and $t_{max} = 0.500$ sec; the printed output for this program would look like

```
INPUTS
  1 1 0 1
        2 0.00 0    1 5 . 000 180.000 5.000 6.000 0.100 0.500
           TIME   CURRENT
           0.00 0    6 . 000
            .10 0    5 . 532
            .20 0    5 . 603
            .30 0    5 . 961
            .40 0    6 . 310
            .50 0    6 . 383
```

2.3   Checking Out a Fortran Program

Program checkout had already been mentioned in very brief fashion in Sec. 1.14 when the $\sqrt{x}$, e^x, and sin x programs were discussed. Because of its great importance and to give it added emphasis, more will be said in this section about program checkout, and this will be done with respect to the electrical circuit program of Sec. 2.2, which at present has no special checkout features, except for the printout of all the input terms. It is desirable to have such a printout in all computer programs. To do a complete job of checking out this electrical circuit program, it would be wise to calculate by hand each of the terms computed by this program (e.g., F, C, D, etc.) to the same accuracy as that done by the digital computer. Since Fortran arithmetic calculations are carried out to eight significant digits, this would require a desk calculator and a good set of trigonometric tables. If this degree of accuracy is used in the hand calculations, then it should be sufficient to do these calculations for three or four values of time t. Now we want to devise a means for printing out all of the terms computed by the program so that they may be checked and compared with those calculated by hand. If two corresponding terms do not agree, then either the computer- or the hand-calculated term is in error. It may be noted that it would have been easier to check out this program if we had broken statement 8, which computes i_p, into the following three statements:

$$8 \quad PARTA = C * COSF(W * T)$$
$$PARTB = D * SINF(W * T)$$
$$PART = PARTA + PARTB$$

We may put a temporary checkout feature in the program by placing the following two statements, which furnish us a detailed printout,

$$PUNCH\ 13,\ F,\ C,\ D,\ A,\ PART,\ HOM$$
$$13 \quad FORMAT\ (6F10.3)$$

just before the PUNCH 12, T, CUR statement. The previous two statements, which should be removed after program checkout is completed, print the terms F, C, D, A, i_p, and i_h, which are useful for program checkout and are not often used for engineering purposes.

Because a computer program may be modified later on and because sometimes a program, especially a large one, is not completely checked out at first, it is useful to have a *permanent checkout feature* in a computer program. We shall use the input term KODE for this purpose. If KODE $\geq$ 0, we shall print the normal engineering output, which is t and i. If the KODE term is a negative input number, we shall print the terms t, i, F, C, D, A, i_p, and i_h for checkout purposes. To do this, we shall replace the statements

$$PUNCH\ 12,\ T,\ CUR$$
$$12 \quad FORMAT\ (2F10.3)$$
$$T = T + DT$$

in the Fortran program of Sec. 2.2 by the following six Fortran statements:

$$IF\ (KODE)2,\ 3,\ 3$$
$$2 \quad PUNCH\ 13,\ T,\ CUR,\ F,\ C,\ D,\ A,\ PART,\ HOM$$
$$GO\ TO\ 4$$
$$3 \quad PUNCH\ 13,\ T,\ CUR$$
$$13 \quad FORMAT\ (8F9.3)$$
$$4 \quad T = T + DT$$

Usually the magnitude ranges are known for the input and output quantities for an engineering problem, but they may not all be known for other quantities. When their magnitude ranges are not known, it is best to print the checkout quantities in a floating-point exponential form. It should be mentioned that all new and modified Fortran programs should be checked over visually before they are ever run on a digital computer. A good way to do this is to write the calculation sequence from the Fortran program

itself, and then check to determine whether it matches the original calculation sequence. It might also be mentioned that the insertion of these
new Fortran statements modifies step (11) of the calculation sequence in
Sec. 2.2 to be

(11) Test the KODE input term: If KODE $\geq$ 0, print t and i.
                                If KODE $<$ 0, print $t, i, F, C, D, A,$
                                i_p, and i_h for checkout purposes.

2.4 Numerical Methods

We would generally solve for the current variation with time for the
electrical circuit of Fig. 2-1 on a digital computer by use of a numerical
method, rather than the method we used in Sec. 2.2. In that section, we
solved the circuit differential equation by analytical means and programmed this solution, which is an exact solution, for digital computer
calculation. If the circuit differential equation were nonlinear, due to a
nonlinear circuit element, then it would have to be solved by numerical
means, since it cannot be solved by classical or Laplace transform techniques. In contrast to exact analytical methods, numerical methods are
often approximate, repetitive step-by-step methods, which can be tedious
to apply when done by hand calculation. They are usually easy to set up
on a digital computer, which can quickly do this labor. We might divide
numerical methods into two broad categories: those used to solve equations and those used to analyze tabulated data.

There are numerous existing numerical methods, and this text describes
only a few of the more elementary methods. This text purposely covers a
wide variety of engineering problems, and these problems require different types of numerical techniques (e.g., interpolation of tabulated data,
solution of an ordinary differential equation, integration of tabulated data,
etc.) for their solution. These are included purposely in order to give this
text a problem-oriented approach. This text covers in detail only a few
numerical techniques of different types, and it illustrates the need for them
by means of engineering problems that require the use of a numerical
method for their solution, but it does not attempt to be a reference for
numerical methods. An elementary numerical method is usually used
when solving an example engineering problem; the text discusses the
limitations of this method. Later it names and often discusses, in brief
fashion, some better techniques that may be used to solve a specific engineering problem. The details of these better methods are discussed more
fully in numerical analysis references, some of which are listed in the back
of this text. The author feels that this is a justified approach for an engineering textbook, since most engineers will probably program only nu-

merical methods that are easy to apply (e.g., the solution of an ordinary differential equation). Methods that are more difficult to apply (e.g., smoothing and curve-fitting tabulated data and inverting a matrix) are often already programmed as subroutines that may be easily utilized by the engineer in his program. Usually there is an accompanying writeup with these subroutines that states how to incorporate the subroutine in a program, the name of the particular numerical method used, and the range of validity and the limitations of the subroutine. The methods and rules for programming a Fortran subprogram are discussed in Chapter 3, while Chapter 4 has several engineering examples that illustrate the use of a Fortran SUBROUTINE subprogram. The mathematician, however, should know both the theory and the details of numerical methods because he is often called upon to program such numerical analysis subprograms.

The various types of numerical methods are categorized differently in various numerical analysis references. This text will arbitrarily classify numerical methods in the twelve categories listed as follows.

1. Evaluation of functions and expressions, summation of series, etc.
2. Solution and roots of single equations.
3. Solution of systems of linear and nonlinear, simultaneous equations.
4. Solution of ordinary differential equations.
5. Solution of partial differential equations.
6. Solution of integral equations.
7. Interpolation of tabulated data.
8. Integration and differentiation of tabulated data.
9. Smoothing and curve- and equation-fitting tabulated data.
10. Matrix methods and linear algebra.
11. Statistical analyses.
12. Simulation and Monte Carlo methods.

This classification is arbitrary, because some of these categories are inter-related. The names and details of some specific numerical methods within these categories are discussed throughout this text. Since this text is written in a problem-oriented fashion and since the numerical techniques are discussed throughout Chapters 2 and 4, the names of the numerical techniques appear in boldface print when they are first discussed, so that the reader may more easily locate them in this text. Categories 1 through 6 are used to solve equations, while categories 7 through 12 are used to analyze tabulated data.

We shall say a little something here about Monte Carlo methods, since this topic will not be mentioned again in this text and since the reader might be unfamiliar with this subject area. *Monte Carlo methods* use statistical mathematics to determine the probabilities in certain situations. Some possible applications are particle motion in molecular physics, statistical thermodynamics, business situations, generation of random numbers, automobile traffic behavior, etc. If this technique is to furnish good results, it is required that the particular situation be repeated many times so that it may be considered to be a game-of-chance process (as the name of this method implies). Hence, the application of Monte Carlo methods can be made much more effective by use of a digital computer. Briefly stated, the basic principle of the Monte Carlo method is that the expected result or score of a game-of-chance situation, no matter how complicated, can in theory be estimated by averaging the results of a large number of situations (i.e., plays of the game). Monte Carlo methods have been applied also to perform such mathematical operations as matrix inversion, solving partial differential equations, evaluating integrals, solving roots of equations, etc., by statistical means.

2.5 Steps in Setting Up and Solving an Engineering Problem on a Digital Computer

We have already programmed some short problems in Fortran for digital computer solution. Now we wish to consider the solution of a typical engineering problem. This text arbitrarily divides the procedure for solving a typical engineering problem into the following eight steps.

1. Definition of the problem and formulation of the physical model, based on a thorough understanding of the problem and its details.
2. Formulation of the mathematical equations, using the physical model as a basis.
3. Determination of the numerical techniques to use, if they are necessary.
4. Determination of the problem inputs and the desired outputs.
5. Writing the calculation sequence and possibly drawing a block diagram.
6. Programming the problem solution.
7. Running the program on the digital computer for both program checkout and problem solution.
8. Interpretation of the results.

The use of the first six steps in programming the solution of a nonlinear electrical circuit is illustrated in Sec. 2.6. Most of these steps are also shown for illustrative purposes when solving the problems in Secs. 2.9, 2.10, and 2.12 of this chapter. Much physical background is also furnished in these sections. The first five steps and step 8 should be done *by* the engineer when solving an engineering problem on a digital computer. Note that knowledge of a programming language is very helpful, but not necessary, for the engineer to do these six steps properly. That is, six of these eight solution steps *can* be performed by an engineer who *thoroughly* knows the details of the physical problem and who knows little about programming and computer operation. In professional practice, the engineer may do step 6 himself, especially for small problems like those in this text, or he may have it done by a person who specializes in programming. For this reason, this text emphasizes steps 1 to 5 more than most texts of this type, which usually emphasize step 6. Some of the digital-computer problem solutions in this text go only as far as the calculation sequence and do not contain a Fortran program. It might also be noted that an engineer has to go through these same six steps (i.e., steps 1 to 5 and 8) if he solves a problem using a desk calculator or any type of digital computer (including those without Fortran capabilities). Most companies prefer to have step 7 done by a trained computer operator, in order to increase the efficiency of computer operation, since it is a high-cost item.

As was indicated previously, very often in professional practice the engineer has a professional programmer write the programs for solving his problems on digital computers. This engineer should, however, be able to set up the problem for digital computer solution. He should also write the calculation sequence and be able to specify or discuss the numerical solution technique. For this reason, this text concentrates heavily on set-up procedures, such as the writing of a calculation sequence. For a more effective communication with the programmer, the engineer should know something about programming languages and should be capable of programming the solution of small engineering problems. Much expensive computer time has been wasted in the engineering profession during the checkout of a program because the engineer does not know how to communicate properly with a programmer. The checkout debugging of a computer program requires knowledge of both the programming language and of the details of the problem. The engineer may have to decide whether an erroneous result is due to a programming error or to an error in his analysis or specification of the problem. The engineer should know the theory of analysis, the problem assumptions and compromises, and the computer program's limitations, whenever he utilizes a computer program, so that he can properly interpret the printed results.

2.6   Solution of a Nonlinear Electrical Circuit Problem

Consider the electrical circuit illustrated in Fig. 2-1, for which we want to find the current variation with time. Suppose that the resistor is a nonlinear circuit element whose resistance R varies with the current and is given by

$$R = F|i|^a$$

where $|i|$ is the absolute value of the current and F and a are arbitrary numerical values. Using *Kirchoff's voltage law*, the *loop equation* for this circuit is

$$L\frac{di}{dt} + F|i|^a i = E_0 \sin \omega t$$

which can be rewritten in the following form

$$\frac{di}{dt} = \frac{1}{L}(E_g - E_R) \tag{2-6}$$

where $E_g = E_0 \sin \omega t$ is the voltage supplied by the voltage source, and $E_R = F|i|^a i$ is the voltage drop across the resistor. Since Eq. (2-6) is a nonlinear differential equation, we cannot solve it by classical or Laplace transform methods. We shall solve it in numerical fashion by use of the *Euler method*. As a background for the Euler method, consider the following equation from calculus

$$f(x + \Delta x) - f(x) = \int_x^{x+\Delta x} f'(\xi) \, d\xi \tag{2-7}$$

If the slope $f'(\xi)$ is constant in the interval from x to $x + \Delta x$, this slope equals $f'(x)$ and this equation gives the following formula when the integral is evaluated

$$f(x + \Delta x) = f(x) + (\Delta x)f'(x) \tag{2-8}$$

which is the equation for the **Euler method** and which is also the sum of the first two terms of a Taylor series. This equation can be rewritten in subscript form as follows

$$f_{x+\Delta x} = f_x + (\Delta x)f'_x \tag{2-9}$$

Essentially this method says that if we know the values of $f(x)$ and $f'(x)$, which are at location x, we can *approximate* $f(x + \Delta x)$ by use of Eq. (2-8). The accuracy of this method, which *assumes* that $f'(x)$ is constant in each Δx interval, improves as Δx is made smaller. This method is graphically illustrated in Fig. 2-3, where the sum of the unshaded areas under the curve is the error that results from using this method.

Applying the Euler method (i.e., Eq. (2-9)) to this electrical circuit problem, we have

$$i_{t+\Delta t} = i_t + (\Delta t)\left(\frac{di}{dt}\right)_t \tag{2-10}$$

where di/dt is given by Eq. (2-6). The inputs to this problem are $KODE$, L, F, a, E_0, ω, Δt, t_0, i_0, and t_{max}. The term $KODE$ is an identification

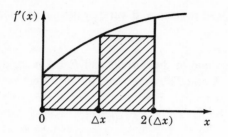

Fig. 2-3

number for each case that is run, t_0 is the initial value of time, i_0 is the value of the current at initial time t_0, and $t_{\max}$ is the value of time at which to end the problem (i.e., the specific case). Since the intent of this problem is to find out the electrical current variation with time, the desired output terms are t and i. We shall also use the *KODE* term for a permanent checkout feature. If the *KODE* input is a negative term, which is done during program checkout, the program will also print the calculated terms E_g, E_R, and di/dt.

Since we have now completed steps 1 to 4 of the *setup and solution procedure* given in Sec. 2.5, we are now ready to write a calculation sequence, which is as follows. The subscript t refers to the value at time t, while the subscript $t + \Delta t$ refers to the value at time $t + \Delta t$.

(1) Load the inputs: $KODE, L, F, a, E_0, \omega, \Delta t, t_0, i_0, t_{\max}$

(2) Punch and print the inputs

(3) $E_{g_t} = E_0 \sin \omega t_t$

(4) $E_{R_t} = F|i_t|^a i_t$

(5) $\left(\dfrac{di}{dt}\right)_t = \dfrac{1}{L}(E_{g_t} - E_{R_t})$

(6) Test *KODE*: If $KODE \geq 0$, go to (9)

  If $KODE < 0$, go to (7)

(7) Punch and print $t_t, i_t, E_{g_t}, E_{R_t},$ and $\left(\dfrac{di}{dt}\right)_t$

(8) Go to (10)

(9) Punch and print t_t and i_t

(10) $t_{t+\Delta t} = t_t + \Delta t$

(11) $i_{t+\Delta t} = i_t + (\Delta t)\left(\dfrac{di}{dt}\right)_t$

(12) Test $(t_{t+\Delta t} - t_{\max})$: If > 0, go to (1) for next case

  If ≤ 0, go to (3) for next Δt time cycle

As the *first* step in writing the computer program, we shall assign symbolic Fortran names to the various terms in the preceding calculation sequence. The symbols KODE, AL, F, A, EO, W, DT, T, CUR, TMAX, EG, ER, and DIDT will be used to represent the terms $KODE$, L, F, a, E_0, ω, Δt, t_t (also t_0 and $t_{t+\Delta t}$), i_t (also i_0 and $i_{t+\Delta t}$), t_{max}, E_{g_t}, E_{R_t}, and $(di/dt)_t$ respectively. It should be noted that input i_0 is the initial value of i_t and that $i_{t+\Delta t}$ is the next value of i_t. Thus, we can use the same Fortran name to represent i_0, i_t and $i_{t+\Delta t}$. For a similar reason, we shall use the same Fortran name to represent t_0, t_t, and $t_{t+\Delta t}$. The following is a Fortran program which is written from the preceding calculation sequence and which may be used to solve this circuit problem. Thus, we have now completed the first six steps of the *setup and solution procedure* given in Sec. 2.5.

```
 1   READ 10, KODE, AL, F, A, EO, W, DT, T, CUR, TMAX
10   FORMAT (I5, 4F8.4/5F8.4)
     PUNCH 11, KODE, AL, F, A, EO, W, DT, T, CUR, TMAX
11   FORMAT (///6HINPUTS/I5/4F13.4/5F13.4//9X4HTIME,
       6X7HCURRENT)
 3   EG = EO * SINF(W * T)
     ER = F * CUR * (ABSF(CUR) ** A)
     DIDT = (EG − ER)/AL
     IF (KODE)7, 8, 8
 7   PUNCH 12, T, CUR, EG, ER, DIDT
     GO TO 9
 8   PUNCH 12, T, CUR
12   FORMAT (2F13.5, 3F10.4)
 9   T = T + DT
     CUR = CUR + DT * DIDT
     IF (T − TMAX)3, 3, 1
     END
```

As a modification to this problem, suppose that the output of the voltage source was a half-wave rectified sine wave. That is, step (3) of the calculation sequence now becomes

$$E_{g_t} = E_0 \sin \omega t_t \quad \text{if } \sin \omega t_t \geq 0$$
$$E_{g_t} = 0 \qquad\qquad \text{if } \sin \omega t_t < 0$$

This modification can be handled by letting the statement after statement 3 in the previous program (i.e., the statement calculating ER) be statement 4, and then inserting the following two statements between statements 3 and 4. It is not uncommon to make slight changes in an engineering program in order to make it solve slightly different problems.

```
     IF (EG)5, 4, 4
 5   EG = 0.0
```

2.7   Printout Control

Oftentimes in an engineering problem, we do not wish the computer to print the output on every computational cycle that the computer undergoes. Otherwise, we may have an excessive amount of unimportant, printed data, and this excessiveness may hamper its readability. We may wish the computer to print the output on every N computational cycles, where N is a previously specified number, or we may have an interval for printout. In the example for this section, we shall use a printout interval, and we shall incorporate it in the electrical circuit problem of Sec. 2.6. This will also give us some idea of what is done when a program is modified. In professional practice, many engineering programs undergo much modification for correction and improvement purposes and to make them more general.

First, we shall discuss the size of the Δt time interval that should be used for the numerical solution of the electrical circuit problem of Sec. 2.6, in order to obtain accurate results. The Euler method, which is given by Eq. (2-8) or (2-9), is a relatively inaccurate numerical solution technique, and better methods will be discussed in Sec. 2.8. As can be seen from Fig. 2-3, the accuracy increases as the interval Δx or Δt is made smaller (i.e., there will be less unshaded area under the curve). For this circuit problem, we shall determine our Δt interval-size by running a problem on the computer with a specified value of Δt and then re-running the problem with a value of Δt that is one-half that of the previously specified one. If both computer results agree within a suitable accuracy, then the first specified value of Δt is satisfactory. If the two results do not agree, then we again halve the value of Δt, and repeat the procedure. This is an *interval-halving technique*.

For this electrical circuit problem, the required value of Δt may be so small that the printout may be excessive, unless we printed the output only when a specified interval $(\Delta t)_p$ is attained. It will also be easier to apply the interval-halving technique to determine the proper value of Δt, when the output for *all* cases is printed at a specified interval $(\Delta t)_p$, since this makes *comparison* of results easier.

To incorporate the print-interval feature in the Fortran program of Sec. 2.6, we shall use the symbol DTPRT for $(\Delta t)_p$ and the symbol TPRT for t_{print}, where t_{print} is the next value of time at which we wish to print output data. That is, we shall print the output *only* whenever $t_i = t_{\text{print}}$. Thus, we shall have to add the term DTPRT to statement 1, which loads the input data, and to the statement that punches the input data. FORMAT statements 10 and 11 will also have to be modified. Suppose that we want to print the output first at time t_0. To do this we shall put the statement

$$\text{TPRT} = \text{T}$$

immediately before statement 3. To print the output at an interval of $(\Delta t)_p$ thereafter, we shall place the following two statements

$$\text{IF (T} - \text{TPRT)9, 6, 6}$$
$$\text{6   TPRT} = \text{TPRT} + \text{DTPRT}$$

immediately before the IF (KODE)7, 8, 8 statement. The first of these two statements tells the program to skip to statement 9 (i.e., jump over the printout statements) if $t_t < t_{\text{print}}$. If $t_t \geq t_{\text{print}}$, the program goes to statement 6, after which it prints the output according to the sign of the KODE term. Statement 6 calculates the new value of t_{print} (i.e., the next value of time at which to print the output) by adding $(\Delta t)_p$ to the old value of t_{print}. Thus, the first value of t_{print} is t_0, the second value is $t_0 + (\Delta t)_p$, the third value is $t_0 + 2(\Delta t)_p$, etc. Figure 2-4 is a block diagram for the Fortran program for this electrical circuit problem, where the print-interval feature is included.

2.8 Numerical Solution of First-Order Ordinary Differential Equations

We have already solved an electrical circuit problem in Sec. 2.6 by use of a numerical technique. Let us now briefly discuss the numerical solution of first-order differential equations in a general fashion. As stated previously, it is advantageous to solve most nonlinear differential equations by numerical methods, since most cannot be solved by classical or Laplace transform means. Numerical means are also very useful if the differential equation is linear, but the coefficients or the forcing function varies with time or displacement (i.e., whichever is the independent variable), since this often greatly complicates an analytical solution procedure. As we shall see later in Secs. 4.1 and 4.2 of Chapter 4, numerical techniques are especially useful if this variation with time or displacement is so involved that it has to be furnished as a graph or a table. Unlike analytical methods, only a little more complication will be added when numerical methods are used to solve such problems.

Numerical methods are approximate solution techniques, so a certain amount of error will result. There are three types of error involved: truncation, roundoff, and inherent. *Truncation error* is the error due to the use of an approximation method. For example, the unshaded area under the curve of Fig. 2-3 is the error due to the use of the Euler method.

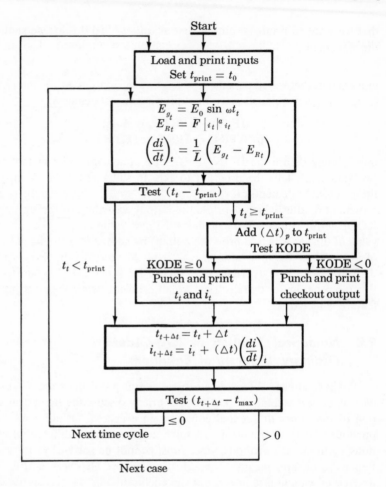

Fig. 2-4

Roundoff error is the error that is due to the use of a finite number of digits in the calculations. For example, this computer would calculate $1/3$ to be 0.33333333. *Inherent error* is that due to the use of an approximately correct term (due to previous truncation and roundoff errors) in a problem equation. For example, when calculating the value of $(di/dt)_t$ at different steps for the problem of Sec. 2.6, there is an inherent error due to the error at each step in the value of current i_t, which is used in the calculation. This type of error is also illustrated in Ill. Ex. 2.1 and Fig. 2-5. These errors generally decrease as the Δt or Δx interval is made smaller, and it is recommended that the interval-halving method mentioned in Sec. 2.7

be used to determine the proper size of this interval when any of the numerical methods mentioned in this section are employed. That is, the computed numerical solution of a differential equation can wander away (i.e., depart further and further) from the true solution, due to the three types of error involved, if the interval size is too large. Most numerical analysis texts furnish equations for the truncation errors of various numerical methods as a function of the interval size and a specified derivative of the dependent variable (i.e., the solution function). If the given differential equation is simple in form, we can use repeated differentiations of this differential equation to calculate the equation for this derivative of a specified degree. For this case, we could calculate the interval size that would be necessary to keep the truncation error, at a particular step of the calculation, below a certain specified amount. This would be difficult to do, however, if the form of the differential equation was involved (e.g., if the coefficients are plotted or tabulated, as they are in many professional engineering problems and which is exemplified in Secs. 4.1 and 4.2, or if the coefficients must be computed from a series of equations) because differentiations of this differential equation would be required.

Fig. 2-5

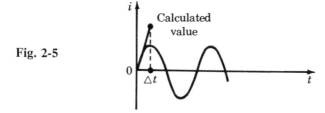

As mentioned previously, the Euler method, which is given by Eq. (2-8), is a rather inaccurate method and better means are desirable. This is especially true for the electrical circuit problem in Sec. 2.6 since the oscillatory voltage source causes a rapidly oscillating loop current, which means that the slope of this current changes rapidly with time. The Euler method might be adequate if the voltage source were a battery in the electrical circuit problem of Sec. 2.6, since the loop current would not be oscillatory for this case, and if the time interval Δt were sufficiently small. Figure 2-5 illustrates why an extremely small Δt interval value must be used if the Euler method is used to solve the oscillatory electrical circuit problem of Sec. 2.6. The Euler method [i.e., Eq. (2-8)] assumes that the slope $f'(x)$ is constant in each Δx interval, which is not what happens usually in physical problems. Because the slope usually varies in an interval, it would be better to use the slope at the midpoint of an interval, instead of the slope at the forward end of the interval as the Euler method does. Let us consider an interval of size $2(\Delta x)$. If we use the slope at the midpoint of this interval as an approximate average-slope value for this interval, substitution in the calculus equation

$$f(x + \Delta x) - f(x - \Delta x) = \int_{x - \Delta x}^{x + \Delta x} f'(\xi) \, d\xi \qquad (2\text{-}11)$$

results in the following equation after the integral is evaluated

$$f(x + \Delta x) = f(x - \Delta x) + 2(\Delta x)f'(x) \qquad (2\text{-}12)$$

where the constant term $f'(x)$ is treated as the average-slope value for $f'(\xi)$. This average-slope would be an exact approximation if $f'(\xi)$ is linear in this $2(\Delta x)$ interval. We shall arbitrarily call the technique given by Eq. (2-12) the *midpoint slope method*. Equation (2-12) can be re-written in subscript form as follows

$$f_{x + \Delta x} = f_{x - \Delta x} + 2(\Delta x)f'_x \qquad (2\text{-}13)$$

The *Adams method* approximates the slope of $f(x)$ by a polynomial of degree n over $(n + 1)$ equally spaced points. For the simplest case, this method assumes that $f'(x)$ has a linear, straight-line variation in each Δx interval, instead of being constant as the Euler method does. A straight line is drawn between $f'(x - \Delta x)$ and $f'(x)$ and is extrapolated to $f'(x + \Delta x)$. Thus, the slope m of this straight line is $(f'(x) - f'(x - \Delta x))/\Delta x$. Using this value of m in the following straight-line equation

$$f'(\xi) = f'(x) + m(\xi - x)$$

and substituting the above equation into Eq. (2-7), we obtain the following result after the integral is evaluated. This result approximates $f(\xi)$ by a quadratic polynomial in the interval from $(x - \Delta x)$ to $(x + \Delta x)$ because the derivation integrated a straight-line approximation for $f'(\xi)$.

$$f(x + \Delta x) = f(x) + \left(\frac{\Delta x}{2}\right)[3f'(x) - f'(x - \Delta x)] \qquad (2\text{-}14)$$

Equation (2-14) can be written in subscript form as follows

$$f_{x + \Delta x} = f_x + \left(\frac{\Delta x}{2}\right)(3f'_x - f'_{x - \Delta x}) \qquad (2\text{-}15)$$

Both the midpoint slope and the Adams methods have a common disadvantage. Suppose that we start the calculations at $x = 0$. For most physical problems, the initial value $f(0)$ is given but not the next value $f(\Delta x)$. Neither method can calculate $f(\Delta x)$, and both methods need a value of $f(\Delta x)$ in order to calculate $f(2\Delta x)$. In other words, both methods need two starting values for $f(x)$. Thus, it is usually necessary to approximate $f(\Delta x)$ by some other means, such as the Euler method, when the

Adams or midpoint slope method is employed. If the given differential equation is simple in form, $f(\Delta x)$ can be approximated by the first three terms of a Taylor series, where we can obtain an equation for $f''(x)$ by differentiating the differential equation.

This section covers only a few of the many numerical methods for solving first-order, ordinary differential equations. Three of the more easily applied methods have been discussed (i.e., Euler, midpoint slope, and Adams), and these methods can be used to solve with sufficient accuracy many rather involved types of differential equations. If we do not wish to use an extremely small interval size, accurate numerical methods will be needed to solve oscillatory problems, as shown in Fig. 2-5, and problems that will require a large number of steps and intervals (e.g., interplanetary space trajectory problems which require both numerous intervals and many significant digits in the calculations). Now we shall discuss two of the more accurate methods—the Milne method and the Runge-Kutta method. We shall not discuss in detail how these methods were derived. It will be noted that these two methods are more difficult to apply.

Milne's method, which has a very small truncation error, passes a quadratic (i.e., second degree) polynomial through three successive, equally spaced points, and this method extrapolates this polynomial to another point, whose x-location shall be denoted by x_{i+1}. Thus, Milne's method uses this polynomial to approximate the value of $f'(x)$ at x_{i+1}, and we shall call this approximated value f'_{i+1}. It can be shown that the area under this quadratic curve segment from point x_{i-3} to point x_{i+1} is equal to $[4(\Delta x)/3](2f'_i - f'_{i-1} + 2f'_{i-2})$, where Δx is the size of the x-interval and f'_{i-2}, f'_{i-1}, and f'_i are the values of $f'(x)$ at x_{i-2}, x_{i-1}, and x_i respectively. Since the area under this curve segment must equal $f(x_{i+1})$ minus $f(x_{i-3})$, we have the approximation

$$f_{i+1} - f_{i-3} = \frac{4(\Delta x)}{3}(2f'_i - f'_{i-1} + 2f'_{i-2})$$

which can be written in a more general non-subscript form as follows

$$f(x + \Delta x) = f(x - 3\Delta x)$$
$$+ \tfrac{4}{3}(\Delta x)[2f'(x) - f'(x - \Delta x) + 2f'(x - 2\Delta x)] \quad \textbf{(2-16)}$$

It should be noted that a big disadvantage of this method is that it requires 4 starting values of $f(x)$ before the method may be applied. That is, if the calculations start at $x = 0$ and if $f(0)$ is given, then the values of $f(\Delta x)$, $f(2\Delta x)$, and $f(3\Delta x)$ must be approximated in order to get the method started. Because these approximations must be rather accurate in order not to destroy the accuracy when Milne's method is applied, these three starting-value terms are often calculated by one of the Runge-Kutta methods, which are discussed next. It may be noted that since Milne's method approximates a cubic polynomial for $f(x)$ over five successive points (because its derivation integrates a quadratic polynomial over this five-point interval), we probably would have to use a rather small interval to apply Milne's method to the oscillatory circuit problem of Sec. 2.6. That is, it can be seen from Fig. 2-5 that we would probably need a rather small value of Δt in order that this cubic polynomial approximation over four successive Δt intervals would adequately approximate this rapidly oscillating current.

Besides being a very accurate method (i.e., has a small truncation error), the **Runge-Kutta method** has a big additional advantage in that it requires only one value of $f(x)$, which is usually given, in order to get the method started. Another very important advantage of this method, whose derivation is based on averaging techniques, is that the interval size may be readily changed at any time because its formula does not contain the value of $f(x)$ or $f'(x)$ in a previous interval, as do the Milne, Adams, and midpoint slope methods. Let us write the first-order, ordinary differential equation, to be solved, in the following generalized, functional-notation form:

$$\frac{dy}{dx} = F(x, y) \qquad (2\text{-}17)$$

We want to solve this differential equation for $y(x)$. The functional term $F(x, y)$ is the solution of the ordinary differential equation for the derivative dy/dx. We are using this functional form because it is easier to express the Runge-Kutta formulae in a functional form. The *second-order accuracy* Runge-Kutta equations are

$$a_1(x) = (\Delta x)F(x, y(x)) \qquad (2\text{-}18a)$$

$$a_2(x) = (\Delta x)F(x + \Delta x, y(x) + a_1(x)) \qquad (2\text{-}18b)$$

$$y(x + \Delta x) = y(x) + \tfrac{1}{2}[a_1(x) + a_2(x)] \qquad (2\text{-}18c)$$

The *third-order accuracy* Runge-Kutta equations are

$$a_1(x) = (\Delta x)F(x, y(x)) \qquad (2\text{-}19a)$$

$$a_2(x) = (\Delta x)F\left(x + \frac{\Delta x}{2}, y(x) + \frac{a_1(x)}{2}\right) \qquad (2\text{-}19b)$$

$$a_3(x) = (\Delta x)F(x + \Delta x, y(x) + 2a_2(x) - a_1(x)) \qquad (2\text{-}19c)$$

$$y(x + \Delta x) = y(x) + \tfrac{1}{6}[a_1(x) + 4a_2(x) + a_3(x)] \qquad (2\text{-}19d)$$

The *fourth-order accuracy* Runge-Kutta equations are

$$a_1(x) = (\Delta x)F(x, y(x)) \qquad (2\text{-}20a)$$

$$a_2(x) = (\Delta x)F\left(x + \frac{\Delta x}{2}, y(x) + \frac{a_1(x)}{2}\right) \qquad (2\text{-}20b)$$

$$a_3(x) = (\Delta x)F\left(x + \frac{\Delta x}{2}, y(x) + \frac{a_2(x)}{2}\right) \qquad \text{(2-20c)}$$

$$a_4(x) = (\Delta x)F(x + \Delta x, y(x) + a_3(x)) \qquad \text{(2-20d)}$$

$$y(x + \Delta x) = y(x) + \tfrac{1}{6}[a_1(x) + 2a_2(x) + 2a_3(x) + a_4(x)] \qquad \text{(2-20e)}$$

Nystrom had modified the Runge-Kutta method to provide more accuracy, but the result is a more involved sixth-order form.

The reader should now carefully go through the illustrative examples of this section since they illustrate the application of the Euler, midpoint slope, Adams, Runge-Kutta, and Milne methods. The reader should also inspect Table 2-1 which tabulates the errors of the numerical calculations that were performed in the examples for this section.

Illustrative Example 2.1.   Suppose that the velocity dy/dt of a particle was equal to $-4y^2t$ ft/sec where t is the time in seconds and y is the displacement in feet of the particle from a reference position. If at time zero, the displacement equals 2 ft, solve for the displacement of this particle from $t = 0$ to $t = 0.200$ sec using the Adams method and an interval of 0.050 sec. Use the Euler method to approximate the second starting value. Calculate the errors of these numerical approximations.

Solution.   Since $dy/dt = -4y^2t$, we are essentially solving the first-order differential equation $dy/dt + 4y^2t = 0$, where $y(0) = 2.000$ ft. To calculate the second starting value, which is $y(0.050)$, we must first substitute in the given differential equation $\dot{y}(t) = -4[y(t)]^2t$ to compute $\dot{y}(0)$ and then apply Eq. (2-8) to approximate $y(0.050)$. These calculations are as follows, where the Euler method approximation for this point was computed from the equation $y(\Delta t) = y(0) + (\Delta t)\dot{y}(0)$ and where this method produced a rather poor approximation since $\dot{y}(0) = 0$ is not a good average velocity for the first interval.

$$\dot{y}(0) = -(4.00)(2.000)^2(0) = 0$$
$$y(0.050) = 2.000 + (0.050)(0) = 2.000 \text{ ft}$$

To apply the Adams method [i.e., Eq. (2-14)] for the rest of this problem, we successively use the following equations

$$\dot{y}(t) = -4[y(t)]^2t$$

$$y(t + \Delta t) = y(t) + \left(\frac{\Delta t}{2}\right)[3\dot{y}(t) - \dot{y}(t - \Delta t)]$$

to obtain the following numerical results:

$$\dot{y}(0.050) = -(4.00)(2.000)^2(0.050) = -0.800 \text{ ft/sec}$$
$$y(0.100) = 2.000 + (0.025)(-2.400 - 0) = 1.940 \text{ ft}$$
$$\dot{y}(0.100) = -(4.00)(1.940)^2(0.100) = -1.506 \text{ ft/sec}$$
$$y(0.150) = 1.940 + (0.025)(-4.518 + 0.800) = 1.847 \text{ ft}$$
$$\dot{y}(0.150) = -(4.00)(1.847)^2(0.150) = -2.047 \text{ ft/sec}$$
$$y(0.200) = 1.847 + (0.025)(-6.141 + 1.506) = 1.731 \text{ ft}$$

In order to determine the errors in our computed results, we must first obtain the exact results. This is why we chose an example problem whose analytical solution may be easily obtained. Since the given differential equation can be rewritten in the following form

$$\frac{dy}{y^2} = -4t \, dt$$

integration of both sides of the previous equation and evaluation of the integration constant from the initial condition $y(0) = 2$ gives us the following exact solution for displacement y:

$$y = \frac{2}{4t^2 + 1}$$

Substitution for time t in the previous equation shows that the exact values for $y(0.050)$, $y(0.100)$, $y(0.150)$, and $y(0.200)$ are 1.980, 1.923, 1.835, and 1.724 ft respectively. Thus, the numerical approximation errors are equal to -0.020, -0.017, -0.012, and -0.007 ft at $t = 0.050, 0.100, 0.150$, and 0.200 sec. Note that the largest of these errors resulted from the use of the Euler method to approximate $y(0.050)$. These errors can be reduced by using a smaller value for Δt and by using a better method to approximate the second starting value. If the Euler method were used throughout, the errors would be -0.020, -0.037, -0.048, and -0.053 ft at $t = 0.050, 0.100, 0.150$, and 0.200 sec. If an interval of 0.00625 sec were used for applying the Euler method throughout this problem, the error would be only -0.006 ft at $t = 2.000$ sec.

Illustrative Example 2.2.   Solve Ill. Ex. 2.1 using the midpoint slope method and an interval of 0.050 sec. Use the Euler method to approximate the second starting value. Calculate the errors of these numerical approximations.

Solution.   We are given that $y(0 = 2.000$ ft. From Ill. Ex. 2.1, we find that $\dot{y}(0) = 0$ and that use of the Euler method approximates the value of $y(0.050)$ to be 2.000 ft. To apply the midpoint slope method [i.e., Eq. (2-12)] for the rest of this problem, we successively use the following two equations:

$$\dot{y}(t) = -4[y(t)]^2 t$$
$$y(t + \Delta t) = y(t - \Delta t) + 2(\Delta t)\dot{y}(t)$$

to obtain the following numerical results

$$\dot{y}(0.050) = -(4.00)(2.000)^2(0.050) = -0.800$$
$$y(0.100) = 2.000 + (0.100)(-0.800) = 1.920$$
$$\dot{y}(0.100) = -(4.00)(1.920)^2(0.100) = -1.475$$
$$y(0.150) = 2.000 + (0.100)(-1.475) = 1.852$$
$$\dot{y}(0.150) = -(4.00)(1.852)^2(0.150) = -2.058$$
$$y(0.200) = 1.920 + (0.100)(-2.058) = 1.714$$

The numerical approximation errors are equal to -0.020, 0.003, -0.017, and 0.010 ft at $t = 0.050, 0.100, 0.150$, and 0.200 sec. That is, the error in the computed value for $y(0.200)$ is $(1.724 - 1.714)$ or 0.010 ft. These errors would be reduced, of course, if we used a smaller interval (i.e., a smaller value for Δt).

If we had obtained our second starting value by using the first three terms of a Taylor series as follows

$$y(\Delta t) = y(0) + (\Delta t)\dot{y}(0) + \frac{(\Delta t)^2}{2} \ddot{y}(0)$$

we would greatly reduce the magnitude of our errors, since the largest error magnitude in our previous calculations was the result of the calculation of $y(0.050)$ by the Euler method. To calculate the value of $\ddot{y}(0)$, we first differentiate the given differential equation to obtain $\ddot{y}(t) = -4[y(t)]^2$ and then substitute $y(0) = 2$ in this result to obtain $\ddot{y}(0) = -4(2)^2 = -16$. Note that it was easy to compute $\ddot{y}(0)$ for this problem because the given differential equation is simple in form (e.g., the coefficients are not plotted or tabulated as they are for many professional engineering problems and as they are for the engineering problems discussed in Secs. 4.1 and 4.2).

Illustrative Example 2.3.   Solve Ill. Ex. 2.1 using Milne's method and an interval of 0.050 sec. Use the second-order accuracy Runge-Kutta method to approximate three of the four needed starting values. Calculate the errors of these numerical approximations.

Solution.   We are given the first starting value which is $y(0) = 2.000$ ft. Now we wish to calculate the other three starting values, $y(0.050)$, $y(0.100)$, and $y(0.150)$, using the second-order accuracy Runge-Kutta method. Since $dy/dt = -4y^2t$, then Eq. (2-17) states that function $F(t, y) = -4y^2t$. Applying Eqs. (2-18a, b, c), we have

$$a_1(t) = (\Delta t)F(t, y(t)) = (\Delta t)[-4y(t)^2t]$$
$$a_2(t) = (\Delta t)F(t + \Delta t, y(t) + a_1(t)) = (\Delta t)[-4(y(t) + a_1(t))^2(t + \Delta t)]$$
$$y(t + \Delta t) = y(t) + \tfrac{1}{2}[a_1(t) + a_2(t)]$$

Using these three equations for each calculation of $y(t + \Delta t)$, we obtain the following numerical results:

$$a_1(0) = -(0.050)(4.00)(2.000)^2(0) = 0$$
$$a_2(0) = -(0.050)(4.00)(2.000 + 0)^2(0.050) = -0.040$$
$$y(0.050) = 2.000 + \tfrac{1}{2}(0 - 0.040) = 1.980 \text{ ft}$$
$$a_1(0.050) = -(0.050)(4.00)(1.980)^2(0.050) = -0.039$$
$$a_2(0.050) = -(0.050)(4.00)(1.980 - 0.039)^2(0.100) = -0.075$$
$$y(0.100) = 1.980 + \tfrac{1}{2}(-0.039 - 0.075) = 1.923 \text{ ft}$$
$$a_1(0.100) = -(0.050)(4.00)(1.923)^2(0.100) = -0.074$$
$$a_2(0.100) = -(0.050)(4.00)(1.923 - 0.074)^2(0.150) = -0.102$$
$$y(0.150) = 1.923 + \tfrac{1}{2}(-0.074 - 0.102) = 1.835 \text{ ft}$$

Comparison of these results with the analytic solution values furnished in Ill. Ex. 2.1 show that these three results for $y(t)$ are exact for the number of decimal places that were carried in the calculations. If we would also calculate $y(0.200)$ by this method, we would obtain a value of 1.724 ft, which is another exact result. Thus, this illustrates, by example, the superior accuracy of the Runge-Kutta method when compared to the methods utilized in Ill. Exs. 2.1 and 2.2.

Applying Eq. (2-16), which is Milne's method, to calculate $y(0.200)$, we obtain the equation

$$y(0.200) = y(0) + \tfrac{4}{3}(\Delta t)[2\dot{y}(0.150) - \dot{y}(0.100) + 2\dot{y}(0.050)]$$

We can calculate the values of the three derivatives $\dot{y}(0.050)$, $\dot{y}(0.100)$, and $\dot{y}(0.150)$ by substitution of time t and the computed $y(t)$ values in the given differential equation, which is

$$\dot{y}(t) = -4[y(t)]^2 t$$

Doing this, we obtain $\dot{y}(0.050) = -0.784$, $\dot{y}(0.100) = -1.48$, and $\dot{y}(0.150) = -2.02$. Thus, application of Milne's method gives

$$y(0.200) = 2.000 + \tfrac{4}{3}(0.050)[2(-2.02) - (-1.48) + 2(-0.784)] = 1.724 \text{ ft}$$

which is also an exact result. Table 2-1 tabulates, for purpose of comparison, the errors that result when the Euler, Adams, midpoint slope, and second-order accuracy Runge-Kutta methods are used to solve this problem when a time interval of 0.050 sec is used. It should be mentioned again that the results for the Adams and midpoint slope methods would improve if the second starting values were more accurately approximated.

Table 2-1

		Errors			
t (sec)	Exact $y(t)$	Euler	Adams	Midpoint Slope	Runge-Kutta
0	2.000	0	0	0	0
0.050	1.980	−0.020	−0.020	−0.020	0.000
0.100	1.923	−0.037	−0.017	0.003	0.000
0.150	1.835	−0.048	−0.012	−0.017	0.000
0.200	1.724	−0.053	−0.007	0.010	0.000

2.9 Solution of a Nonlinear Mechanical Vibration Problem

Consider the mechanical vibration system illustrated in Fig. 2-6 that consists of a weight, a linear spring, a nonlinear damper, and an oscillating external force of magnitude $F_0 \cos \omega t$. This example will show us how to numerically solve a second-order, ordinary differential equation using a digital computer.

Since both the spring and the damper resist the motion of the weight W, using Newton's second law the equation of motion for this mechanical system is

$$\frac{W}{g}\ddot{x} = F_0 \cos \omega t - F_d - F_s \tag{2-21}$$

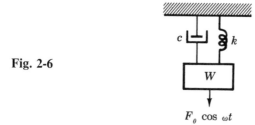

Fig. 2-6

where F_d and F_s are the magnitudes of the damping and spring forces respectively. For a linear spring, $F_s = kx$, where x is the displacement between the two ends and k is the *spring constant*. Most college textbooks use linear dampers, where $F_d = c\dot{x}$, and where *damping coefficient c* is constant, in order to linearize the differential equation of motion and thus permit a straightforward analytical solution. In most actual physical situations, however, dampers are nonlinear, and often the magnitude of the damping force F_d is approximately proportional to the square of the velocity. For this velocity-squared damping, $F_d = a|\dot{x}|\dot{x}$, where $\dot{x}$ is the relative velocity between the two ends of the damper and where $|\dot{x}|$ was used so that F_d can oppose the direction of velocity $\dot{x}$ in Eq. (2-21). To be more general, we shall let $F_d = a|\dot{x}|^b\dot{x}$ (i.e., $c = a|\dot{x}|^b$). Substitution of $F_s = kx$ and $F_d = c\dot{x}$, where $c = a|\dot{x}|^b$, into Eq. (2-21) gives

$$\frac{W}{g}\ddot{x} + a|\dot{x}|^b\dot{x} + kx = F_0 \cos \omega t \qquad (2\text{-}22)$$

Since the previous differential equation is nonlinear, it is best to solve it by numerical means. This is a second-order differential equation, and we shall solve for $\dot{x}$ using the Euler method and for x using the trapezoidal method, which will be discussed next.

Consider the equation

$$f(x + \Delta x) - f(x) = \int_x^{x+\Delta x} f'(\xi)\, d\xi \qquad (2\text{-}23)$$

If we assume that the average value of slope $f'(\xi)$ in the interval from x to $x + \Delta x$ is equal to $[f'(x) + f'(x + \Delta x)]/2$ and substitute this result in Eq. (2-23), we obtain the following approximation after the integral is evaluated:

$$f(x + \Delta x) = f(x) + \left(\frac{\Delta x}{2}\right)[f'(x) + f'(x + \Delta x)] \qquad (2\text{-}24)$$

The **trapezoidal method** is given by Eq. (2-24), which can be rewritten in subscript form as follows:

$$f_{x+\Delta x} = f_x + \left(\frac{\Delta x}{2}\right)(f'_x + f'_{x+\Delta x}) \qquad (2\text{-}25)$$

The trapezoidal method is graphically illustrated in Fig. 2-7, and comparison of the size of the unshaded area under this curve with that of Fig.

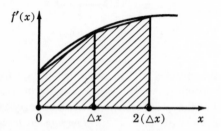

Fig. 2-7

2-3 clearly shows the superiority of the trapezoidal method over the Euler method. The trapezoidal method cannot be directly applied in the solution of first-order differential equations of the general type

$$f'(x) \equiv \frac{df}{dx} = F(x,f)$$

This is because we need the value of $f(x + \Delta x)$ in order to calculate $f'(x + \Delta x)$. The trapezoidal method can be used to improve a value of $f(x + \Delta x)$ that was calculated by another method. For example, when we solve a problem using the midpoint slope method, we must approximate $f(\Delta x)$ in order to obtain a second starting value. We can calculate $f(\Delta x)$ first by the Euler method, and then improve this approximation by recalculating it by the trapezoidal method. This will be explained in more detail in Sec. 2.11.

The trapezoidal method, however, is very useful in the solution of higher-order differential equations. For a third-order differential equation written in the following general form

$$f'''(x) \equiv \frac{d^3f}{dx^3} = F(x,f,f',f'')$$

we can numerically obtain $f''(x + \Delta x)$ using the Euler, midpoint slope, or Adams method; and we can numerically obtain both $f'(x + \Delta x)$ and $f(x + \Delta x)$ by using the trapezoidal method (i.e., by use of Eq. (2-24)). If a method as accurate as Milne's method were used to calculate $f''(x + \Delta x)$, then $f'(x + \Delta x)$ and $f(x + \Delta x)$ should be calculated by methods like the Milne method or Simpson's one-third method (which is discussed in Sec. 4.5).

Using Eq. (2-22) and the Euler and the trapezoidal methods to solve the previously mentioned mechanical vibration problem, we have the following equations for the solution of this problem:

$$\ddot{x}_t = \frac{g}{W}(F_0 \cos \omega t_t - a|\dot{x}_t|^b \dot{x}_t - k x_t) \qquad (2\text{-}26)$$

$$\dot{x}_{t+\Delta t} = \dot{x}_t + (\Delta t)\ddot{x}_t \qquad (2\text{-}27)$$

$$x_{t+\Delta t} = x_t + \left(\frac{\Delta t}{2}\right)(\dot{x}_t + \dot{x}_{t+\Delta t}) \qquad (2\text{-}28)$$

where damping coefficient $c = a|\dot{x}|^b$. As was discussed in Sec. 2.8, this problem will require a very small time interval Δt, since an oscillatory motion (i.e., a vibration) will result. Thus, it is preferable to approximate $\dot{x}_{t+\Delta t}$ by a better method than the Euler method. The inputs for this problem are $KODE$, W, a, b, k, F_0, ω, Δt, t_0, x_0, $\dot{x}_0$, $t_{\max}$, and $(\Delta t)_p$. The terms x_0 and $\dot{x}_0$ are the values of the displacement and velocity at initial time t_0, and $(\Delta t)_p$ is the time-interval for output printout. The $KODE$ term will be used for both case identification and program checkout purposes. The desired output terms are time t and displacement x and possibly the system forces, velocity, and acceleration.

Now we are ready to write a calculation sequence from which a Fortran program may be written. We shall not include a Fortran program in this section, since it is an exercise for the student. The concepts used in writing this program are very similar to those used in writing the Fortran program for the nonlinear electrical circuit problem in Secs. 2.6 and 2.7. The following is a calculation sequence for solving this vibration problem. The values of t_t, x_t, and $\dot{x}_t$ are initialized by using the same Fortran names for t_0 and t_t, for x_0 and x_t, and for $\dot{x}_0$ and $\dot{x}_t$.

(1)   Load the inputs: $KODE$, W, a, b, k, F_0, ω, Δt, t_0, x_0, $\dot{x}_0$, $t_{\max}$, $(\Delta t)_p$

(2)   Punch and print the inputs

(3) $t_{\text{print}} = t_0$

(4) $F_{E_t} = F_0 \cos \omega t_t$

(5) $F_{d_t} = a|\dot{x}_t|^b \dot{x}_t$

(6) $F_{s_t} = k x_t$

(7) $\ddot{x}_t = \left(\dfrac{32.2}{W}\right)(F_{E_t} - F_{d_t} - F_{s_t})$

(8)   Test $(t_t - t_{\text{print}})$: If ≥ 0, go to (9)
             If < 0, go to (14)

(9)   Add $(\Delta t)_p$ to t_{print}

(10) Test $KODE$: If $KODE \geq 0$, go to (13)
             If $KODE < 0$, go to (11)

(11) Punch and print t_t, x_t, $\dot{x}_t$, $\ddot{x}_t$, F_{E_t}, F_{d_t}, and F_{s_t}

(12) Go to (14)

(13) Punch and print t_t and x_t

(14) $t_{t+\Delta t} = t_t + \Delta t$

(15) $\dot{x}_{t+\Delta t} = \dot{x}_t + (\Delta t)\ddot{x}_t$

(16) $x_{t+\Delta t} = x_t + \left(\dfrac{\Delta t}{2}\right)(\dot{x}_t + \dot{x}_{t+\Delta t})$

(17) Test $(t_{t+\Delta t} - t_{max})$: If >0, go to (1) for next case

   If ≤ 0, go to (4) for next Δt time cycle

Illustrative Example 2.4.   Write a calculation sequence for a digital computer program to solve the following nonlinear, third-order differential equation numerically, by using the Euler method once and the trapezoidal method twice, when the initial values $y(0)$, $\dot{y}(0)$, and $\ddot{y}(0)$ are given.

$$\frac{d^3y}{dt^3} = y^2t + \left(\frac{dy}{dt}\right)^3\left(\frac{d^2y}{dt^2}\right).$$

Solution.   Applying Eqs. (2-8) and (2-25), this calculation sequence may be written as follows, where the subscript form is used in these equations, where step (6) applies the Euler method, and where steps (7) and (8) apply the trapezoidal method.

(1) Load the inputs: $y(0)$, $\dot{y}(0)$, $\ddot{y}(0)$, Δt, and t_{max}

(2) Set $t_t = 0$

(3) $\dddot{y}_t = y_t^2 t_t + \dot{y}_t^3 \ddot{y}_t$

(4) Print t_t, y_t, $\dot{y}_t$, $\ddot{y}_t$ and $\dddot{y}_t$

(5) $t_{t+\Delta t} = t_t + \Delta t$

(6) $\ddot{y}_{t+\Delta t} = \ddot{y}_t + (\Delta t)\dddot{y}_t$

(7) $\dot{y}_{t+\Delta t} = \dot{y}_t + \left(\dfrac{\Delta t}{2}\right)(\ddot{y}_t + \ddot{y}_{t+\Delta t})$

(8) $y_{t+\Delta t} = y_t + \left(\dfrac{\Delta t}{2}\right)(\dot{y}_t + \dot{y}_{+\Delta t})$

(9) Test $(t_{t+\Delta t} - t_{max})$: If >0, go to (1) for the next case

   If ≤ 0, go to (3) for the next Δt time cycle

Illustrative Example 2.5.   Suppose that the acceleration $\ddot{y}$ of a particle was equal to $-4y^2$ ft^2/sec^2 where t is the time in seconds and y is the displacement in feet of the particle from a reference position. If the initial velocity is zero and the initial displacement is 2 ft, solve for the displacement of this particle from $t = 0$ to $t = 0.200$ sec using the trapezoidal and Euler methods and an interval of 0.050 sec. Calculate the errors of these numerical approximations.

Solution.   In mathematical form, this problem requires us to solve the differential equation $\ddot{y} + 4y^2 = 0$, where $\dot{y}(0) = 0$ and $y(0) = 2.000$. Thus, from the given differential equation, we have

$$\ddot{y}(t) = -4[y(t)]^2$$

Application of Eq. (2-8) gives

$$\dot{y}(t + \Delta t) = \dot{y}(t) + (\Delta t)\ddot{y}(t)$$

Applying Eq. (2-24), we obtain

$$y(t + \Delta t) = y(t) + \left(\frac{\Delta t}{2}\right)[\dot{y}(t) + \dot{y}(t + \Delta t)]$$

Using these three previous equations, we obtain the following numerical results

$$\ddot{y}(0) = -(4.00)(2.000)^2 = -16.000$$
$$\dot{y}(0.050) = 0 + (0.050)(-16.000) = -0.800$$
$$y(0.050) = 2.000 + (0.025)(0 - 0.800) = 1.980$$
$$\ddot{y}(0.050) = -(4.00)(1.980)^2 = -15.680$$
$$\dot{y}(0.100) = -0.800 + (0.050)(-15.680) = -1.584$$
$$y(0.100) = 1.980 + (0.025)(-0.800 - 1.584) = 1.920$$
$$\ddot{y}(0.100) = -(4.00)(1.920)^2 = -14.746$$
$$\dot{y}(0.150) = -1.584 + (0.050)(-14.746) = -2.321$$
$$y(0.150) = 1.920 + (0.025)(-1.584 - 2.321) = 1.822$$
$$\ddot{y}(0.150) = -(4.000)(1.822)^2 = -13.279$$
$$\dot{y}(0.200) = -2.321 + (0.050)(-13.279) = -2.985$$
$$y(0.200) = 1.822 + (0.025)(-2.321 - 2.985) = 1.787$$

The solution for the given nonlinear differential equation is $2/(4t^2 + 1)$, which is the same as the solution for Ill. Ex. 2.1. This is to be expected since differentiation of the differential equation in Ill. Ex. 2.1 gives $\ddot{y} = -4y^2$ and since substitution in this differential equation gives $\dot{y}(0) = 0$. Thus, the exact values for $y(0.050)$, $y(0.100)$, $y(0.150)$, and $y(0.200)$ are 1.980, 1.923, 1.835, and 1.724 ft respectively. Thus, the numerical approximation errors are equal to 0.000, -0.003, -0.013, and -0.035 ft at $t = 0.050$, 0.100, 0.150, and 0.200 sec. These errors could be reduced by using a smaller value for the interval Δt or by using the Adams or midpoint slope method instead of the Euler method to compute $\dot{y}(t + \Delta t)$.

2.10   Solution of a Two-Wall Heat Transfer Problem

The physical problem in this section will illustrate how simultaneous, ordinary differential equations are solved by numerical means on a digital computer. It will be seen that, unlike analytical methods, the resultant procedure is only slightly more involved than that when solving a single differential equation by numerical means. A two-wall heat transfer problem is used here as the physical example; but we could also have used an electrical circuit that has two or more loops, a spring-mass system that has two or more masses, etc., since these problems also require the solution of simultaneous, ordinary differential equations.

Consider the heat transfer system illustrated in Fig. 2-8 that contains two walls of large areas whose temperatures are T_A and T_B. Each wall is thin enough and has a sufficiently high value of thermal conductivity to consider the amount of resistance to heat conduction in each wall to be

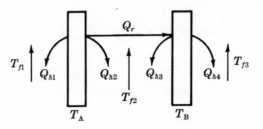

Fig. 2-8

negligible. Thus, each wall can be considered to be at a uniform temperature, and the heat balance equation for each wall is

$$Wc\frac{dT}{dt} = \sum Q_{in} - \sum Q_{out} \tag{2-29}$$

where T is the wall temperature in °F or °R, W is the weight of the wall in lb, c is the wall heat capacity in Btu/lb-°R, t is time in hr, $\sum Q_{in}$ is the sum of the heat flow rates entering the wall in Btu/hr, and $\sum Q_{out}$ is the sum of the heat flow rates leaving the wall. Thus, Eq. (2-29) shows that the wall temperature increases with time if the rate of heat inflow exceeds the rate of heat outflow. A fluid at temperature T_{f2} flows between the two walls, while fluids at temperatures T_{f1} and T_{f3} flow outside these two walls, as shown in Fig. 2-8. Before applying Eq. (2-29), we must assume the relative temperature magnitudes. Assume that $T_A > T_B > T_{f1} > T_{f2} > T_{f3}$. For this case, there will be a radiation heat flow rate, Q_r, that goes from wall A to wall B, as is shown in Fig. 2-8. It flows in this direction if $T_A > T_B$ because heat always flows from the higher temperature region to the lower temperature region. There will also be four convection heat flow rates Q_{h1}, Q_{h2}, Q_{h3}, and Q_{h4} that flow from the wall to the adjacent fluid, as is shown in Fig. 2-8, because we have assumed that the wall temperatures are larger than the fluid temperatures. Using Eq. (2-29) and Fig. 2-8 the wall heat balance equations are

$$W_A c_A \frac{dT_A}{dt} = -Q_{h1} - Q_{h2} - Q_r \tag{2-30}$$

$$W_B c_B \frac{dT_B}{dt} = Q_r - Q_{h3} - Q_{h4} \tag{2-31}$$

The equation for the radiation heat flow rate Q_r is

$$Q_r = \sigma F_A F_E A (T_A^4 - T_B^4) \qquad (2\text{-}32)$$

where $\sigma = 0.1714 \times 10^{-8}$, F_A is the shape factor, F_E is the emissivity factor, A is the wall surface area in ft^2, and T_A and T_B are the absolute wall temperatures in °R. It should be noted that this Q_R term, since both T_A and T_B have an exponent of 4, makes each of the two wall heat balance equations [i.e., Eqs. (2-30) and (2-31)] nonlinear. Thus, this problem requires the solution of a pair of simultaneous, nonlinear ordinary differential equations, which means that it is best to solve them by numerical means. Since convection heat flow rate Q_h equals $hA(T_s - T_f)$, where h is the convection coefficient in Btu/hr-ft^2-°R, A is the wall surface area in ft^2, T_s is the wall surface temperature in °R or °F, and T_f is the fluid temperature in °R or °F; the equations for the four convection heat flow rate terms in this problem are

$$Q_{h1} = h_1 A (T_A - T_{f1}) \qquad (2\text{-}33)$$

$$Q_{h2} = h_2 A (T_A - T_{f2}) \qquad (2\text{-}34)$$

$$Q_{h3} = h_3 A (T_B - T_{f2}) \qquad (2\text{-}35)$$

$$Q_{h4} = h_4 A (T_B - T_{f3}) \qquad (2\text{-}36)$$

We shall choose the Euler method as the numerical technique to be used for this problem. Since the calculated temperatures will not oscillate in value, the Euler method should provide sufficiently accurate results if the interval-halving method is properly used to determine the value of interval Δt. Use of the Euler method gives

$$T_{A_{t+\Delta t}} = T_{A_t} + (\Delta t)\left(\frac{dT_A}{dt}\right)_t \qquad (2\text{-}37)$$

$$T_{B_{t+\Delta t}} = T_{B_t} + (\Delta t)\left(\frac{dT_B}{dt}\right)_t \qquad (2\text{-}38)$$

where from Eqs. (2-30) and (2-31), we have

$$\left(\frac{dT_A}{dt}\right)_t = \frac{1}{W_A c_A}(-Q_{h1_t} - Q_{h2_t} - Q_{r_t}) \qquad (2\text{-}39)$$

$$\left(\frac{dT_B}{dt}\right)_t = \frac{1}{W_B c_B}(Q_{r_t} - Q_{h3_t} - Q_{h4_t}) \qquad (2\text{-}40)$$

This two-wall heat transfer problem will be solved using Eqs. (2-32) to (2-40). The inputs for this problem are $KODE$, A, h_1, h_2, h_3, h_4, W_A, W_B, c_A, c_B, F_A, F_E, T_{f1}, T_{f2}, T_{f3}, t_0, T_{A_0}, T_{B_0}, t_{max}, Δt, and $(\Delta t)_p$. The $KODE$ term is used for both case identification and program checkout purposes, T_{A_0} and T_{B_0} are the values of the two wall temperatures at initial time t_0, t_{max} is the time at which to end the problem, and $(\Delta t)_p$ is the time-interval for output printout. The desired output terms are time t and wall temperatures T_A and T_B. We are now ready to write a calculation sequence, from which a Fortran program may be written. The following is a calculation sequence for solving this heat transfer problem, and it is similar in form to the calculation sequences in both Secs. 2.6 and 2.9.

(1) Load the inputs: $KODE$, A, h_1, h_2, h_3, h_4, W_A, W_B, c_A, c_B, F_A, F_E, T_{f1}, T_{f2}, T_{f3}, t_0, T_{A_0}, T_{B_0}, t_{max}, Δt, and $(\Delta t)_p$

(2) Punch and print the inputs

(3) $t_{print} = t_0$

(4) $Q_{h1_t} = h_1 A(T_{A_t} - T_{f1})$

(5) $Q_{h2_t} = h_2 A(T_{A_t} - T_{f2})$

(6) $Q_{h3_t} = h_3 A(T_{B_t} - T_{f2})$

(7) $Q_{h4_t} = h_4 A(T_{B_t} - T_{f3})$

(8) $Q_{r_t} = (0.1714 \times 10^{-8})F_A F_E A(T_{A_t}^4 - T_{B_t}^4)$

(9) $\left(\dfrac{dT_A}{dt}\right)_t = \dfrac{1}{W_A c_A}(-Q_{h1_t} - Q_{h2_t} - Q_{r_t})$

(10) $\left(\dfrac{dT_B}{dt}\right)_t = \dfrac{1}{W_B c_B}(Q_{r_t} - Q_{h3_t} - Q_{h4_t})$

(11) Test $(t_t - t_{print})$: If ≥ 0, go to (12)
                        If < 0, go to (17)

(12) Add $(\Delta t)_p$ to t_{print}

(13) Test $KODE:$ If $KODE \geq 0$, go to (16)
              If $KODE < 0$, go to (14)

(14) Punch and print t_t, T_{A_t}, T_{B_t}, Q_{r_t}, Q_{h1_t}, Q_{h2_t}, Q_{h3_t}, Q_{h4_t}, $(dT_A/dt)_t$, and $(dT_B/dt)_t$

(15) Go to (17)

(16) Punch and print t_t, T_{A_t}, and T_{B_t}

(17) $t_{t+\Delta t} = t_t + \Delta t$

(18) $T_{A_{t+\Delta t}} = T_{A_t} + (\Delta t)\left(\dfrac{dT_A}{dt}\right)_t$

(19) $T_{B_{t+\Delta t}} = T_{B_t} + (\Delta t)\left(\dfrac{dT_B}{dt}\right)_t$

(20) Test $(t_{t+\Delta t} - t_{max})$: If > 0, go to (1) for next case
                        If ≤ 0, go to (4) for next Δt time cycle

Now we are ready to write a Fortran program for the solution of this problem. The symbols KODE, A, H1, H2, H3, H4, WA, WB, CA, CB, FA, FE, TF1, TF2, TF3, T, TA, TB, TMAX, DT, DTPRT, QH1, QH2, QH3, QH4, QR, DTADT, DTBDT, and TPRT will be used to represent the terms $KODE$, A, h_1, h_2, h_3, h_4, W_A, W_B, c_A, c_B, F_A, F_E, T_{f1}, T_{f2}, T_{f3}, t_t (and t_0 and $t_{t+\Delta t}$), T_{A_t} (and T_{A_0} and $T_{A_{t+\Delta t}}$), T_{B_t} (and T_{B_0} and $T_{B_{t+\Delta t}}$), t_{max}, Δt, $(\Delta t)_p$, Q_{h1_t}, Q_{h2_t}, Q_{h3_t}, Q_{h4_t}, Q_{r_t}, $(dT_A/dt)_t$, $(dT_B/dt)_t$, and t_{print}, respectively. The following is a Fortran program for solving this heat transfer problem.

```
 1   READ 10, KODE, A, H1, H2, H3, H4, WA, WB, CA, CB, FA,
       FE, TF1, TF2, TF3, T, TA, TB, TMAX, DT, DTPRT
10   FORMAT (I5/(5F8.4))
     PUNCH 11, KODE, A, H1, H2, H3, H4, WA, WB, CA, CB, FA,
       FE, TF1, TF2, TF3, T, TA, TB, TMAX, DT, DTPRT
11   FORMAT (///6HINPUTS/I5/(5F14.4))
     PUNCH 12
12   FORMAT (//10X4HTIME, 12X2HTA, 12X2HTB)
     TPRT = T
 4   QH1 = H1 * A * (TA − TF1)
     QH2 = H2 * A * (TA − TF2)
     QH3 = H3 * A * (TB − TF2)
     QH4 = H4 * A * (TB − TF3)
     QR = (0.1714E−8) * FA * FE * A * (TA ** 4 − TB ** 4)
     DTADT = (−QH1 − QH2 − QR)/(WA * CA)
     DTBDT = (QR − QH3 − QH4)/(WB * CB)
     IF (T − TPRT)8, 5, 5
 5   TPRT = TPRT + DTPRT
     IF (KODE)6, 7, 7
 6   PUNCH 13, T, TA, TB, QR, QH1, QH2, QH3, QH4, DTADT,
       DTBDT
13   FORMAT (4F14.5/F28.5, 3F14.5/F28.5, F14.5)
     GO TO 8
 7   PUNCH 14, T, TA, TB
14   FORMAT (3F14.5)
 8   T = T + DT
     TA = TA + DT * DTADT
     TB = TB + DT * DTBDT
     IF (T − TMAX)4, 4, 1
     END
```

As can be seen from this example, the solution of simultaneous first-order ordinary differential equations by most numerical methods (e.g., Euler, midpoint slope, and Adams) is rather straightforward. An exception is when the Runge-Kutta method is used. Suppose we wanted to solve the following pair of ordinary differential equations written in functional form

$$\frac{dy_1}{dt} = F(t, y_1, y_2) \qquad (2\text{-}41a)$$

$$\frac{dy_2}{dt} = G(t, y_1, y_2) \qquad (2\text{-}41b)$$

If we solved this pair of ordinary differential equations by the second-order accuracy **Runge-Kutta method,** the sequence of calculations would be

$$a_1(t) = (\Delta t)F(t, y_1(t), y_2(t)) \qquad (2\text{-}42a)$$

$$b_1(t) = (\Delta t)G(t, y_1(t), y_2(t)) \qquad (2\text{-}42b)$$

$$a_2(t) = (\Delta t)F(t + \Delta t, y_1(t) + a_1(t), y_2(t) + b_1(t)) \qquad (2\text{-}42c)$$

$$b_2(t) = (\Delta t)G(t + \Delta t, y_1(t) + a_1(t), y_2(t) + b_1(t)) \qquad (2\text{-}42d)$$

$$y_1(t + \Delta t) = y_1(t) + \tfrac{1}{2}[a_1(t) + a_2(t)] \qquad (2\text{-}42e)$$

$$y_2(t + \Delta t) = y_2(t) + \tfrac{1}{2}[b_1(t) + b_2(t)] \qquad (2\text{-}42f)$$

These previous equations should be compared with Eqs. (2-18a, b, c) which solve a single ordinary differential equation by this same method. From this comparison, it should not be difficult for the reader to see how simultaneous, ordinary differential equations are solved by the third- and fourth-order-accuracy Runge-Kutta methods.

Illustrative Example 2.6.   Suppose that we had masses 1, 2, and 3 which are elastically coupled and whose accelerations are known to be as follows:

$$\ddot{x}_1 = 0.581(x_2 - x_1)$$
$$\ddot{x}_2 = 0.581(x_1 - x_2) + 0.273(x_3 - x_2)$$
$$\ddot{x}_3 = 0.273(x_2 - x_3)$$

Write a calculation sequence for a digital computer program to solve these three simultaneous, second-order differential equations numerically, by using the trapezoidal and Euler methods, when the initial values $x_1(0)$, $\dot{x}_1(0)$, $x_2(0)$, $\dot{x}_2(0)$, $x_3(0)$, and $\dot{x}_3(0)$ are given.

Solution.   Applying Eqs. (2-9) and (2-25), this calculation sequence may be written as follows, where the subscript form is used in these equations.

(1)   Load the inputs: $x_1(0)$, $x_2(0)$, $x_3(0)$, $\dot{x}_1(0)$, $\dot{x}_2(0)$, $\dot{x}_3(0)$, Δt, and t_{max}

(2)   Set $t_t = 0$

(3) $\ddot{x}_{1_t} = 0.581(x_{2_t} - x_{1_t})$

(4) $\ddot{x}_{2_t} = 0.581(x_{1_t} - x_{2_t}) + 0.273(x_{3_t} - x_{2_t})$

(5) $\ddot{x}_{3_t} = 0.273(x_{2_t} - x_{3_t})$

(6)   Print t_t, x_{1_t}, x_{2_t}, and x_{3_t}

(7) $t_{t+\Delta t} = t_t + \Delta t$

(8) $\dot{x}_{1_{t+\Delta t}} = \dot{x}_{1_t} + (\Delta t)(\ddot{x}_{1_t})$

(9) $\dot{x}_{2_{t+\Delta t}} = \dot{x}_{2_t} + (\Delta t)(\ddot{x}_{2_t})$

(10) $\dot{x}_{3_{t+\Delta t}} = \dot{x}_{3_t} + (\Delta t)(\ddot{x}_{3_t})$

(11) $x_{1_{t+\Delta t}} = x_{1_t} + \left(\dfrac{\Delta t}{2}\right)(\dot{x}_{1_t} + \dot{x}_{1_{t+\Delta t}})$

(12) $x_{2_{t+\Delta t}} = x_{2_t} + \left(\dfrac{\Delta t}{2}\right)(\dot{x}_{2_t} + \dot{x}_{2_{t+\Delta t}})$

(13) $x_{3_{t+\Delta t}} = x_{3_t} + \left(\dfrac{\Delta t}{2}\right)(\dot{x}_{3_t} + \dot{x}_{3_{t+\Delta t}})$

(14) Test $(t_{t+\Delta t} - t_{max})$: If >0, go to (1) for the next case
      If ≤ 0, go to (3) for the next Δt time cycle

2.11 Further Remarks on the Numerical Solution of Ordinary Differential Equations

Let us first summarize briefly how we have covered this topic in this text up to this point. Section 2.6 applied the Euler method to solve a nonlinear electrical circuit problem, and Sec. 2.8 discussed better methods for solving first-order ordinary differential equations by numerical means. The Adams, midpoint slope, Milne, and Runge-Kutta methods were covered, including brief remarks on their advantages and disadvantages, and there were illustrative examples to exemplify their application. A mechanical spring-mass system was used in Sec. 2.9 to show how second- and higher-order differential equations may be solved by numerical means, and this section also introduced the trapezoidal method. Section 2.10 utilized a heat transfer problem to illustrate how to solve simultaneous, ordinary differential equations by numerical means, and that section also contains a further discussion of this subject.

The methods that we have covered, so far, are sometimes called *predictor methods*. That is, they predict successive values of $f(x + \Delta x)$ at each step by use of a numerical approximation equation. Section 2.9 briefly mentioned that the trapezoidal method can be used at each step to improve the calculation of $f(x + \Delta x)$ by the Euler, midpoint slope, or Adams method. When used for this purpose, the trapezoidal method can be considered to be a *corrector method*, and this use is exemplified in Ill. Ex. 2.7. A corrector method may be applied once, a specified number of times, or in an iterative fashion as is done in Ill. Ex. 2.7. It was shown in Ill. Exs. 2.1 and 2.2 that the use of the Euler method to calculate a second starting value, when the Adams and midpoint slope methods are applied, can add a relatively large error to the results. This error could be reduced if the second starting value were first approximated by the Euler method and then corrected once or twice by the trapezoidal method. As was mentioned previously, it is not always easy to approximate the second starting value by the first three or four terms of a Taylor series for professional engineering problems.

For methods as accurate as the Milne and Runge-Kutta methods, Simpson's one-third method, which is discussed in Sec. 4.5, can be used as the corrector method. In fact, Milne's method is often considered to be the combination of Eq. (2-16) and Simpson's one-third method, which is

$$f(x + \Delta x) = f(x - \Delta x) + \frac{\Delta x}{3}[f'(x - \Delta x) + 4f'(x) + f'(x + \Delta x)]$$

Even though the truncation error at each calculation step will be rather small, the use of the Milne method corrected by Simpson's method can result in unstable solutions for some problems, especially if the problem requires many calculation steps or intervals. A numerical solution technique is considered to be *relatively stable* if the rate at which the total error grows during the application of that method is less than the rate of change for the true solution. For an unstable method, the error will tend to increase for specific types of differential equation applications. Because it is both a stable and an accurate method, **Hamming's method,** which uses the following corrector equation when Milne's method is used as a predictor method, is a recommended method for solving differential equations.

$$f(x + \Delta x) = \tfrac{1}{8}\{9f(x) - f(x - 2\Delta x)$$
$$+ 3(\Delta x)[f'(x + \Delta x) + 2f'(x) - f'(x - \Delta x)]\} \quad \textbf{(2-43)}$$

The mechanical vibration problem that was solved in Sec. 2.9 is classified as an initial-value problem, because it is described by a second-order ordinary differential equation where both of the problem conditions (i.e., x_0 and $\dot{x}_0$) are given at the same value of time. That is, for an *initial-value problem,* all of the needed conditions to solve the given differential equation, of order 2 or higher, are given for one value of the independent variable. Such problems, even if they are nonlinear, can be easily solved by numerical means. This has already been shown in Sec. 2.9. Suppose that we have a problem that is described by the following second-order differential equation written in functional form:

$$\frac{d^2y}{dx^2} = F\left(x, y, \frac{dy}{dx}\right)$$

If the two problem conditions are given at $x = x_1$ and $x = x_2$ (i.e., the values of $y(x_1)$ and $y(x_2)$ are both given), such a problem is called a *two-point boundary-value problem.* This type of problem is much more difficult to solve than an initial-value problem—in fact, there is no known direct approach for its solution. Worse yet, the solution may not exist at all—or the solution may not be unique (i.e., there may be several solutions). For example, the differential equation $\ddot{y} + y = 0$, whose form is linear and rather simple, has an infinite number of solutions for some

pairs of boundary conditions [e.g., $y(0) = -y(\pi) = 1$] and no solution
for other pairs of boundary conditions. That is, the solution $A \cos t +$
$B \sin t$ will satisfy the two boundary conditions $y(0) = 1$ and $y(\pi) = -1$
for all finite values of coefficient B, but this solution cannot satisfy the
boundary conditions $y(0) = y(\pi) = 4$. As a physical example of a two-
point boundary value problem, consider a loaded, elastic beam. We know
from our strength of materials course that $d^4y/dx^4 = w(x)/EI$, where x is
the distance from the left end of the beam, y is the transverse displacement
of the beam due to an applied load distribution $w(x)$, I is the moment of
inertia about the centroid for the beam cross-section, and E is the modulus
of elasticity of the beam material. Since this is a fourth-order differential
equation, we need four conditions to solve problems of this type. The
method of beam support furnishes us with two conditions at each end of
the beam. For example, if a beam of length L is rigidly supported at both
ends, then we have the four conditions $y(0) = 0$, $y'(0) = 0$, $y(L) = 0$, and
$y'(L) = 0$. Since the given differential equation is linear and since this is
a two-point boundary-value problem, then the problem should be solved
by analytical means unless the applied load distribution $w(x)$ is so complex
in form that it is graphed or tabulated or unless the EI values vary with
length x of the beam. Nonlinear two-point boundary-value problems,
however, usually have to be solved by numerical means.

For two-point boundary-value problems of the form $y'' = F(x, y, y')$,
where $y(x_1)$ and $y(x_2)$ are both given, a trial-and-error procedure will
sometimes work. In this procedure, we assume a value for $y'(x_1)$, solve
the problem like an initial-value problem (e.g., use the Adams or Runge-
Kutta method), and see how close our calculated value of $y(x_2)$ matches
with the given value. We keep redoing the problem for another value of
$y'(x_1)$ until a match is obtained. If the problem is not well-behaved, however, this procedure may blow up. A few applications of a trial-and-error
method should determine this behavior. Several methods have been pro-
posed as an aid to choose the next assumed value for $y'(x_1)$. One of the
best of these methods is the *multiple shooting method,* whose details
may be found in numerical analysis references and which first redefines the
original two-point boundary value problem to be a set of n two-point
boundary value problems to which trial-and-error techniques are applied.
The easiest method for obtaining $y'(x_1)$ assumptions is based on linear
interpolation. Suppose that the assumption $y'(x_1) = G$ gives $y(x_2) = K$,
and the assumption $y'(x_1) = H$ gives $y(x_2) = L$. Then the *linear inter-*
polation method calculates the next value of $y'(x_1)$ from the following
linear interpolation equation:

$$y'(x_1) = G + \left(\frac{y(x_2) - K}{L - K}\right)(H - G) \qquad \textbf{(2-44)}$$

Since there is no established numerical technique for solving two-point boundary value problems, trial-and-error methods are usually tried first because they are the easiest to apply. If these do not work, more difficult methods must be employed. The *finite-difference method* is one of the more commonly applied methods for this purpose. Essentially, this method subdivides the problem interval (e.g., x_1 to x_2) into n equal or unequal subintervals and replaces the derivatives in the given differential equation with finite-difference approximations. Section 4.4 furnishes us with some finite-difference approximations that may be used for these derivatives, but sometimes better approximations may be necessary. If the original differential equation is nonlinear, then special techniques must be employed to linearize the approximation equations. If we substitute the x-values for the n subintervals into the linearized approximation equation, we will have a set of simultaneous, linear algebraic equations, as is shown in Ill. Ex. 2.8. We assume a set of values for a solution and iteratively solve these algebraic equations for a set of new values. The next set of values are the average of the assumed and the calculated values. Methods for the solution of simultaneous, linear algebraic equations are discussed in Sec. 4.8.

Another method for solving two-point boundary value problems consists of rewriting the given differential equation as an integral equation. That is, the highest-order derivative is considered to be the unknown, and lower-order derivatives are obtained by integration. Each integral in this integral equation is approximated by numerical means, and such approximation formulae (e.g., Simpson's methods) are furnished in Sec. 4.5.

Illustrative Example 2.7.   For the problem given in Ill. Ex. 2.1, evaluate the second starting value $y(0.050)$ numerically by using the Euler method as a predictor method and the trapezoidal method as an iterative corrector method.

Solution.   It is given that $y(0) = 2.000$. Since the given differential equation shows that $dy/dt = -4y^2t$, $\dot{y}(0) = 0$, and application of Eq. (2-8) gives

$$y(0.050) = 2.000 + (0.050)(0) = 2.000$$

Since $dy/dt = -4y^2t$, we obtain

$$\dot{y}(0.050) = -(4.00)(2.000)^2(0.050) = -0.800$$

Now using Eq. (2-24) to recalculate $y(0.050)$, we obtain

$$y(0.050) = 2.000 + (0.025)(0 - 0.800) = 1.980$$

Recalculation of $\dot{y}(0.050)$ gives

$$\dot{y}(0.050) = -(4.00)(1.980)^2(0.050) = -0.785$$

Again using Eq. (2-24) to recalculate $y(0.050)$, where the new value of $\dot{y}(0.050)$ is used, we obtain

$$y(0.050) = 2.000 + (0.025)(0 - 0.785) = 1.980$$

Since two successive calculations of $y(0.050)$ are in agreement, we have obtained a value for this term. This value also agrees with the exact analytical result. We can now calculate $y(0.100)$ by the same method, if we desire.

Illustrative Example 2.8.   Start the solution of the following second-order differential equation using the finite-difference method, where $y(0) = 0$ and $y(1) = -0.400$.

$$\frac{d^2y}{dx^2} + y = x^2$$

Solution.   First we shall divide the interval from 0 to 1, for this two-point boundary value problem, into five equal subintervals. Applying Eq. (4-16) in Sec. 4.4, we can approximate the second derivative d^2y/dx^2 at location x_i by the approximation $(y_{i+1} - 2y_i + y_{i-1})/(\Delta x)^2$, where y_{i-1}, y_i, and y_{i+1} are the values of y at locations x_{i-1}, x_i, and x_{i+1} and where $\Delta x = 0.200$ since we have five equal subintervals. Thus, the given differential equation can be written in the following approximate form for location x_i:

$$\frac{y_{i+1} - 2y_i + y_{i-1}}{(0.200)^2} + y_i = x_i^2$$

which can be rewritten as follows, where $y_i \equiv y(x_i)$.

$$25y_{i+1} - 49y_i + 25y_{i-1} = x_i^2$$

We know that $y_1 \equiv y(0) = 0$. Since $\Delta x = 0.200$, then $x_1 = 0$, $x_2 = 0.200$, $x_3 = 0.400$, $x_4 = 0.600$, $x_5 = 0.800$, and $x_6 = 1.00$. We also know that $y_6 \equiv y(1.00) = -0.400$. Thus, substitution in the previous approximation equation for $i = 2, 3, 4$, and 5 gives us the following four linear algebraic equations, which can be solved for y_2 to y_5 by methods we learned in algebra. It would be wise to re-solve this problem for a Δx interval of 0.100 and see if the results are the same as those for $\Delta x = 0.200$.

$$
\begin{aligned}
-49y_2 + 25y_3 \qquad\qquad\quad &= (0.200)^2 = 0.040 \\
25y_2 - 49y_3 + 25y_4 \qquad\quad &= (0.400)^2 = 0.160 \\
25y_3 - 49y_4 + 25y_5 &= (0.600)^2 = 0.360 \\
25y_4 - 49y_5 &= -25(-0.400) + (0.800)^2 = 10.64
\end{aligned}
$$

2.12 Trial-and-Error Solution of a Fluid Flow Problem

Consider the constant-area pipe having bends and other energy-loss devices that is illustrated in Fig. 2-9. Station 1 is the pipe entrance and station 2 is the pipe exit. That is, the fluid flows from station 1 to station 2. The problem here is to find the pipe diameter D required to pass a given volumetric flow rate Q of a specified liquid when the entrance and exit pressures p_1 and p_2 are given. This might be considered to be a problem of economics for aircraft or for fluid (e.g., water and petroleum) transport for consumer usage, because money will be saved if the pipe lines are not over-sized. An over-sized pipe line also adds excess weight to an aircraft and penalizes its performance. Though this problem will solve for diameter D for only one set of p_1, p_2, and Q values, the determination of the required diameter size must be made for a range of operating conditions. For water and petroleum transport, these operating conditions may be expressed by curves of p_1 and p_2 versus Q. For aircraft fuel lines, which are connected to fuel pumps and fuel tanks which are points of known pressure, these operating conditions may be expressed by curves of p_1, p_2, and Q versus time t.

Fig. 2-9

Since we are limiting this problem to liquid flow in this pipe, the fluid may be treated as being incompressible. The continuity equation for an incompressible fluid is

$$A_1 V_1 = A_2 V_2 = Q \tag{2-45}$$

where A is the cross-sectional area of the pipe in ft², V is the fluid velocity in ft/sec, and Q is the volumetric flow rate of the fluid in ft³/sec. This equation, which results from the law of conservation of mass, states that the volumetric inflow rate into the pipe equals the outflow rate. Going further, the volumetric flow rate $Q = AV$ is constant at all points inside this pipe. Also, for incompressible fluid flow, we have the *Bernoulli equation*, which is

$$\frac{p_1}{\gamma} + \frac{V_1^2}{2g} + z_1 = \frac{p_2}{\gamma} + \frac{V_2^2}{2g} + z_2 + h_{L_{1-2}} \tag{2-46}$$

where p is the fluid pressure in lb/ft², γ is the specific weight of the fluid in lb/ft³, z is the elevation of the pipe centerline in ft, and $h_{L_{1-2}}$ is the head loss between stations 1 and 2 in ft. The term z is the fluid potential energy per lb of fluid flowing, and the term $V^2/2g$ is the fluid kinetic energy per lb of fluid. The p/γ (or pv, where v is specific volume) term is the fluid flow energy per lb of fluid, which is the amount of energy required to move a pound of fluid across a system boundary. Thus, Eq. (2-46) may be derived from energy conservation considerations. The head loss term is the energy loss between stations 1 and 2 per lb of fluid flowing, since Eq. (2-46) shows that it is the difference between the total fluid energy (i.e., the sum of the flow, kinetic, and potential energies) at station 1 and at station 2. Since Q = AV or V = Q/A and since the pipe area A is constant, fluid velocity V is constant throughout the pipe. Thus, Eq. (2-46) becomes

$$\frac{p_1}{\gamma} + z_1 = \frac{p_2}{\gamma} + z_2 + h_{L_{1-2}}$$

which can be rewritten as

$$\frac{(p_1 - p_2)}{\gamma} + (z_1 - z_2) = h_{L_{1-2}} \tag{2-47}$$

The total energy loss between stations 1 and 2 equals the sum of the energy losses caused by various means. Most individual energy head losses can be expressed by an equation of the following form

$$h_L = K_L \left(\frac{V^2}{2g} \right) \tag{2-48}$$

where the dimensionless term K_L is called the *loss coefficient*. Thus, for a series of n individual losses between stations 1 and 2

$$h_{L_{1-2}} = \sum_{i=1}^{n} K_{L_i} \left(\frac{V_i^2}{2g} \right) = \frac{V^2}{2g} \sum_{i=1}^{n} K_{L_i} = \frac{Q^2}{2gA^2} \sum_{i=1}^{n} K_{L_i} \tag{2-49}$$

where use was made of the fact that velocity V, which equals Q/A, is constant in this pipe.

Let us now consider some energy or head loss devices. For a *pipe bend*, K_L is usually furnished as a function of the bend angle θ and the ratio r/D, where r is the radius of the bend. Thus, if we keep both θ and r/D constant in our pipe-system design, then the bend K_L term will be constant. For a *pipe entrance* (e.g., when fluid flows from a tank into a pipe), $K_L = 0.500$ if this entrance is a sharp-edged connection, and $K_L = 0.050$ if this entrance is a smooth, rounded connection. For fluid *exit* from a pipe, $K_L = 1.00$. For most energy loss devices, the loss coefficient K_L is a function of the geometry of the device, as was shown previously for a bend, entrance, and exit. Thus, the loss coefficients for most of the energy loss devices in this system can be kept constant if we keep their geometries constant. One major exception is *pipe friction*, where $K_L = f\ell/D$. The term ℓ is the pipe length, D is the internal pipe diameter, and f is a dimensionless term called the *friction factor*. This latter term is a function of the fluid properties, pipe geometry, fluid velocity, and the roughness of the pipe internal surface. Thus, we shall modify Eq. (2-49) to the following form

$$h_{L_{1-2}} = \frac{8Q^2}{\pi^2 g D^4} \left(f \frac{\ell}{D} + \sum K \right) \tag{2-50}$$

where the term $\pi D^2/4$ was substituted for pipe area A, and the term $\sum K$ is the sum of all the loss coefficients for the pipe except that of pipe friction. Now we need an equation for friction factor f. The smoother the pipe, the smaller will be the required pipe diameter for this system, since this will result in a minimum energy loss. Thus, we shall use the following equation which holds for turbulent flow in a smooth pipe:

$$\frac{1}{\sqrt{f}} = -0.800 + 2.00 \log_{10}(N_R\sqrt{f}) \tag{2-51}$$

where N_R is a dimensionless term called *Reynolds number*. Equation (2-51) can be used when $N_R > 5000$, which includes most cases for our practical interest. The equation for Reynolds number is defined to be $N_R = VD\rho/\mu$ where ρ is the fluid density in slug/ft^3 and μ is the absolute viscosity of the fluid in lb-sec/ft^2. Since $\rho = \gamma/g$, $V = Q/A$, and $A = \pi D^2/4$; this equation may be rewritten as follows:

$$N_R = \frac{4Q\gamma}{\pi g\mu D}$$

Solving the previous equation for diameter D gives

$$D = \frac{4Q\gamma}{\pi g\mu N_R} \tag{2-52}$$

We can combine Eqs. (2-47) and (2-50), and solve the resultant equation for friction factor f. This gives

$$f = \frac{D}{\ell}\left[\frac{\pi^2 g D^4}{8Q^2}\left(\frac{p_1 - p_2}{\gamma} + z_1 - z_2\right) - \sum K\right] \tag{2-53}$$

Solving Eq. (2-51) for $\log_{10}(N_R)$, and using the relation $\log_e x = 2.3026 \log_{10} x$, we obtain

$$\log_{10} N_R = 0.400 + \frac{1}{2\sqrt{f}} - \frac{\log_e \sqrt{f}}{2.3026} \tag{2-54}$$

This fluid flow problem is now reduced to that of simultaneously solving Eqs. (2-52), (2-53), and (2-54) for the three terms f, N_R, and D when the values of Q, p_1, p_2, z_1, z_2, ℓ, $\sum K$, γ, and μ are specified. That is, we know the values of z_1, z_2, ℓ, and $\sum K$ from the geometry of the pipe system, and we know the values of γ and μ from the type of fluid used. From an inspection of these three equations, it can be seen that they cannot be solved in direct fashion to obtain these three desired terms. Thus, a trial-and-error procedure must be employed. It is a trial-and-error problem because we must know D to calculate f in Eq. (2-53) and because it is difficult to calculate f from Eq. (2-54). We shall first try a *brute-force iteration procedure*, which works for many such engineering problems. The following describes a brute-force iteration procedure for this problem where the term ϵ is a previously specified accuracy criteria.

(1) Assume a value for diameter D. Call it D_A.

(2) Calculate friction factor f from Eq. (2-53).

(3) Calculate $\log_{10} N_R$ from Eq. (2-54).

(4) $N_R = 10^{\log_{10} N_R}$.

(5) Calculate diameter D from Eq. (2-52). Call it D_B.

(6) If $\left| \dfrac{D_B}{D_A} - 1 \right| < \epsilon$, go to step (8) since the solution has converged. If $\geq \epsilon$, go to step (7).

(7) Let the new value of D_A equal D_B, and go to step (2) for the next trial-and-error calculation cycle.

(8) If $N_R > 5000$, then the calculated values of D_B, N_R, and f are the solutions for the pipe diameter, Reynolds number, and friction factor for this problem.

We shall consider the previous calculation sequence to be adequate enough to write a Fortran program to try this brute-force iteration procedure. The inputs for this program are $KODE$, Q, p_1, p_2, z_1, z_2, ℓ, $\sum K$, D_A, γ, μ, the maximum number of iterations, and ϵ, which will be represented in this Fortran program by the symbols KODE, Q, P1, P2, Z1, Z2, AL, SK, DA, GAM, U, IMAX, and ER, respectively. If $KODE \geq 0$, the program will print only the iterated values for D_B, N_R, and f, along with the error calculation and the number of iterations represented by the symbol ITN. If $KODE < 0$, all of the calculated terms will be printed for each cycle of the iteration for the purpose of program checkout. The symbols DB, RN, OGNR, F, and SQF will be used to represent the computed terms D_B, N_R, $\log_{10} N_R$, f, and $\sqrt{f}$, respectively. The following is a Fortran program for solving this fluid flow problem by a brute-force iteration method, where IMAX is a specified maximum number of iterations that can be tried in case the iteration does not converge.

```
 1  READ 10, KODE, IMAX, Q, P1, P2, Z1, Z2, AL, SK, DA, GAM,
    U, ER
10  FORMAT (2I5/8F9.3/3F9.6)
    PUNCH 11, KODE, IMAX, Q, P1, P2, Z1, Z2, AL, SK, DA, GAM,
    U, ER
11  FORMAT (///6HINPUTS/2I5/4F13.3/4F13.3/3F13.6)
    CONST = (4.0 * Q * GAM)/(3.1416 * 32.2 * U)
    TERMA = ((P1 - P2)/GAM) + (Z1 - Z2)
    TERMB = (3.1416 ** 2) * (4.025)/(Q ** 2)
```

```
      ITN = 1
      IF (KODE)2, 3, 3
  2   PUNCH 12, CONST, TERMA, TERMB
 12   FORMAT (/9HCONSTANTS/3F13.5///15HITERATED
        VALUES)
  3   F = (DA/AL) * ((TERMA * TERMB * DA ** 4) − SK)
      SQF = SQRTF(F)
      OGF = LOGF(SQF)
      OGNR = 0.400 + (1.0/(2.0 * SQF)) − (OGF/2.3026)
      RN = 10.0 ** OGNR
      DB = CONST/RN
      RATIO = DB/DA
      CRIT = ABSF(RATIO − 1.0)
      IF (KODE)4, 5, 5
  4   PUNCH 13, ITN, DB, RN, F, SQF, OGNR, OGF, RATIO, CRIT
 13   FORMAT (I5, 2E12.4, F9.5/F20.3, 4F9.3)
  5   IF (ITN − IMAX)21, 9, 9
 21   ITN = ITN + 1
      IF (CRIT − ER)9, 7, 7
  7   DA = DB
      GO TO 3
  9   IF (RN − 5000.0)6, 6, 8
  6   PUNCH 14
 14   FORMAT (//12HLOW NR VALUE)
  8   PUNCH 15, DB, RN, F, CRIT, ITN
 15   FORMAT (5X8HDIAMETER, 5X8HREYNOLDS, 5X8HFRIC-
        TION, 8X5HERROR, 2X6HCYCLES/4F13.5, I8)
      GO TO 1
      END
```

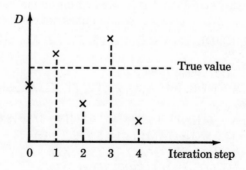

Fig. 2-10

Sometimes for poorly behaved problems, a brute-force, trial-and-error procedure such as this one will cause the iteration to diverge in a manner as shown in Fig. 2-10, instead of converge. For this reason, an *average-value method* is recommended to improve the convergence of such iterations. For this method, the next trial value used is the average of the old value and the newly calculated value, instead of the newly calculated value, as was done previously. To use this average-value method, step (7) of the previous calculation sequence must be changed to become

(7)   Let new $D_A = \frac{1}{2}$(old $D_A + D_B$), and go to step (2) for the next trial-and-error calculation cycle.

Thus, to use the average-value method for this fluid flow problem in a computer program, we only have to change statement 7 of the previous Fortran program to be

$$7 \quad DA = (DA + DB)/2.0$$

The reader will find, when he runs this Fortran program, that this fluid flow problem is too poorly-behaved to attain much success with either the brute-force or the average-value method. If the assumed diameter is too small, the calculated, iterated diameters will decrease, instead of increase, in value. If the assumed diameter is too large, the iterated diameters will increase in value. Thus, even though these two methods will work for many engineering problems, the iterations diverge from the solution when they are applied to this particular problem because friction factor f varies very slowly with Reynolds number N_R. Thus, the reader is now referred to Sec. 2.13 which discusses better methods for solving trial-and-error problems.

Illustrative Example 2.9.   Show how we may calculate the roots of the cubic polynomial equation $y^3 - 9.7y - 34.3 = 0$ by using a brute-force iteration method and by using an average-value iteration method.

Solution.   As stated previously, these two iteration methods, in spite of their crudeness, can be used successfully to solve many trial-and-error type mathematical and physical problems. Since the given equation is a cubic polynomial with real coefficients, we know from Sec. 2.15 that there is at least one real root. We can obtain the other two roots using the quadratic formula. To solve for a real root by an iterative method, we must guess a value for the solution and then use this guessed value to obtain a calculated approximate solution, which is to be compared with the previously guessed solution. This usually requires a special arrangement of the problem equations. For example, since the given cubic polynomial can be expressed in the factored form $y(y^2 - 9.7) = 34.3$, we can rewrite the given equation as $y = 34.3/(y^2 - 9.7)$ to allow a trial-and-error iteration. That is, we assume a first value y_1 for the solution and calculate new guesses by use of the equation

$$y_{n+1} = \frac{34.3}{y_n^2 - 9.7}$$

The brute-force method uses the newly calculated value y_{n+1} for its next guess, while the average-value method uses $(y_n + y_{n+1})/2$ (i.e., the average of two successive guessed values) for its next guess. A solution results when the calculated value of y_{n+1} equals the previous guess y_n. Again it should be mentioned that in both this problem and the fluid flow problem of this section, the problem equations had to be rewritten in a different form so that an iteration can be performed. For some large problems that occur in the engineering profession, this can be a challenge.

Illustrative Example 2.10. Write a complete calculation sequence for the Fortran program in this section. As has been suggested previously, one very good way to desk check a Fortran program before it is ever run on a digital computer is to write a calculation sequence from the Fortran program itself and then determine whether it does what was originally intended.

Solution. The following calculation sequence was written from the Fortran program in this section, where steps (3) to (5) calculate terms that have to be computed only once for this iteration problem.

(1) Load the inputs: $KODE$, maximum number of iterations, Q, p_1, p_2, z_1, z_2, ℓ, $\sum K$, D_A (the first guess for D), γ, μ, and ϵ.

(2) Punch and print the inputs.

(3) $K = 4Q\gamma/\pi g\mu$

(4) $KA = [(p_1 - p_2)/\gamma] + (z_1 - z_2)$

(5) $KB = \pi^2(g/8)/Q^2$

(6) Set ITN = 1

(7) Punch and print K, KA, and KB if the $KODE$ input is negative.

(8) $f = (D_A/\ell)[(KA)(KB)(D_A^4) - \sum K]$

(9) Calculate $\sqrt{f}$

(10) Calculate $\log_e \sqrt{f}$

(11) $\log_{10} N_R = 0.400 + \dfrac{1}{2\sqrt{f}} - \dfrac{\log_e \sqrt{f}}{2.3026}$

(12) $N_R = 10^{\log_{10} N_R}$

(13) $D_B = K/N_R$

(14) $R = D_B/D_A$

(15) CRIT = $|R - 1|$

(16) If the $KODE$ input is negative, punch and print the iteration count, D_B, N_R, f, $\sqrt{f}$, $\log_{10} N_R$, $\log_e \sqrt{f}$, R, and $|R - 1|$.

(17) Go to step (22) if the iteration count equals or exceeds the maximum specified. Otherwise, go to step (18).

(18) Add 1 to ITN, the iteration count.

(19) Test (CRIT $- \epsilon$) $\equiv \left|\dfrac{D_B}{D_A} - 1\right| - \epsilon$: If <0, go to step (22). If ≥ 0, go to step (20).

(20) Set D_A, the next assumed value, to equal D_B.

(21) Go to step (8) for the next iteration.

(22) If $N_R \leq 5000$, punch and print the warning message: "LOW NR VALUE".

(23) Punch and print the final iterated values for D_B, N_R, and f and also CRIT and the number of iterations used.

(24) Go to step (1) for the next case.

2.13 Discussion of Trial-and-Error Methods and Solutions and Roots of Equations

The methods covered in this section fall within the roots-of-single-equations, numerical analysis category and within the category for solving simultaneous, nonlinear equations. These roots and solutions must be real numbers. The solutions of polynomial equations, whose roots can be real or complex, are covered in Sec. 2.15. In Sec. 2.12, we attempted to apply a brute-force and an average-value iteration method in order to solve a fluid-flow, trial-and-error problem. These two methods will not work for this poorly-behaved fluid flow problem, but they will work for many other physical problems. These two methods are exemplified again in Ill. Ex. 2.9. Let us now discuss these two methods in general terms, before we discuss better solution methods. Let the equation $f(x) = 0$ represent an equation or a system of equations. Suppose that we can solve this equation for x in terms of a function of x. That is, we obtain

$$x = F(x) \tag{2-55}$$

where $F(x)$ may be a system of equations like that of the fluid flow problem in Sec. 2.12. That is, this system consists of Eqs. (2-52), (2-53), and (2-54), where $x = D$ and where these three equations represent $x = F(x)$. The previous section showed that it sometimes takes much manipulation to obtain an equation (or equations) of the form $x = F(x)$. First, we guess that the solution is x_1, and substitute it in $F(x)$ to obtain $x_2 = F(x_1)$. Repeating this process, we obtain $x_3 = F(x_2)$, etc. Summarizing, we have

$$x_{n+1} = F(x_n) \tag{2-56}$$

A solution is obtained when $x_{n+1} = x_n$, though some other criteria may be used, as was done by the fluid flow example in Sec. 2.12. This method may also be applied to find the n roots for a system of n equations. For example, it may be used to find roots x, y, and z for

$$f(x, y, z) = 0 \tag{2-57a}$$

$$g(x, y, z) = 0 \tag{2-57b}$$

$$h(x, y, z) = 0 \tag{2-57c}$$

by using the iteration formulas $x_{n+1} = F(x_n)$, $y_{n+1} = G(y_n)$, and $z_{n+1} = H(z_n)$.

For the solution of $f(x) = 0$ by the **average-value method**, we assume x_1 and calculate $x_2 = F(x_1)$ as before. Value x_3 is calculated by

$$x_3 = F\left(\frac{x_1 + x_2}{2}\right)$$

This process is repeated and may be summarized by the equation

$$x_{n+1} = F\left(\frac{x_{n-1} + x_n}{2}\right) \qquad (2\text{-}58)$$

This method may also be applied to solve Eqs. (2-57a, b, c) for roots x, y, and z.

A very good procedure for finding the root of a single equation $f(x) = 0$, if $f'(x)$ can be computed and if $f'(x) \neq 0$ near a root, is to use *Newton's method*. Application of this method, which is also called the **Newton-Raphson method** and which is given by Eq. (1-1), is illustrated in Sec. 1.14, where it is used to calculate the square root of a number. Newton's method can also be modified to solve a system of equations (linear or nonlinear) like those given by Eqs. (2-57a, b, c). Note that Newton's method requires a calculation of $f(x)$ and $f'(x)$ for each iteration. Thus, it must be possible to calculate these two terms, and the derivative must exist for all of the iterated points. Note that it would be difficult to calculate $f'(x)$ if $f(x)$ or its coefficients consisted of tabulated data or a series of equations, as is the case for many professional engineering problems.

Very often these types of problems are solved graphically (i.e., sometimes graphic or tabular means are used to find the approximate location of a root). Suppose that we wanted to solve the equation $f(x) = 0$ (which can consist of several equations) for x. We can let y represent $f(x)$, guess a solution for x, compute y, and keep doing this until we find a value of x for which $y = 0$. For the fluid flow problem of Sec. 2.12, for example, we can let y be the difference of the two N_R values calculated by Eqs. (2-52) and (2-54), where $x = D$. We can compute values of y for equally spaced values of x and then approximate the root r by drawing a curve, as is shown in Fig. 2-11. In this figure, we know that there is a root between $x = 3$ and $x = 4$, because y changes sign at these two points; that is, $y(3)$ and $y(4)$ have opposite signs. Similarly, in a computer program, we can calculate values of y for an equally spaced set of x-values. The program can then scan the calculated values of y for sign-changes and thus determine the approximate location (i.e., interval location) for the roots of $f(x)$.

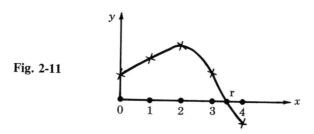

Fig. 2-11

Suppose now that for a given problem, a computer program had found the approximate location of a root. This computer program can then find the value of this root by using the **linear-slope** or **false-position method**. To summarize, we are solving the equation $f(x) = 0$, we have let $y = f(x)$, and the computer program has located points s and t where $f(s)$ and $f(t)$ have opposite signs, as shown in Fig. 2-12.

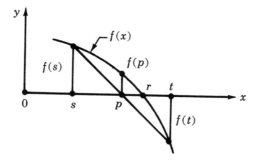

Fig. 2-12

The actual root of $f(x)$ is r. Since we know that there is a root between s and t, we apply this method by drawing a straight line between $f(s)$ and $f(t)$ and approximating the root by p, which is the intersection of this line with the x-axis. Since $f(p)$ is positive for this case, as shown in Fig. 2-12, we know now that the root is between p and t. We next let the new value of s equal p and repeat this procedure until a convergence to $f(p) = 0$ occurs. Since Fig. 2-12 shows that

$$\frac{f(s)}{p - s} = \frac{f(s) - f(t)}{t - s}$$

the linearly approximated root p can be obtained from the following equation, which can be incorporated into a computer program. This program must also choose the points s and t such that $f(s)$ and $f(t)$ are opposite in sign. To do this, test the sign of $f(p)$. If $f(p)$ is positive, let the next value of s equal p. If $f(p)$ is negative, let the next value of t equal p. We could also do this by testing the sign of the product $f(s)f(p)$. Note that $f(s)$ and $f(p)$ must have the same sign if this product is positive and opposite signs if this product is negative.

$$p = s - \left[\frac{t - s}{f(t) - f(s)} \right] f(s) \qquad (2\text{-}59)$$

A simpler, but possibly a more slowly converging, method to program would be to use Eq. (2-59) to obtain the next trial value p for the root of $f(x) = 0$, where s and t are now the *last two* values calculated. Thus, this program would not require an inspection of the $f(p)$, $f(s)$, and $f(t)$ values to determine the interval in which this root lies, as was required by the false-position method. Since this method does not require the root to be between s and t, it is an easier method to start. This could be incorporated into the fluid flow program in Sec. 2.12 by using Eq. (2-59) to calculate the new value of diameter D_A to use for the next iteration. Here, we can let y or $f(D)$ be the difference of two types of N_R calculations, and this difference would equal zero when a solution is attained.

The previous method can be improved by using the three successively calculated points p, s, and t and drawing a quadratic curve through these points. The next approximation for this root is the intersecton of this quadratic curve with the x-axis. This can be done mathematically by using the second-order Lagrange interpolation method, which is a polynomial interpolation procedure and is discussed later in Sec. 4.3.

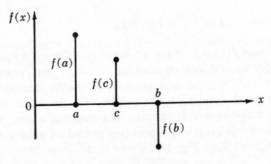

Fig. 2-13

The last method that we shall cover is an interval-reduction technique that is called the **bisection method.** To start with, we know that the root is located between points a and b, since $f(a)$ and $f(b)$ have opposite signs, as shown in Fig. 2-13. We then take the midpoint c of this interval (i.e., $c = (a + b)/2$) and calculate $f(c)$. Since $f(c)$ and $f(b)$ have opposite signs for this case, we know that the root is between c and b. Thus, we let the next value of a equal c and repeat the procedure until $b \approx a$ or $f(c) = 0$. This procedure, which is not difficult to program, converges surprisingly rapidly, because the size of the interval (a, b) is halved after each iteration.

Illustrative Example 2.11. The bisection method locates a root by successively dividing an interval in half and then choosing the half-interval in which this root lies. Write a calculation sequence for a computer program to apply this method such that the proper half-interval will always be chosen. Also briefly mention how the bisection method may be used to solve the fluid flow problem in Sec. 2.12.

Solution. Referring to Fig. 2-13, we shall denote the end points for each successively chosen interval to be a and b, where we know beforehand that the root lies between points a and b for the first or largest interval. For each iteration, we calculate $f(c)$, where $c = (a + b)/2$. If $f(c) = 0$, we have a root. If $f(c)$ is positive, the root lies between points c and b, as shown in Fig. 2-13. If $f(c)$ is negative, the root lies between points a and c. Thus, a brief calculation sequence to apply the bisection method is as follows:

(1)   Load the initial values for a and b, where it is known that $f(a) > 0$ and that $f(b) < 0$.
(2) $c = (a + b)/2$
(3)   Calculate $f(c)$ from the given equations.
(4)   Test $f(c)$: > 0, set $a = c$ and go to step (2).
           $= 0$, go to step (5).
           < 0, set $b = c$ and go to step (2).
(5)   Print c and $f(c)$.
(6)   Go to step (1) for the next case.

We could add a limit on the number of iterations that can be performed in the previous calculation sequence, and we could also modify it to go to step (5) if $|b - a|$ was less than a prescribed value ϵ since the root is then essentially located. The computer program could also calculate $f(a)$ and $f(b)$ to make sure that the step (1) conditions are met. It may be noted that we could also simplify the step (1) condition to require that $f(a)$ and $f(b)$ only have to be opposite in sign, if we change step (4) to test the product $f(a)f(c)$. That is, $f(c)$ and $f(a)$ have the same sign if their product is positive and opposite signs if their product is negative. To utilize either calculation sequence to solve the fluid flow problem, we only have to determine the function $f(D)$ for step (3) and also the initial values for diameters a and b. Thus, for step (1), we shall use a very small diameter, that is slightly above zero, and a very large diameter for our inputs. In Sec. 2.12, it has been shown that this fluid flow problem may be expressed mathematically by Eqs. (2-52), (2-53), and (2-54) which must be solved by trial-and-error (i.e., iterative) means. The function $f(D)$ might consist of the following series of equations for a specific, assumed value for diameter D, where we wish to find the value of D for which $f(D) = 0$. It can be easily seen that the equations that follow utilize Eqs. (2-52), (2-53), and (2-54).

$$\left(\frac{N_R}{10^4}\right)_A = \frac{4Q\gamma}{(10^4)(\pi g\mu D)}$$

$$f = \frac{D}{\ell}\left[\frac{\pi^2 g D^4}{8Q^2}\left(\frac{p_1 - p_2}{\gamma} + z_1 - z_2\right) - \sum K\right]$$

$$\log_{10} N_R = 0.400 + \frac{1}{2\sqrt{f}} - \frac{\log_e \sqrt{f}}{2.3026}$$

$$\left(\frac{N_R}{10^4}\right)_B = 10^{\log_{10} N_R}/10^4 = 10^{\log_{10} N_R - 4}$$

$$f(D) = \left(\frac{N_R}{10^4}\right)_A - \left(\frac{N_R}{10^4}\right)_B$$

2.14   Determination of the Natural Frequencies of a Linear Mechanical System

Consider the mechanical, undamped spring-mass system, consisting of two masses and two linear springs, that is illustrated in Fig. 2-14. The reader has probably had another engineering course that furnishes the background to show that this linear mechanical system is mathematically analogous to a two-loop electrical circuit consisting of a voltage source, two inductors, and two capacitors (where one capacitor is in both loops). If either mass is displaced from its equilibrium position, this system will vibrate. Because this system has two degrees of freedom (i.e., either mass could vibrate while the other mass is held motionless), this system has two natural frequencies. The *natural frequencies* are specific vibration frequencies of the system when the applied force F is removed. That is, if the system has no applied force and if both masses vibrate (in the same or opposite directions) such that each mass attains its maximum displacement or amplitude always at the same time, then the frequency of vibration for this situation is one of the natural frequencies of the system. To write the equations of motion for this system, we displace each mass in the positive direction, determine the direction of the forces that result, and apply Newton's second law (i.e., $m_i\ddot{x}_i = \sum F_i$) for each mass.

The equations of motion for this spring-mass system, using Newton's second law, are as follows.

$$m_1\ddot{x}_1 = -k_1 x_1 - k_2(x_1 - x_2)$$
$$m_2\ddot{x}_2 = F + k_2(x_1 - x_2)$$

Figure 2-14 also shows the free-body diagram from which the equations of motion were written, and this diagram shows the directions of all the forces. We have assumed here that $x_1 > x_2$, which physically means that the lower spring will be compressed an amount $(x_1 - x_2)$. The compressed lower spring pushes mass m_1 upward and pushes mass m_2 downward.

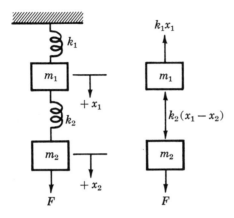

Fig. 2-14

Thus, both springs oppose the downward motion of mass m_1 (i.e., both of these spring forces on mass m_1 act in the upward or negative direction). The magnitude of the force on a linear spring is equal to the product of the spring constant and the displacement between its two ends.

Since we are interested only in the two natural frequencies for this system, we shall now omit applied force F in the second equation. Thus, the equations of motion for a free vibration of this system (i.e., a vibration when no external force is applied) can be written as follows.

$$\ddot{x}_1 + \left(\frac{k_1 + k_2}{m_1}\right) x_1 - \frac{k_2}{m_1} x_2 = 0 \tag{2-60}$$

$$\ddot{x}_2 + \frac{k_2}{m_2} x_2 - \frac{k_2}{m_2} x_1 = 0 \tag{2-61}$$

Since each of the two previous equations are homogeneous differential equations of a rather standard form, it is known that their solutions are of the harmonic forms $x_1 = A_1 \sin(\omega t + \phi)$ and $x_2 = A_2 \sin(\omega t + \phi)$, where A_1 and A_2 are vibration amplitudes, ω is a natural frequency of the system, and ϕ is a phase angle. Calculations (i.e., two differentiations) show that $\ddot{x}_1 = -\omega^2 A_1 \sin(\omega t + \phi)$ and $\ddot{x}_2 = -\omega^2 A_2 \sin(\omega t + \phi)$. Substitution of these results for $\ddot{x}_1$, $\ddot{x}_2$, x_1, and x_2 into Eqs. (2-60) and (2-61) and cancellation of sin $(\omega t + \phi)$ in each term gives us the following two algebraic equations:

$$\left(-\omega^2 + \frac{k_1 + k_2}{m_1}\right) A_1 - \frac{k_2}{m_1} A_2 = 0 \qquad (2\text{-}62)$$

$$-\frac{k_2}{m_2} A_1 + \left(-\omega^2 + \frac{k_2}{m_2}\right) A_2 = 0 \qquad (2\text{-}63)$$

If a vibration type of solution (i.e., not the non-vibrational solution $A_1 = A_2 = 0$) exists, then the determinant of the coefficients of A_1 and A_2 must equal zero. That is

$$\begin{vmatrix} \dfrac{k_1 + k_2}{m_1} - \omega^2 & -\dfrac{k_2}{m_1} \\[2ex] -\dfrac{k_2}{m_2} & \dfrac{k_2}{m_2} - \omega^2 \end{vmatrix} = 0 \qquad (2\text{-}64)$$

Expansion of the previous determinant equation gives us the following polynomial equation, called the *characteristic equation*, of degree 4 in ω and degree 2 in ω^2.

$$\omega^4 - \left(\frac{k_1 + k_2}{m_1} + \frac{k_2}{m_2}\right) \omega^2 + \frac{k_1 k_2}{m_1 m_2} = 0 \qquad (2\text{-}65)$$

Since Eq. (2-65) is of degree 2 in ω^2, we can use the quadratic formula to solve for the roots ω_1^2 and ω_2^2. Thus, we have four roots $+\omega_1$, $-\omega_1$, $+\omega_2$, and $-\omega_2$, but only the two positive roots are physical solutions for this problem. Hence, the two natural frequencies for this system are ω_1 and ω_2.

Since we have gone this far, we should briefly discuss the solutions of Eqs. (2-60) and (2-61), which will describe the motions of the two masses during a free vibration of this system. Since each differential equation is linear and since there are two natural frequencies, ω_1 and ω_2, each solution is a linear combination of two possible solutions as follows:

$$x_1 = A_{11} \sin(\omega_1 t + \phi_1) + A_{12} \sin(\omega_2 t + \phi_2)$$
$$x_2 = A_{21} \sin(\omega_1 t + \phi_1) + A_{22} \sin(\omega_2 t + \phi_2)$$

where Eqs. (2-62) and (2-63) can be used to express coefficients A_{21} and A_{22} in terms of A_{11} and A_{12}. Doing this gives $A_{11}/A_{21} = k_2/(k_1 + k_2 - m_1 \omega_1^2)$ and $A_{12}/A_{22} = k_2/(k_1 + k_2 - m_1 \omega_2^2)$. The values of the four unknowns (i.e., amplitudes A_{11} and A_{12} and phase angles ϕ_1 and ϕ_2) can be determined from the values of $x_1(0)$, $\dot{x}_1(0)$, $x_2(0)$, and $\dot{x}_2(0)$ (i.e., the initial values of the two displacements and the two velocities) for the particular problem.

If we add, below mass m_2, an extra spring k_3 and an extra mass m_3 to this system, then the system has three degrees of freedom and the characteristic equation will be of degree 6 in ω and of degree 3 in ω^2. That is, the characteristic equation for a spring-mass system possessing n degrees of freedom is a polynomial of degree $2n$ in ω and of degree n in ω^2. Thus, we must learn methods for solving for the roots of polynomial equations, which is discussed in Sec. 2.15, if we wish to obtain the natural frequencies of mechanical systems possessing more than two degrees of freedom.

We may express Eq. (2-64) in the following form, where $\lambda = \omega^2$ and where it can be seen by comparison that the B_{ij} elements are coefficients of x_1 and x_2 in Eqs. (2-60) and (2-61), which are the equations of motion. Thus, we could have obtained Eq. (2-64) directly from the equations of motion for this mechanical system.

$$\begin{vmatrix} B_{11} - \lambda & B_{12} \\ B_{21} & B_{22} - \lambda \end{vmatrix} = 0$$

The previous determinant equation, when expanded, is a polynomial of order 2 in λ, and its two roots are called the *eigenvalues* of the following array or matrix consisting of two rows and two columns

$$\begin{matrix} B_{11} & B_{12} \\ B_{21} & B_{22} \end{matrix}$$

where element B_{11} equals $(k_1 + k_2)/m_1$ and is the coefficient of x_1 in Eq. (2-60); element B_{12} equals $-k_2/m_1$ and is the coefficient of x_2 in Eq. (2-60); and elements B_{21} and B_{22} equal $-k_2/m_2$ and k_2/m_2 and are the coefficients of x_1 and x_2 in Eq. (2-61), respectively.

The calculation of the eigenvalues of a matrix is discussed in more detail in Sec. 3.7. Thus, we have another means for calculating the natural frequencies, since the eigenvalues λ_i are equal to the square of the natural frequencies. An n degree of freedom system has n natural frequencies (and hence n eigenvalues), and its matrix of B_{ij} elements will consist of n rows and n columns. Since there are Fortran subprograms available that calculate the eigenvalues of a matrix, we can obtain the natural frequencies of a spring-mass system by calculating the B_{ij} matrix elements from the equations of motion. It may be noted that these natural frequencies are inherent properties of the system, and they are not affected by any external forces nor by the values of the initial displacements and velocities.

2.15 Methods for Obtaining Roots of Polynomial Equations

In Sec. 2.14, we had a physical engineering problem where we had to obtain the roots of a polynomial equation in order to obtain the natural frequencies for the system. This type of numerical problem falls in the solution-of-an-equation category, but it is covered in an individual section for special reasons. First, the solution of this type of numerical problem is required in many types of engineering problems (e.g., vibration analysis, control system design, system stability analyses, etc.). Second, the methods covered in Sec. 2.13 are usually applied to solve an involved equation having only real roots or a set of n nonlinear equations possessing n real roots. The problem here is to solve a single equation of specified form for several roots, where these roots can be real, imaginary, or complex. A *polynomial equation,* $f(x) = 0$, *of degree n* has the following form

$$f(x) = a_0 x^n + a_1 x^{n-1} + \ldots + a_{n-1} x + a_n = 0 \qquad (2\text{-}66)$$

If the n roots of this polynomial equation are r_1 to r_n, then this polynomial equation can be rewritten in the following factored form:

$$f(x) = a_0(x - r_1)(x - r_2) \ldots (x - r_n) = 0 \qquad (2\text{-}67)$$

Thus, our problem is to find roots r_1 to r_n when the values of degree n and coefficients a_0 to a_n are specified.

We might mention here three useful properties of polynomial equations. If the coefficients a_0 to a_n are all real, then all complex roots occur in *conjugate complex pairs.* That is, if $(a + ib)$ is a root, then another root is $(a - ib)$. This also implies that there is at least one real root when degree n is an odd number. The second property is Descartes' rule, which requires that the sign changes for the sequence $a_0, a_1, a_2, \ldots, a_n$ be counted. That is, if a_i and a_{i+1} have opposite signs (one plus and one negative) then there is a sign change. Coefficients of zero-value are disregarded. *Descartes' rule* states that if coefficients a_0 to a_n are all real, then the number of positive real roots is equal to or less than the number of these previously mentioned sign changes. If the number of these positive real roots is less than these sign changes, then it is less by an even number. The third property is that the sum of the n roots is equal to $-a_1/a_0$ and the product of these n roots is equal to $(-1)^n a_n/a_0$.

Let us now discuss how one might solve a polynomial equation of degree n by methods presently known to us; that is, by *Newton's method* and the *quadratic formula.* The first $(n - 2)$ roots are obtained by using Newton's method, which is expressed by Eq. (1-1). That is, to solve Eq. (2-66), we use the iteration equation $x_{n+1} = x_n - f(x_n)/f'(x_n)$. The use of Newton's method (also called the ***Newton-Raphson method***) for solving a polynomial equation of the form $(x^2 - a) = 0$ for roots r_1 and r_2 is shown in Sec. 1.14. We shall not derive the Newton-Raphson method in this text because the reader has already done this in a previous calculus course. It may be warned that the Newton-Raphson method may not converge to a solution if $f'(x) = 0$ near a root. After the first root of the polynomial equation, r_1, is obtained, we divide the polynomial equation by $(x - r_1)$ to obtain a second polynomial of degree $(n - 1)$. This division can be performed by use of synthetic division procedures, which is exemplified in Ill. Ex. 2.12. The next root, r_2, is obtained by Newton's method, and another division is performed to obtain a polynomial of degree $(n - 2)$. This procedure is repeated until we are left with a second-degree polynomial of the form

$$cx^2 + dx + e = 0 \tag{2-68}$$

whose roots can be computed from the **quadratic formula**

$$r_{n-1}, r_n = \frac{-d \pm \sqrt{d^2 - 4ce}}{2c} \tag{2-69}$$

The previous solution procedure, including the synthetic divisions and the applications of the Newton-Raphson method and the quadratic formula, can be programmed in Fortran. The real roots should be solved first. If there are at most two complex roots, they can then be obtained by the quadratic formula, and the procedure is rather straightforward. Newton's method can also be used to solve for the complex roots of a polynomial equation. A complex starting value must be assumed, and the rest of the procedure is similar to that for finding a real root. The calculations are longer and more laborious, because of the complex arithmetic operations that are required. The solution of a polynomial by Newton's method is exemplified in Ill. Ex. 2.13.

There are many available methods for solving polynomial equations. Some of the more important ones, besides the Newton-Raphson method, are the Bairstow, Bernoulli, Birge-Vieta, Graeffe, Lehmer, and Lin methods. The details for applying these methods can be found in texts on numerical analysis. The **Birge-Vieta** method is a procedure for applying the Newton-Raphson method. Essentially, this method uses a recursion formula that is similar to that used in Ill. Ex. 1.19 to calculate the polynomials $f(x_n)$ and $f'(x_n)$ during each iteration when the Newton-Raphson method is applied. This calculation of $f(x_n)$ and $f'(x_n)$ can be performed in a rather easy manner by use of synthetic division, as shown in Ill. Ex. 2.13. The **Bairstow** and the **Lin** methods are advantageous for finding the complex roots of a polynomial equation with real coefficients. Since these roots will occur in complex conjugate pairs if all of the polynomial coefficients are real, then $(a - bi)$ is a root if $(a + bi)$ is a root. Thus, the given polynomial equation will have the following *quadratic factor:*

$$(x - a - bi)(x - a + bi) = x^2 + mx + n \tag{2-70}$$

Both the Bairstow and Lin methods solve for coefficients m and n. Once these two coefficients have been determined, the pair of roots can be obtained by use of the quadratic formula [i.e., Eq. (2-69)]. Lin's method, which is exemplified in Ill. Ex. 2.14, obtains these quadratic factors (i.e., coefficients m and n) by an iteration of a brute-force or successive-approximation type and, hence, is easier to apply and program than the Bairstow method. The Bairstow method first assumes coefficients m and n, as does the Lin method, and then after each division of the given polynomial by an assumed quadratic factor $(x^2 + mx + n)$, it computes a new set of assumed coefficients for the next trial quadratic factor. That is, the Bairstow method employs a two-dimensional form of the Newton-Raphson method to derive equations that calculate the correction terms δm and δn. These correction terms are added to the previously assumed values for m and n to obtain the pair of m and n values to use in the next iteration. The iteration converges to a solution for coefficients m and n when the computed values of δm and δn both approach zero. The use of this method is exemplified in Ill. Ex. 2.15.

Lehmer's method is very advantageous for finding the roots of a polynomial that has complex coefficients. This is not an easy type of problem to solve. Though this method does not converge as rapidly as Newton's method, it has the advantage that little modification is required when special cases are encountered. Most methods encounter a difficulty when two or more roots of a polynomial equation are close together; that is, it is not easy to find them to a high degree of accuracy. *Graeffe's method* alleviates this difficulty by transforming the original polynomial equation into an equation whose roots are squares of the original roots. This transformation is exemplified in Ill. Ex. 2.16. Thus, the roots of the transformed equation are more widely separated. Because the *Bernoulli method* is self-starting and because it considers only two types of cases, this method is well suited for use in a digital computer program or subprogram. For these reasons, this method is sometimes used to provide starting values for a Newton-Raphson iteration. This method computes the real root r_1, or a pair of complex roots, of the given polynomial that has the largest absolute value. If the polynomial is divided by $(x - r_1)$, the method can be reapplied to this second polynomial to obtain the root that has the second largest absolute value. The use of this method is exemplified and explained in more detail in Ill. Ex. 2.17. The methods that have been mentioned previously in this section furnish only one polynomial root at a time, and each calculated root is divided out before another root is determined. A method devised recently by H. Rutishauser is based on the *Quotient-Difference algorithm* which simultaneously approximates all of the roots of a polynomial. Even though this method may not furnish all of the roots when some are nearly equal in magnitude, it will usually find a majority of these polynomial roots. Because of the slow convergence and round-off errors of the Rutishauser method, it is best to use this method to furnish starting values for another iteration method (e.g., Newton-Raphson, Lin, etc.).

Unfortunately, no single method can be programmed to satisfactorily find, with complete certainty, all of the roots of a polynomial equation for all of the possibilities that may be encountered. Too many visual decisions are required. The Bairstow, Birge-Vieta, Lin, and Newton-Raphson methods will not always converge for every initial guess for a root. The Bernoulli, Graeffe, and Lehmer methods will converge to a solution with certainty (though sometimes it may be slow for a pair of nearly equal roots), but the size of the numbers involved grows very large during each successive iteration cycle. For this reason, it is best to find the roots of a polynomial equation on a digital computer by using a subprogram that combines two or more solution methods. Such subprograms are available as Fortran SUBROUTINE subprograms, which can then be utilized by engineers in their own programs and which are discussed in Sec. 3.6. The inputs to such a SUBROUTINE subprogram are the degree and coefficients of the specified polynomial, and the outputs are the real or complex roots. Any computed root can be checked by substitution into the original polynomial equation.

Illustrative Example 2.12.   Use synthetic division to verify that the roots of the following polynomial equation are 1, 2, and 3.

$$f(x) = x^3 - 6x^2 + 11x - 6 = 0$$

Solution.   As the reader had learned previously in an algebra course, the synthetic division procedure for the division of $f(x)$ in Eq. (2-66) by $(x - r)$ may be summarized by the following tabular form. The fact that synthetic division involves only additions and multiplications makes this method relatively easy to program.

a_0	a_1	a_2	a_3	$\ldots$	a_{n-1}	a_n
	rb_0	rb_1	rb_2	$\ldots$	rb_{n-2}	rb_{n-1}
b_0	b_1	b_2	b_3	$\ldots$	b_{n-1}	b_n

Note that the first row consists of the a_i coefficients for the polynomial $f(x)$. The b_i terms in the third row are obtained by addition of the two terms above it; that is, b_1 to b_n are computed from the equation $b_i = a_i + rb_{i-1}$. The second row terms are obtained by the multiplication of b_{i-1} by r, as shown. The answer or quotient for this division is the polynomial $b_0x^{n-1} + b_1x^{n-2} + \ldots + b_{n-1}$ with a remainder of b_n. This remainder b_n is equal to $f(r)$, so that synthetic division can also be used to calculate the value of $f(x)$ for a specific value of x. Such a calculation is required when Newton's method is applied. Use of synthetic division to divide the given polynomial by $(x - 3)$ gives

$$\begin{array}{rrrr} 1 & -6 & 11 & -6 \\ & 3 & -9 & 6 \\ \hline 1 & -3 & 2 & 0 \end{array}$$

Thus, since the remainder equals zero, we know that $x = 3$ is a root of this polynomial. Since the quotient is $x^2 - 3x + 2$, we can now use synthetic division as follows to divide this quotient by $(x - 2)$.

$$\begin{array}{rrr} 1 & -3 & 2 \\ & 2 & -2 \\ \hline 1 & -1 & 0 \end{array}$$

Since the remainder equals zero, we know that $x = 2$ is another root of the given polynomial equation. Since the quotient is $x - 1$, we know that $x = 1$ is the third root of the given polynomial equation. It can be seen from this example how, by using the equations $b_0 = a_0$ and $b_i = a_i + rb_{i-1}$, for $i \geq 1$, to obtain the b_0 to b_n output terms, one can program a synthetic division procedure in which the inputs are r and the a_i coefficients for polynomial $f(x)$.

Illustrative Example 2.13. Use the Newton-Raphson method to obtain the roots of the following polynomial equation:

$$f(x) = x^4 - x^3 - 8x^2 - 4x - 48 = 0$$

Solution. The Newton-Raphson method employs the iterative equation

$$x_{n+1} = x_n - \frac{f(x_n)}{f'(x_n)}$$

Since $f'(x) = 4x^3 - 3x^2 - 16x - 4$, the previous equation may be rewritten as follows, when we substitute for $f(x_n)$ and $f'(x_n)$.

$$x_{n+1} = x_n - \frac{x_n^4 - x_n^3 - 8x_n^2 - 4x_n - 48}{4x_n^3 - 3x_n^2 - 16x_n - 4}$$

Assumption of $x_1 = 5.00$ gives

$$x_2 = 5.00 - \frac{(5)^4 - (5)^3 - 8(5)^2 - 4(5) - 48}{4(5)^3 - 3(5)^2 - 16(5) - 4} = 5.00 - \frac{232}{341} = 4.32$$

If we keep applying the iteration equation, we will come to a step where $x_{n+1} = x_n = 4.00$. Thus, one root is $x = 4.00$. To obtain another root, we first divide the given polynomial $f(x)$ by $(x - 4)$ to obtain the following quotient $g(x)$

$$g(x) = \frac{f(x)}{x - 4} = x^3 + 3x^2 + 4x + 12$$

where this operation can be performed by synthetic division as shown in Ill. Ex. 2.12. To obtain the next root by the Newton-Raphson method, we employ the iteration equation

$$x_{n+1} = x_n - \frac{g(x_n)}{g'(x_n)}$$

which can be rewritten as follows, after we substitute for $g(x_n)$ and $g'(x_n)$.

$$x_{n+1} = x_n - \frac{x_n^3 + 3x_n^2 + 4x_n + 12}{3x_n^2 + 6x_n + 4}$$

Assumption of $x_1 = -4.00$ gives

$$x_2 = -4.00 - \frac{(-4)^3 + 3(-4)^2 + 4(-4) + 12}{3(-4)^2 + 6(-4) + 4} = -4.00 - \left(\frac{-20}{28}\right) = -3.28$$

If we keep applying the previous iteration equation, we will come to a step where $x_{n+1} = x_n = -3.00$. Thus, a second root is $x = -3$. If we divide $g(x)$ by $(x + 3)$, we obtain $g(x)/(x + 3) = x^2 + 4$. Thus, the last two roots are the solutions of the equation $x^2 + 4 = 0$, which are $x = 2i$ and $x = -2i$. Thus, the four roots are 4, -3, $2i$, and $-2i$, and the given polynomial equation $f(x) = 0$ may be expressed in the factored form $(x - 4)(x + 3)(x^2 + 4) = 0$.

The previous procedure for applying Newton's method can be simplified by using the Birge-Vieta method with synthetic division. That is, we shall use synthetic division to calculate both $f(x_n)$ and $f'(x_n)$. Let us now use synthetic division to divide $f(x)$ by $(x - 5)$ and also the quotient by $(x - 5)$, as follows, where synthetic division details have already been discussed in Ill. Ex. 2.12.

$$
\begin{array}{rrrrr}
1 & -1 & -8 & -4 & -48 \\
 & 5 & 20 & 60 & 280 \\
\hline
1 & 4 & 12 & 56 & 232 = f(5) \\
 & 5 & 45 & 285 & \\
\hline
1 & 9 & 57 & 341 & = f'(5)
\end{array}
$$

The values of $f(5)$ and $f'(5)$ are located at the denoted places in the previous calculation. That is, the remainder in the first division by $(x - x_n)$ equals $f(x_n)$ or $f(5)$, and the remainder in the second division equals $f'(x_n)$ or $f'(5)$. Thus, it is seen that a synthetic division subprogram can be effectively used to calculate $f(x_n)$, $f'(x_n)$, and the coefficients of the next polynomial for a Newton-Raphson iteration. In like manner, $g(-4)$ and $g'(-4)$ may be computed as follows:

$$
\begin{array}{rrrr}
1 & 3 & 4 & 12 \\
 & -4 & 4 & -32 \\
\hline
1 & -1 & 8 & -20 = g(-4) \\
 & -4 & 20 & \\
\hline
1 & -5 & 28 & = g'(-4)
\end{array}
$$

Illustrative Example 2.14.   Obtain the roots of the polynomial equation in Ill. Ex. 2.13 using Lin's method.

Solution.   Lin's method requires that degree n of Eq. (2-66) must be both even and larger than three. If the degree n is odd, there is at least one real root, and we can use Newton's method to obtain one root r_1 and then divide the given polynomial $f(x)$ by $(x - r_1)$ to obtain a polynomial $g(x)$ of even degree $(n - 1)$, so that Lin's method can be applied. Lin's method consists of repeated divisions by trial quadratic divisors until the remainder approaches zero. It is a controlled, trial-and-error division technique that factors a polynomial of even degree into a product of quadratic expressions. We can use the last three terms of the given polynomial to obtain a first trial divisor as follows:

$$(-8x^2 - 4x - 48)/(-8) = x^2 + 0.50x + 6$$

Division of $f(x)$ by this trial divisor gives

$$
\begin{array}{r}
x^2 - \quad 1.5x - 13.25 \\
x^2 + 0.50x + 6\,\overline{\big)\,x^4 - \quad x^3 - \quad 8x^2 - \quad 4x - 48} \\
\underline{x^4 + 0.5x^3 + \quad 6x^2} \\
-1.5x^3 - \quad 14x^2 - \quad 4x \\
\underline{-1.5x^3 - 0.75x^2 - \quad 9x} \\
-13.25x^2 + \quad 5x - 48 * \\
\underline{-13.25x^2 - 6.625x - 79.5} \\
11.625x + 31.5
\end{array}
$$

Since the remainder is not close to zero, we are not close to a solution. A second quadratic trial divisor is obtained from the expression in the preceding division that is denoted by an asterisk as follows:

$$(-13.25x^2 + 5x - 48)/(-13.25) = x^2 - 0.377x + 3.62$$

If we keep applying this procedure, the trial divisor will approach $(x^2 + 4)$, the quotient will approach $(x^2 - x - 12)$, and the remainder will approach zero. Thus, the given polynomial equation $f(x) = 0$ can now be expressed in the factored form $(x^2 + 4)(x^2 - x - 12) = 0$. At this point, two of the roots may be obtained from the quadratic equation $x^2 + 4 = 0$. This gives us the roots $x = 2i$ and $x = -2i$. The other two roots can be obtained from the quadratic equation $x^2 - x - 12 = 0$. Use of the quadratic formula gives us the roots $x = 4$ and $x = -3$. These four roots agree with those of Ill. Ex. 2.13.

Illustrative Example 2.15.   Redo Ill. Ex. 2.14 using the Bairstow method.

Solution.   If we divide a given polynomial $f(x)$ of degree n as defined by Eq. (2-66), by a trial quadratic divisor $(x^2 + mx + n)$, we shall obtain a quotient of the form

$$b_1x^{n-2} + b_2x^{n-3} + \ldots + b_{n-1}$$

and a remainder of the form $(r_1x + r_2)$. If the trial quadratic divisor were a factor of polynomial $f(x)$, then both r_1 and r_2 would equal zero. To apply Bairstow's method, we form a new polynomial $g(x)$, which is given by

$$g(x) = b_1x^n + b_2x^{n-1} + \ldots + b_{n-1}x^2 + r_1x + r_2$$

The procedure then divides polynomial $g(x)$ by the trial quadratic divisor $(x^2 + mx + n)$ to obtain a quotient of the form

$$d_1x^{n-2} + d_2x^{n-3} + \ldots + d_{n-2}x + d_{n-1}$$

and a remainder of the form $(p_1x + p_2)$. When this has been done, δm and δn, which are the correction terms for coefficients m and n in the trial divisor, may be computed from the following equations. The method uses $[x^2 + (m + \delta m)x + (n + \delta n)]$ as the next trial divisor.

$$\delta m = [r_1(d_{n-1} - md_{n-2}) - r_2d_{n-2}]/f$$
$$\delta n = [r_2d_{n-1} - r_1(p_1 - r_1 + md_{n-1})]/f$$
$$f = [d_{n-1}(d_{n-1} - md_{n-2}) - d_{n-2}(p_1 - r_1 + md_{n-1})]$$

Let us use the same first trial divisor as was used in Ill. Ex. 2.14. Thus, for this case where $m = 0.50$ and $n = 6$, we obtain $b_1 = 1$, $b_2 = -1.5$, $b_3 = -13.25$, $r_1 = 11.625$, and $r_2 = 31.5$, as is shown by the division procedure in Ill. Ex. 2.14. Thus, the new polynomial $g(x)$ is given by

$$g(x) = x^4 - 1.5x^3 - 13.25x^2 + 11.625x + 31.5$$

Division of the previous $g(x)$ polynomial by $(x^2 + 0.50x + 6)$ gives the quotient $(x^2 - 2x - 18.25)$ and the remainder $(32.75x + 141)$. Thus, $d_1 = 1$, $d_2 = -2$, $d_3 = -18.25$, $p_1 = 32.75$, and $p_2 = 141$. Substitutions of these values in the equations for f, δm, and δn gives

$$f = [-18.25(-18.25 + 1) + 2(32.75 - 11.625 - 9.125)] = 339$$
$$\delta m = [11.625(-18.25 + 1) - 31.5(-2)]/339 = -0.408$$
$$\delta n = [31.5(-18.25) - 11.625(32.75 - 11.625 - 9.125)]/339 = -2.12$$

Thus, the next value to use for coefficient m equals $(0.500 - 0.408)$ or 0.092, and the next value to use for coefficient n equals $(6.00 - 2.12)$ or 3.88. The next trial divisor is now $(x^2 + 0.092x + 3.88)$. If we keep repeating this procedure until $\delta m = \delta n = 0$, then the trial divisor will be $(x^2 + 4.00)$, the quotient will be $(x^2 - x - 12)$, and the remainder will approach zero. Thus, we obtain the quadratic factors $(x^2 + 4)$ and $(x^2 - x - 12)$ for $f(x)$ and the four roots, $x = 2i$, $-2i$, 4, and -3, as we did in Ill. Ex. 2.14, when Lin's method was applied.

Illustrative Example 2.16.   Show how Eq. (2-67) may be transformed into an equation $F(x)$ whose roots are the squares of the roots $r_1, r_2, \ldots,$ and r_n for Eq. (2-66).

Solution.   This can be done by multiplying Eq. (2-67) by $(-1)^n f(-x)$, where it can be shown that

$$(-1)^n f(-x) = a_0^2(x + r_1)(x + r_2) \ldots (x + r_n)$$

Denoting the result of the multiplication $[f(x)][(-1)^n f(-x)]$ as $F(x)$, we obtain the following polynomial equation in x^2

$$F(x) = a_0^2(x^2 - r_1^2)(x^2 - r_2^2) \ldots (x^2 - r_n^2) = 0$$

If we let z equal x^2, the previous equation can be rewritten as follows, where $F(x)$ is now a polynomial of degree n in z

$$F(x) = a_0(z - r_1^2)(z - r_2^2) \ldots (z - r_n^2)$$
$$= d_0z^n + d_1z^{n-1} + \ldots + d_{n-1}z + d_n = 0$$

where it can be seen that the roots of the previous polynomial equation in z are

r_1^2, r_2^2, . . . , and r_n^2, which are the squares of the roots for Eqs. (2-66) and (2-67). Thus, we only have to solve the previous polynomial equation for its n roots, and then take the square roots of these results to obtain the roots for Eq. (2-66). Included in Graeffe's method is a procedure and equation for computing the d_i coefficients, for the previous polynomial equation of degree n in z, directly from the a_i coefficients for Eq. (2-66). For example, note the pattern of the following equations, which calculate the first four d_i values.

$$d_0 = a_0^2$$
$$d_1 = -a_1^2 + 2a_0a_2$$
$$d_2 = a_2^2 - 2a_1a_3 + 2a_0a_4$$
$$d_3 = -a_3^2 + 2a_2a_4 - 2a_1a_5 + 2a_0a_6$$

Illustrative Example 2.17.   Use the Bernoulli method to find the root r_1 of the following polynomial equation which has the largest absolute value.

$$x^3 - 6x^2 + 11x - 6 = 0$$

Solution.   Since the given polynomial equation can be written in the factored form $(x - 3)(x - 2)(x - 1) = 0$, which is verified in Ill. Ex. 2.12, we know that our answer should be $r_1 = 3$. Essentially the Bernoulli method considers the following two basic cases, where reference is made to Eq. (2-67), where the a_i coefficients are all real, and where $|r_1| \geq |r_2| \geq |r_3| \geq \ldots \geq |r_n|$. For the first case, $|r_1| > |r_2|$ and this method will compute root r_1, which is called the *dominant root* because it is the largest in absolute value. For the second case, roots r_1 and r_2 are complex conjugates, and $|r_2|$ is larger than $|r_3|$. The second case calculates the complex roots r_1 and r_2. To handle other cases, the given polynomial can be transformed to a form that satisfies one of these two basic cases. This method can perform poorly if one or more roots almost equal the dominant root r_1 in value. The problem for this example falls within the category of the first case. The given procedure would have to be modified to handle the second case, which calculates a pair of complex conjugate roots. To solve for the dominant root of a polynomial by the Bernoulli method, it is best to first try the method for case 1. If the method for case 1 fails to converge, then the dominant root is probably complex, and the method for case 2 should be employed. If any of the a_i coefficients are complex, we could obtain the dominant root by using case 1 for the Bernoulli method along with complex arithmetic.

The Bernoulli method for case 1 calculates a sequence G_i. The ratio G_{i+1}/G_i converges to the value of the dominant root for large values of i. The procedure for case 2 is similar except that different sequences T_i and V_i are formed. That is, different equations are used to calculate T_i and V_i than for G_i. For a cubic polynomial of the form $x^3 + a_1x^2 + a_2x + a_3$, $G_1 = -a_1$, $G_2 = -a_1G_1 - 2a_2$, and $G_3 = -a_1G_2 - a_2G_1 - 3a_3$. Other values of G_i can be computed from the following recursion equation:

$$G_i = -(a_1G_{i-1} + a_2G_{i-2} + a_3G_{i-3})$$

Since $a_1 = -6$, $a_2 = 11$, and $a_3 = -6$ for this problem, we obtain $G_1 = 6$, $G_2 = 44$, $G_3 = 216$, and other values of G_i can be computed from the recursion formula

$$G_i = 6G_{i-1} - 11G_{i-2} + 6G_{i-3} = 6(G_{i-1} + G_{i-3}) - 11G_{i-2}$$

Use of this recursion formula gives $G_4 = 848$ and $G_5 = 2976$. Since $G_2/G_1 = 7.33$, $G_3/G_2 = 4.92$, $G_4/G_3 = 3.92$, and $G_5/G_4 = 3.52$, it is seen that the sequence G_{i+1}/G_i is converging toward the value of the dominant root, which is 3.00. As was mentioned previously, the Bernoulli method can be used for a few iterations to obtain starting values for the application of Newton's method, which can be used to calculate the root in more accurate fashion (i.e., more significant digits). Thus, we would be combining two solution methods in order to find the roots of a polynomial equation.

PROBLEMS

2.1. Keypunch the Fortran program in Sec. 2.2. Also keypunch the input data cards using the same values as those given in that section, except make the KODE term negative. Run this program on the computer and plot the currents i, i_h, and i_p versus time t, where the checkout feature of Sec. 2.3 is included in the program.

2.2. Consider a one-loop electrical circuit composed of a battery whose output voltage is E_0, a resistor of resistance R, and an inductor of inductance L that are connected in series. Write the loop equation for this circuit and solve it analytically by classical or Laplace transform means. After writing the calculation sequence, write a Fortran program that computes the solution of this differential equation. Choose a set of input values and check out your program on the computer, using ideas from Sec. 2.3.

2.3. Same as Prob. 2.2, except that there is a capacitor instead of a resistor in the circuit.

2.4. Keypunch the Fortran program in Sec. 2.6, adding to it the print-interval feature mentioned in Sec. 2.7. Also keypunch the input data cards, where $L = 15$ henries, $F = 2$, $a = 1.50$, $E_0 = 180$ volts, $\omega = 5$ rad/sec, $t_0 = 0$, $i_0 = 6$ amperes, $t_{max} = 1.500$ sec, and $(\Delta t)_p = 0.050$ sec. Start with a Δt value of 0.050 sec, and use the interval-halving technique mentioned in Sec. 2.6 to establish the proper value of Δt.

2.5. Redo Prob. 2.4 for the case where the output of the voltage source is a half-wave rectified sine wave.

2.6. Redo Prob. 2.4 for the case where the inputs are the same, except that $F = 20$ and $a = 0$. It should be noted that this problem is now the same as the linear circuit problem of Prob. 2.1 and has the same inputs. Calculate the difference in the current values when both programs are used. The student may elect to combine both programs and do the subtraction within the program itself.

2.7. Modify the program in Sec. 2.6 to solve Prob. 2.2 numerically by the Euler method. Use a print-interval feature in the program to ease the determination of Δt by the interval-halving method. Using the same set of inputs, run this program and the program of Prob. 2.2 and compare the results. Why can a larger value of Δt be used for the calculation of this problem by the Euler method than that of Prob. 2.4 for a similar set of inputs?

2.8. Write a Fortran program to solve the electrical circuit problem of Sec. 2.6 numerically by using the midpoint slope method. Use the Euler method to approximate the value of current $i(\Delta t)$. Use $\Delta t = 0.050$ sec and the set of linear inputs specified in Prob. 2.6. Run this program and the programs and inputs of Probs. 2.1 and 2.6. Calculate the errors that result from using the Euler method and the midpoint slope method for different values of Δt.

2.9. Same as Prob. 2.8, except use the Adams method instead of the midpoint slope method.

2.10. Same as Prob. 2.8, except use the second-order-accuracy Runge-Kutta method instead of the midpoint slope method.

2.11. Using the given calculation sequence as a basis, program the solution of the nonlinear mechanical vibration problem in Sec. 2.9. Choose a set of input values and check out your program on the computer. Note that if input b equals zero, the vibration is linear.

2.12. Write a Fortran program to solve the nonlinear mechanical vibration problem of Sec. 2.9 numerically by using the midpoint slope and trapezoidal methods. Use the Euler method to compute the value of $\dot{x}(\Delta t)$. For the same set of input values, run this program and that of Prob. 2.11, each for two values of Δt where the second value is half that of the first. Compare your results.

2.13. Choose a set of inputs for the programs of Probs. 2.11 and 2.12, where $b = 0$ to obtain a linear damper. For this set of inputs, solve the problem analytically, run both programs, and calculate the errors in the computer results for different values of Δt.

2.14. Same as Prob. 2.12, except use the Adams method instead of the midpoint slope method.

2.15. Program the numerical solution of the standard, nonlinearized, oscillating pendulum problem using the midpoint slope and trapezoidal methods. Calculate the value of $\dot{\theta}(\Delta t)$ using the Euler method. First, write the calculation sequence. Check out the program after choosing a set of input values.

2.16. Keypunch the heat transfer program in Sec. 2.10 and also input data cards, where area $A = 2.10$ ft^2, convection coefficients h_1, h_2, h_3, and h_4 equal 12.4, 8.6, 9.7, and 11.6 Btu/hr-ft^2-°R, wall weights W_A and W_B equal 4.1 and 3.7 lb, specific heats c_A and c_B equal 0.154 and 0.191 Btu/lb-°R, $F_A = 0.910$, $F_E = 0.870$, $T_{f1} = 510$ °R, $T_{f2} = 515$ °R, $T_{f3} = 520$ °R, $t_0 = 0$, $T_{A_0} = 640$ °R, $T_{B_0} = 580$ °R, $t_{max} = 0.03000$ hr, and

$(\Delta t)_p = 0.00100$ hr. Start with a Δt interval of 0.00100 hr, and use the interval-halving technique mentioned in Sec. 2.6 to establish the proper value of Δt.

2.17. Write a Fortran program to solve the heat transfer problem of Sec. 2.10 numerically by using the midpoint slope method. Use the Euler method to compute the values of $T_1(\Delta t)$ and $T_2(\Delta t)$. For the same set of input values as Prob. 2.16, use the interval-halving technique to determine the value of Δt that should be used for this program, and compare this with the value of Δt that should be used for the program in Sec. 2.10.

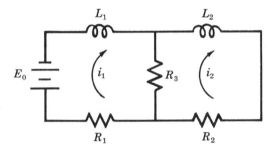

Fig. 2-15

2.18. Write a calculation sequence and a Fortran program to solve for the timewise variation of currents i_1 and i_2 in the electrical circuit of Fig. 2-15. In this program, solve the two loop equations numerically using the Euler method.

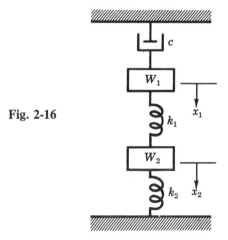

Fig. 2-16

2.19. If weights W_1 and W_2 in Fig. 2-16 are given initial displacements x_{1_0} and x_{2_0} respectively, the illustrated mechanical system will undergo a linear, free vibration. Using the Euler and the trapezoidal methods, write a calculation sequence and a Fortran program to numerically solve for the timewise variation of displacements x_1 and x_2.

2.20. Consider the design of a minimum diameter pipe line to carry a fluid, of specific gravity 1.27 and a viscosity of 0.000313 lb-sec/ft^2, at a flow rate of 2.00 ft^3/sec. The pipe is 350 ft long, $z_1 = 108.4$ ft, $z_2 = 103.8$ ft, and $\sum K = 3.15$. The pressures at stations 1 and 2 (i.e., the front and back ends) are 3,008 psfa and 1,000 psfa, respectively. Keypunch the fluid flow program in Sec. 2.12 and the inputs given in this problem. Run this brute-force iteration program to solve for diameter D, using initial guesses of 0.450 ft, 0.498 ft, 0.499 ft, 0.500 ft, and 0.550 ft. Print your iterations and comment on the behavior of this problem. Modify the program to use the average-value method, and run this modified program to print the iterations when using D_A inputs of 0.450, 0.497, 0.498, 0.499, 0.500, 0.501, and 0.550 ft.

2.21. Write a calculation sequence and a Fortran program to solve the fluid flow problem in Sec. 2.12 using the linear-slope or false-position method. Use the inputs of Prob. 2.20 to check out your program.

2.22. Write a Fortran program to solve the fluid flow problem in Sec. 2.12 using the bisection method. Use the inputs of Prob. 2.20 to check out your program.

2.23. Modify the programs in Sec. 2.12 and in Prob. 2.22 to handle pipes of various roughnesses by using the Colebrook equation for turbulent fluid flow, which is

$$\frac{1}{\sqrt{f}} = -2 \log_{10}\left[\frac{e}{3.70D} + \frac{2.51}{N_R\sqrt{f}} \right]$$

where e is the average height in ft of the roughness protuberances inside the pipe. It may be noted that this program will be quite general and that this equation reduces to Eq. (2-51) when the pipe is smooth (i.e., when $e \approx 0$). It may also be mentioned that for laminar pipe flow, where $N_R < 2100$, $f = 64/N_R$.

2.24. Write a Fortran program to calculate the two natural frequencies of the mechanical vibration system in Sec. 2.14.

2.25. Redo Prob. 2.24 for a mechanical system consisting of three masses and three springs. Use the Newton-Raphson method to solve for the first natural frequency and the quadratic formula to solve for the other two natural frequencies.

CHAPTER 3

More Fortran Instructions

3.1 *Introduction*

In the first part of this chapter, we shall learn about arrays and subscripted variables and about DIMENSION, DO, and CONTINUE statements. These statements are very useful when some of the input, output, or computed data in a computer program represent a table of data, a graph, a matrix, etc. This will be further seen in the examples given in Chapter 4.

The last part of this chapter will deal with SUBROUTINE and FUNCTION subprogram statements. These statements, which are not available in Fortran I, can be advantageously used in several ways to obtain a more efficient program. One of the chief advantages of these statements for engineers is that a matrix inversion (or an evaluation of the roots of a polynomial, etc.) can be programmed as a SUBROUTINE subprogram by someone with a competent mathematical background. This subprogram can be utilized by engineers in any of their programs that require the type of computation that is performed in that subprogram. Computer installations generally have subprograms that will perform interpolations, numerical integrations, numerical differentiations, matrix arithmetic, matrix inversions, curve-fit tabulated data, calculate roots of polynomials, determine eigenvalues, evaluate determinants, etc., for use in other programs.

The subprogram statements are also used for segmenting a program, such that repeated calculations in a problem are programmed in detail only once in the resulting Fortran program. As an example of the latter advantage, suppose that we had a problem that required the inversion of three different matrices. The SUBROUTINE statement allows us to solve this problem in a main program, while the details of the matrix inversion procedure are contained only in a Fortran subprogram that is run along with the main program on the computer. The last part of this chapter deals with several matrix arithmetic subroutines.

3.2   Arrays and Subscripted Variables and DIMENSION Statements

Suppose we had quantities A_1, A_2, A_3, . . . , A_9, and A_{10} as data. We can represent these subscripted quantities in Fortran by A(1), A(2), A(3), . . . , A(9), and A(10). Note that the specific term A_3 is represented by A(3) and that the term inside the parentheses is a *fixed-point constant*. We can also represent the arbitrarily subscripted quantity A_i by A(I), and it should be noted that the term inside the parentheses is a *fixed-point variable*. If a Fortran instruction refers to A(I) at a time when I = 3, then the instruction refers to A(3) at that time. Here we have used a *subscripted variable* (with only the name A) to represent the ten quantities A(1) to A(10). The complete set of ten quantities is called an *array*, and the name of this array is A. An individual quantity in an array, such as A(4), is called an *element* of that array. The first element is A(1), the second element is A(2), etc.

Now suppose that we had the following matrix consisting of two rows and four columns:

$$B_{11} \quad B_{12} \quad B_{13} \quad B_{14}$$
$$B_{21} \quad B_{22} \quad B_{23} \quad B_{24}$$

The arbitrarily subscripted term B_{ij}, where i is the row number and j is the column number, can be represented in Fortran by B(I, J). Thus, for the term B(I, J), the first subscript I is the row number and the second subscript J is the column number. Note that the subscripts are separated by commas within the parentheses. We can represent the first row of the above matrix in Fortran by B(1, 1), B(1, 2), B(1, 3), and B(1, 4); and the second row can be represented by B(2, 1), B(2, 2), B(2, 3), and B(2, 4).

The name of a subscripted variable must follow the same rules as those previously given for an unsubscripted Fortran variable. Thus, the name of an array consisting of fixed-point elements must start with the letter I, J, K, L, M, or N. An array cannot consist of both fixed- and floating-point elements. A subscripted variable may have one, two, or three subscripts, and we shall call these variables one-, two-, and three-dimensional arrays, respectively. Thus, in this case n-dimensional means n-subscripts. Fortran I does not permit more than two subscripts. A *subscript*, which must always be positive and a fixed-point quantity, may be written in the following forms:

$$k$$
$$m$$
$$m + k$$
$$m - k \qquad \text{variable}$$
$$k * m$$
$$k * m + k$$
$$k * m - k$$

where k means any positive (and non-zero) fixed-point constant, and m means any positive fixed-point variable. Fortran I permits only the first four of the previous subscript-forms. Thus, Fortran II permits the following notations for the elements of subscripted variables:

$$AB(I - 4)$$
$$XR(4 * J, K, 4)$$
$$MS(6 * K + 2)$$

but does not permit the following notations:

$$AB(4 - I)$$
$$RX(J * 4)$$
$$TM(4 * B - 1)$$
$$SK(I + J + K)$$

because the subscripts do not fulfill any of the seven permissible forms.

The **DIMENSION** *statement* is an unexecuted statement which specifies the maximum number of elements in an array and, thus, tells the computer, during machine-language translation, how many storages to allocate for that array. All subscripted variables in a program must appear in a DIMENSION statement, and this DIMENSION statement must appear before any other appearance of this variable in the program. For this reason, it is wise to locate the DIMENSION statements at the beginning of a program. The following statements may be used to specify the maximum size of arrays A, X, Y, and Z:

$$\text{DIMENSION A(15, 10, 12)}$$
$$\text{DIMENSION X(20), Y(30), Z(11, 8)}$$

The same statement states that array X has at most twenty elements, array Y has at most thirty elements, and array Z has at most eleven rows and eight columns (i.e., 88 elements). Note that several arrays may be mentioned in a DIMENSION statement and that the maximum size is specified by a positive fixed-point number within the parentheses.

Illustrative Example 3.1.   Write Fortran instructions to compute the following equations:

$$A_{11}X_1 + A_{12}X_2 + A_{13}X_3 = R_1$$
$$A_{21}X_1 + A_{22}X_2 + A_{23}X_3 = R_2$$

Solution.   This may be done as follows, where use was made of arrays A, R, and X:

$$R(1) = A(1, 1) * X(1) + A(1, 2) * X(2) + A(1, 3) * X(3)$$
$$R(2) = A(2, 1) * X(1) + A(2, 2) * X(2) + A(2, 3) * X(3)$$

These Fortran instructions should be preceded in the program by a DIMENSION statement such as

$$\text{DIMENSION R(2), X(3), A(2, 3)}$$

Illustrative Example 3.2.   The following points were taken from a graph of y versus x: (0, 6.1), (1, 8.7), (3, 3.2), (7, −1.1), and (12, −7.3). Show how to represent this graph in a Fortran program.

Solution.   We can represent the x-points by array X, where $X(1) = 0.0$, $X(2) = 1.0$, $X(3) = 3.0$, $X(4) = 7.0$, and $X(5) = 12.0$. We can represent the y-points by array Y, where $Y(1) = 6.1$, $Y(2) = 8.7$, $Y(3) = 3.2$, $Y(4) = −1.1$, and $Y(5) = −7.3$. Since $X(3) = 3.0$ and $Y(3) = 3.2$, we know that $y = 3.2$ when $x = 3.0$. Thus, we have shown how an array may be used to represent points on a graph and other types of tabulated data.

Illustrative Example 3.3.   For a certain type of material, the values of its specific heat and its thermal conductivity were tabulated for 35 different values of temperature. Show how to represent this tabulated data in a Fortran program.

Solution.   We can represent the temperature values by an array called TEMP, the specific heat values by an array called SPHET, and the thermal conductivity values by an array called TCON. Thus, SPHET(12) and TCON(12) are the values of specific heat and thermal conductivity at temperature TEMP(12). The DIMENSION statement for this problem can be written as:

$$\text{DIMENSION TEMP(35), SPHET(35), TCON(35)}$$

Illustrative Example 3.4. Suppose that we have quantities A_1, A_2, A_3, ..., A_n as data. Write Fortran instructions to calculate the average value of these n quantities.

Solution. Using N to represent n, array A to represent A_1 to A_n, and the following equation to calculate the average value

$$A_{av} = \frac{1}{n} \sum_{j=1}^{n} A_j$$

we obtain the following portion of a Fortran program:

```
      J = 0
      SUM = 0.0
   15 J = J + 1
      SUM = SUM + A(J)
      IF(J − N)15, 16, 16
   16 AN = N
      AVG = SUM/AN
```

The above program portion represents A_j by A(J), $\sum A_j$ by SUM, and A_{av} by AVG. The first two statements set both j and $\sum A_j$ equal to zero, while the third, fourth, and fifth statements are executed n times (because of the IF statement) to calculate $\sum A_j$. During the first trip or cycle through the loop, $j = 1$, A_1 is added to SUM, and the IF statement causes the program to go to statement 15 (which sets $j = 2$ and starts the second trip through the loop). During the nth trip or cycle, $j = n$, A_n is added to SUM, and control goes from the IF statement to statement 16 (since $j = n$) which obtains n in floating-point form. The last statement calculates the average value.

3.3 DO and CONTINUE Statements

In Ill. Ex. 3.4, we had calculated the average value of the elements in array A (i.e., A(1) to A(N)). This could have been done more easily using a **DO** *statement* (instead of an IF statement) as follows:

```
      SUM = 0.0
      DO 17 J = 1, N
   17 SUM = SUM + A(J)
      AN = N
      AVG = SUM/AN
```

First, note that the program-portion in Ill. Ex. 3.4 has two more statements than the previous one. The first statement sets $\sum A_j$ (i.e., SUM) to initially equal zero. The last two statements obtain n as a floating-point number and calculate the average value using the equation

$$A_{av} = \frac{1}{n} \sum_{j=1}^{n} A_j$$

The DO statement and statement 17 calculate the term $\sum\limits_{j=1}^{n} A_j$. These two statements are executed n times (i.e., the DO statement causes the program to go through n loops or cycles). The first time or cycle, J = 1 and A(1) is added to SUM (i.e., A_1 is added to $\sum A_j$), the second time J = 2 and A(2) is added to the SUM term, and during the last cycle J = N and A(N) is added to the SUM term. After the Nth cycle is completed, the SUM term will equal A(1) + A(2) + ... + A(N), and the program will go to the AN = N statement (instead of going from statement 17 to the DO statement as was done during the first N − 1 cycles). Thus, we have shown that the DO statement is a rather powerful one.

Let us now discuss the features of a DO statement more thoroughly. Note in the previous example that the DO statement caused certain consecutive statements to be repeated several times and that a fixed-point variable was increased in value between repetitions. The **DO** *statement* can be written in one of the following two forms

$$\text{DO } s\, j = n1,\, n2$$
$$\text{DO } s\, j = n1,\, n2,\, n3$$

where s is a *statement number*, j is a *fixed-point variable* which is called the *index*, and $n1$, $n2$, and $n3$ may be *fixed-point constants* or *variables*. If $n3$ is not stated in a DO statement, then $n3 = 1$. The DO statement instructs the computer to repeatedly execute the statements that follow the DO statement, up to and including the statement numbered s. These repeated statements are called the *range* of the DO statement. The first time these range statements are executed with index j equal to $n1$, and the second time with $j = n1 + n3$. That is, for each succeeding execution of the range statements, j is increased by $n3$. After the range statements have been executed with j equal to the highest value that does not exceed $n2$, the program stops the repetition and goes to the statement located after statement s. The reader should now look again at the previous Fortran example and see how this paragraph applies to the DO statement and statement 17, which calculates $\sum A_j$.

If instead of DO 17 J = 1, N, we had changed the DO statement in the previous Fortran example (i.e., the one that calculates A_{av}) to be

$$\text{DO } 17 \text{ J} = 2, \text{N}, 2$$

and changed the fourth statement to be AN = N/2, then this Fortran program-portion would calculate the average of all the even-numbered elements in array A. This is because the DO statement and statement 17 forms the sum of all the elements with even-numbered subscripts. The first time statement 17 is executed, J = 2; the second time, J = 2 + 2 = 4;

and the third time, $J = 4 + 2 = 6$; etc., since 2 is added to index J after each execution of statement 17.

As stated previously, for the DO statement

$$DO \ s \ j = n1, \ n2, \ n3$$

whenever enough loops are executed so that the next value of index j will exceed $n2$, then the program will go to the statement that follows statement s (which is the last statement in the DO range) and, thus, transfer out of the DO loop. Thus, for the statement DO 19 J = 1, 17, the program will transfer out of the DO range (to the statement following statement 19) after 17 loops or cycles are executed. An IF or a GO TO statement, inside the DO range, may be used to cause a transfer outside the DO range. This usage is illustrated in Ill. Ex. 3.6. A rather valuable feature is that the value of index j is available for use in computations whenever an IF or GO TO statement is used for transfer outside a DO loop. We are not allowed, however, to transfer into the range of a DO statement by use of a transfer statement located outside the range of that DO statement. Thus, neither

```
        GO TO 17
        DO 17 J = 1, N
   17   SUM = SUM + A(J)
```

nor the following program portion

```
        DO 17 J = 1, N
   17   SUM = SUM + A(J)
        GO TO 17
```

is permissible. Illustrative Example 3.6 shows a valid transfer from the inside to the outside of a DO range. The last statement in a DO range, however, cannot be a transfer statement (e.g., IF, GO TO, etc.). If this results, then this particular transfer statement should be followed by a CONTINUE statement. The **CONTINUE** *statement* does nothing (i.e., causes no action) when the Fortran program is executed, and it is used merely to satisfy the rule that the last statement in a DO range cannot be a transfer statement. This usage of the CONTINUE statement as the last statement in a DO range is exemplified in Ill. Ex. 3.6. Illustrative Example 3.5 shows another use of the CONTINUE statement as a dummy, no-operation instruction.

If a DO statement lies within the range of another DO statement, then *all* statements in the range of the inner DO statement must lie *within* the range of the outer DO statement. The range of the two DO loops can end with the same statement, as shown in Ill. Ex. 3.8, but the last statement of the inner DO loop must not be located after the last statement of the outer DO loop.

Illustrative Example 3.5. Suppose that we had quantities A_1, A_2, A_3, ..., A_n as data. Write Fortran instructions to calculate the average of all the positive non-zero quantities in this array.

Solution. We can accomplish this by adding an IF statement, a CONTINUE statement, and two other statements to the first Fortran example in this section. Thus, we have

$$
\begin{aligned}
&\quad\text{SUM} = 0.0\\
&\quad\text{NPOS} = 0\\
&\quad\text{DO 17 J} = 1, \text{N}\\
&\quad\text{IF (A(J))17, 17, 18}\\
&18\quad\text{SUM} = \text{SUM} + \text{A(J)}\\
&\quad\text{NPOS} = \text{NPOS} + 1\\
&17\quad\text{CONTINUE}\\
&\quad\text{AN} = \text{NPOS}\\
&\quad\text{AVG} = \text{SUM/AN}
\end{aligned}
$$

The CONTINUE statement was used, because statement 17 must be executed during each cycle of the DO loop. The term NPOS is a count of the number of positive terms.

Illustrative Example 3.6. Suppose that we had quantities $x_1, x_2, x_3, \ldots, x_n$ as data, where $x_1 < x_2 < \ldots < x_n$. Write Fortran statements to determine between which x_i values the value of a quantity p lies.

Solution. In the following Fortran statements, array X is used to represent the x_i terms, N represents n, and P represents p.

$$
\begin{aligned}
&\quad\text{DO 23 I} = 1, \text{N}\\
&\quad\text{IF (P} - \text{X(I)) 24, 24, 23}\\
&23\quad\text{CONTINUE}\\
&24
\end{aligned}
$$

Since the X(I) (i.e., x_i) elements are arranged in an increasing-value order, the statements in the DO range will be repeated (where index I is increased by one after each repetition) until the IF statement finds the first X(I) term in the array that equals or exceeds quantity P. When this happens, the IF statement causes a transfer to statement 24 which is outside the DO loop. The value of index I is also available for use in a computation. When statement 24 is reached, we know that the value of quantity P either equals X(I) or it lies between the values of X(I − 1) and X(I). In Chapter 4, we utilize Fortran statements similar to those in this example as the first part of a linear or a polynomial interpolation routine for application to tables and graphs.

Illustrative Example 3.7. Suppose that we had quantities A_1 to A_{32}, B_1 to B_{32}, and C_1 to C_{32}. Write Fortran statements to compute

$$\sum_{i=1}^{32} (A_i B_i + C_i)$$

Solution. This computation may be programmed as follows

```
        SUM = 0.0
        DO 41 I = 1, 32
  41    SUM = SUM + A(I) * B(I) + C(I)
```

Illustrative Example 3.8. Write Fortran statements to compute

$$\sum_{j=1}^{21} \sum_{i=1}^{12} A_{ij} B_i$$

Solution. This computation may be performed by the following Fortran statements, where it should be noted that the inner DO loop is contained within the range of the outer DO loop.

```
        SUM = 0.0
        DO 37 J = 1, 21
        DO 37 I = 1, 12
  37    SUM = SUM + A(I, J) * B(I)
```

3.4 Input and Output Statements for Handling Arrays

If a **READ** or **PRINT** *statement* contains specifically given elements of an array, the elements will be read or printed according to the sequence listed in the Fortran statement. If this data is input, it must be punched on the IBM card in the corresponding sequence (i.e., the first data field on the card goes with the first variable name, etc.), but this sequence is arbitrary if these elements are *explicitly stated.* Thus, the following Fortran statement is a valid one.

READ 11, B(9), B(7), B(21), A(3, 8), R, B(2), F

For Fortran II, a one-dimensional array may be read into the computer as follows

```
        READ 18, (A(K), K = 1, N)
  18    FORMAT (8F8.3)
```

which means that the first N elements of array A are read from IBM cards and that each card contains eight elements. The first quantity read is A(1), the second is A(2), the third is A(3), etc. Thus, the first card should contain A(1) to A(8), the second card (if necessary) should contain A(9) to A(16), etc. Note that the array's variable name and the indexing information are all enclosed in parentheses. Similar statements may be made when a one-dimensional array is printed or punched. The same type of indexing can be used to read or print a row or a column of a matrix and other types of two-dimensional arrays. Thus, the statement

$$\text{PRINT } 14, (B(I, 4), I = 1, 8)$$

prints eight elements from column 4 of matrix B, and the statement

$$\text{PRINT } 15, (C(6, J), J = 1, 9)$$

prints nine elements from the sixth row of matrix C.

In Fortran II, it is also permissible to use indexing so that an entire two-dimensional or three-dimensional array may be read by one READ statement or printed by one PRINT statement. For example, matrix R can be printed as follows, where six elements are printed on each line.

$$\text{PRINT } 31, ((R(K, L), L = 1, M), K = 1, 7)$$
31   FORMAT (6F11.4)

In principle, the inner and outer indexes of the above PRINT statement act like the inner and outer DO statements, respectively, of a double DO loop. Thus, matrix R will be printed row-wise in this example, and seven rows (i.e., $K = 1$ to 7) of this matrix will be printed. Note that if $M = 4$ at this instant, then the first two lines of printout will be as follows:

$$R_{11} \quad R_{12} \quad R_{13} \quad R_{14} \quad R_{21} \quad R_{22}$$
$$R_{23} \quad R_{24} \quad R_{31} \quad R_{32} \quad R_{33} \quad R_{34}$$

This printout would be more readable if the Fortran statements were written such that each line of printout will contain elements of only one row of R, no matter what the value of M is at that instant. This can be done as follows

$$\text{DO } 7 \text{ K} = 1, 7$$
7   PRINT 31, (R(K, L), L = 1, M)
31   FORMAT (6F11.4)

Each cycle of the DO loop prints one row (i.e., M elements) of matrix R. If $M \leq 6$, this row will be printed on one line. Thus, if $M = 4$, the first line will contain R_{11} to R_{14}, the second line will contain R_{21} to R_{24}, etc.

Illustrative Example 3.9.   Write Fortran I statements to read the first N elements of array D.

Solution.   In Fortran I, we are limited to reading or printing only specific elements of an array. The number N is a fixed-point variable, and several IBM cards must be read if N were quite large. This could be handled by using a DO statement as follows, where five elements are read from each card. For this reason, increment n_3 is set to equal 5 in the DO statement. Quantities $D(1)$ to $D(5)$ are read during the first cycle of the DO loop, quantities $D(6)$ to $D(10)$ are read during the second cycle, etc., until all N elements of array D have been loaded into the computer.

$$\text{DO } 9 \text{ I} = 1, \text{N}, 5$$
9   READ 13, D(I), D(I + 1), D(I + 2), D(I + 3), D(I + 4)
13   FORMAT (5F8.2)

Illustrative Example 3.10. Write a complete program to do the calculations of Ill. Ex. 3.8.

Solution. One possible Fortran program to do this is as follows:

```
    DIMENSION B(12), A(12, 21)
 1  READ 11, (B(I), I = 1, 12)
11  FORMAT (6F8.2)
    DO 7 I = 1, 12
 7  READ 11, (A(I, J), J = 1, 21)
    SUM = 0.0
    DO 37 J = 1, 21
    DO 37 I = 1, 12
37  SUM = SUM + A(I, J) * B(I)
    PRINT 12, SUM
12  FORMAT (22HDOUBLE SUM OF PRODUCTS/F15.2)
    GO TO 1
    END
```

This program first reads array B and two-dimensional array A; then it performs the calculations of Ill. Ex. 3.8, prints the result, and goes to statement 1 for the next case.

3.5 Arithmetic FUNCTION Statements and FUNCTION Subprograms

As previously stated in Sec. 3.1, Fortran I for the IBM 1620 Computer does not have the capability to use the Fortran statements that are explained in this section. To start with an example, suppose that we wish to calculate the quantities (tan A + tan B) and tan C. Since none of the seven library functions provide for the calculation of the tangent of an angle, we must use other means, unless the particular computer installation has added this as another library function. These two terms may be computed by the following program which utilizes an *arithmetic statement function*

```
    TANF(X) = SINF(X)/COSF(X)
 1  READ 11, A, B, C
11  FORMAT (3F8.5)
    R = TANF(A)
    V = TANF(B)
    D = R + V
    E = TANF(C)
    PRINT 11, D, E
    GO TO 1
    END
```

The first statement of this program is an arithmetic statement function, and it utilizes the equation $\tan x = \sin x / \cos x$. This type of statement must be located before the first executable statement of a program, and it only defines a function (i.e., it does not cause any calculations to result). In the rest of the program, note that the function TANF(X) is used in the same manner that a library function is, and that X was a dummy variable for later specification of the argument (or angle in this example) for the given function. Its appearance in the R, V, and E Fortran statements calls for the use of the TANF(X) function. It may be noted that the term D could have been calculated by one Fortran statement as follows:

$$D = TANF(A) + TANF(B)$$

The *arithmetic statement function* is limited in application to functions that have only one value and which can be expressed by only one statement. Its form is $e(g) = f$, where e is the *function name*, g is the *argument*, and f is a *Fortran expression*. The name is arbitrary except that it must not contain more than six characters; the first character must be alphabetic, and the last character must be F. The first letter must be X if the function is fixed-point in value. Argument g follows name e and is enclosed in parentheses. If there are several arguments, they must be separated by commas. Both the arguments and the terms in expression f may not include subscripted variables. Expression f may use other functions if they have been previously defined by other arithmetic function statements or are library functions. This had been previously done in this section to calculate $\tan x = \sin x / \cos x$.

Now let us program the solution of the same problem using a **FUNCTION** *subprogram*. The main program could be the same as the previously given program with the first statement removed. The only other difference is that we cannot use TANF(X) in the calculation of R, V, and E, because the name ends in F, so we can replace it by TANG(X) in these three Fortran statements. The function TANG(X) is defined elsewhere, but it can be used in the main program in the same way that a library function or an arithmetic statement function is used. This function is defined in a subprogram, and this subprogram is compiled *independently* of the main program (even though it is a part of the total Fortran program). The FUNCTION subprogram can only be used for functions that have one value, but it can use several Fortran statements to define the function. The form of this FUNCTION subprogram could be

FUNCTION TANG(X)
.
.
.
RETURN
END

The subprogram could have only the following statement between the FUNCTION and the RETURN statements to calculate tan x (which is represented by the name TANG)

$$TANG = SINF(X)/COSF(X)$$

or the subprogram can calculate tan x by using an infinite series equation or other techniques. In the latter case, there will be several Fortran statements between the FUNCTION and the RETURN statements in the subprogram.

The **RETURN** *statement* is the last *executed* statement when a FUNCTION or a SUBROUTINE subprogram is utilized or executed, and, thus, it usually precedes the END statement. This RETURN statement terminates a subprogram and returns control to the program that asked for use of this subprogram. Thus, a RETURN statement is used to state at what point in the subprogram to return to the main program (or the calling subprogram). There can be several RETURN statements or exits in a subprogram.

The FUNCTION subprogram will not be discussed any further. Though they are utilized (or referred to) differently in a main program (or a subprogram that asks for their use), the FUNCTION and the SUBROUTINE subprograms themselves are very similar. The main difference is that the FUNCTION subprogram can return only one computed term to the main program (or the calling subprogram), while the SUBROUTINE subprogram can return several computed terms (including arrays). Because of these similarities and because the SUBROUTINE statement is much more useful, the reader will find further rules for using FUNCTION subprograms in the discussion of SUBROUTINE subprograms. A subprogram (FUNCTION or SUBROUTINE) can be defined to be a Fortran program that is used by another program or subprogram.

3.6 SUBROUTINE Subprograms

Let us first write a Fortran program to do the example problem in Sec. 3.5, but using this time a Fortran **SUBROUTINE** *subprogram*. This can be done as follows:

```
 1   READ 11, A, B, C
11   FORMAT (3F8.5)
     CALL TANG(A, R)
     CALL TANG(B, V)
     D = R + V
     CALL TANG(C, E)
     PRINT 11, D, E
     GO TO 1
     END
```

The difference between this program and the program using the FUNCTION subprogram is that three **CALL** *statements* were used to replace the following three statements

$$R = TANG(A)$$
$$V = TANG(B)$$
$$E = TANG(C)$$

Each **CALL** *statement* in the above program is of the form CALL (X, Y), where X is the angle and Y = tan X (i.e., Y is the calculated value of tan X). The form of the SUBROUTINE subprogram could be as follows, where X and Y are dummy variables

SUBROUTINE TANG(X, Y)
.
.
.
RETURN
END

The statements between the SUBROUTINE and the RETURN statements calculate the tangent of angle X, and this tangent is represented by the symbol Y. The RETURN statement was previously explained in Sec. 3.5.

The general form of a **FUNCTION** *statement* (which is the first statement in a FUNCTION subprogram) is

FUNCTION Name (A1, A2, A3, . . .)

and the general form of a **SUBROUTINE** *statement* (which is the first statement in a SUBROUTINE subprogram) is

SUBROUTINE Name (A1, A2, A3, . . .)

where, in both cases, Name is the *symbolic name* of the subprogram and A1, A2, etc., are the *arguments*. The subprogram name can consist of one to six alphabetic or numeric characters, but the first character must be alphabetic. The subprogram arguments are the names of nonsubscripted, fixed- or floating-point variables, and these arguments can be considered to be inputs and outputs for the subprogram.

As was previously illustrated, a SUBROUTINE subprogram is utilized by the main program or another subprogram by the use of a CALL statement. Note how this differs from how a FUNCTION subprogram is utilized. The **CALL** *statement*, when executed, transfers control to the subprogram, and it specifies the name of the SUBROUTINE and its arguments. Its general form is as follows

CALL Name (B1, B2, B3, . . .)

The dummy arguments (A1, A2, etc.) of the SUBROUTINE statement are replaced by the arguments (B1, B2, etc.) given in the CALL statement when this subprogram is executed. Thus, the arguments in the CALL statement must agree in *number, order,* and *mode* with the corresponding arguments of the SUBROUTINE statement. The arguments in the CALL statement may be one of the following types: fixed- and floating-point constants, fixed- and floating-point variables (which may have subscripts), and arithmetic expressions. If an argument in a CALL statement is the name of an array, then the dimensions assigned to this array must be the same as the size of the corresponding array given in a DIMENSION statement in the called SUBROUTINE.

The use of the SUBROUTINE statement for subprograms is a rather powerful feature, and it may be used advantageously in several ways. For example, if a problem required the interpolation of several graphs, then the interpolation procedure can be programmed once in a SUBROUTINE subprogram, and CALL statements in the main program cause its use when needed. Thus, the SUBROUTINE subprogram can be used as an easy means for handling repeated calculations (e.g., several matrix additions) that occur in a problem. Of particular advantage to us is that persons of competent mathematical background can program such calculations as a matrix inversion, the roots of a polynomial, a curve-fit, etc., as SUBROUTINE subprograms. These subprograms can be supplied to the computer installation, and engineers can use a particular subprogram (if its use is needed) with his own program. Thus, a subprogram can be used once in many main programs. Since there are several SUBROUTINE subprogram examples in Sec. 3.7 and in Chapter 4, the illustrative examples in this section are of an elementary nature. Thus, the reader is referred to Secs. 3.7, 4.2, etc. for further examples using subprograms.

In large problems and usually with large computers, the SUBROUTINE statement is often used to divide or segment a program into smaller parts (i.e., subprograms) in order to ease the checkout of the overall program. When this is done, the subprograms are compiled and checked out individually. This practice of breaking a program into a short main program and several SUBROUTINE subprograms is also done often when two or more persons are writing different parts of the program. This program-division procedure can be made easier by use of a COMMON statement.

To illustrate what the **COMMON** *statement* does, suppose that the main program contains the statement

COMMON RA, M, T, PN

and a SUBROUTINE subprogram contains the statement

$$COMMON\ D,\ I,\ E,\ F$$

These two statements cause D and RA to have the same storage location. This means that the term D in the subprogram corresponds to the term RA in the main program. The same can be said for I and M, for E and T, and for F and PN. Thus, a COMMON statement can be used so that a SUBROUTINE statement and the corresponding CALL statements will not need to contain any arguments or parentheses (e.g., SUBROUTINE TANG). These arguments are now located in the COMMON statements. When a program is segmented, the COMMON statement is long and usually contains the names of all the program variables. The same COMMON statement is used in the main program and all subprograms, thus allowing all CALL and SUBROUTINE statements to be written without arguments and parentheses.

Illustrative Example 3.11. Illustrative Example 3.2 shows how we can represent a graph of y versus x by tabulating N points and representing these points by arrays X and Y, where each array consists of N elements. Write a Fortran subroutine to read N points from a y-versus-x curve into a computer and to also print these values.

Solution. The subroutine only has to read array X and array Y into the computer, and to print these values. To keep the points together, we have chosen the order of data reading to be: X(1), Y(1), X(2), Y(2), etc. A subroutine to do this is as follows:

```
        SUBROUTINE CURVRD(X, Y, N)
        DIMENSION X(20), Y(20)
        READ 10, N, (X(I), Y(I), I = 1, N)
   10   FORMAT (I5/(8F8.3))
        PRINT 11, N, (X(I), Y(I), I = 1, N)
   11   FORMAT (///11HINPUT CURVE/I6/(6F12.3))
        RETURN
        END
```

Illustrative Example 3.12. Suppose we had a FUNCTION subprogram to interpolate the y-versus-x curve in Ill. Ex. 3.11. That is, it will use arrays X and Y to find the value of y for any value of x. The first statement of this subprogram is

$$FUNCTION\ ENTRP(X,\ Y,\ XA,\ N)$$

and it calculates the interpolated value of y for the given x-value XA. Write a statement to interpolate a seventeen-point, C-versus-T curve in a main program.

Solution. If we call the interpolated point TA, and the interpolated value CA, the statement is

$$CA = ENTRP(T,\ C,\ TA,\ 17)$$

Illustrative Example 3.13.   An interpolation of a curve has only one answer, so it can be written as a FUNCTION subprogram, as well as a SUBROUTINE subprogram. If we convert the subprogram in Ill. Ex. 3.12 to a SUBROUTINE subprogram, write the first statement in the new subprogram. Let YA denote the interpolated value. Also solve Ill. Ex. 3.12 using the new subprogram.

Solution.   The new subprogram starts with the statement

SUBROUTINE ENTRP(X, Y, XA, YA, N)

and the new solution of Ill. Ex. 3.12 is

CALL ENTRP(T, C, TA, CA, 17)

Methods for interpolating curves are discussed in Secs. 4.1, 4.2, and 4.3.

3.7   *Matrix Arithmetic and Matrix Subprograms*

The purpose of this section is to program matrix arithmetic subroutines. These subroutines are furnished in the illustrative examples for this section. The next to last illustrative example in this section (i.e., Ill. Ex. 3.18) shows how these subroutines might be used in a problem that requires matrix calculations. Let us now review some basic fundamentals of matrix notation and matrix arithmetic.

A *matrix* is merely a rectangular grouping of numbers arranged in rows and columns to form an array. Each number is called an *element* of the matrix. Matrices do not have a specific value, as do determinants, but they are very useful as a shorthand notation for carrying out certain types of calculations. The following matrix

$$\begin{bmatrix} -5 & 3 & 7 \\ 2 & 0 & -9 \end{bmatrix}$$

consists of two rows, three columns, and six elements. The first column consists of -5 and 2, while the second row consists of 2, 0, and -9. Note that the above array is enclosed in brackets to denote that it is a matrix. The *size* of a matrix is specified by its *number of rows and columns*. Thus, the above matrix is of size two-by-three. In general, a matrix of m rows and n columns (i.e., size m by n) can be represented as follows:

$$[B] = \begin{bmatrix} B_{11} & B_{12} & \ldots & B_{1n} \\ B_{21} & B_{22} & \ldots & B_{2n} \\ \cdot\cdot & \cdot\cdot & \ldots & \cdot\cdot \\ B_{m1} & B_{m2} & \ldots & B_{mn} \end{bmatrix}$$

In the above matrix, each element is identified by two subscripts, where the first subscript denotes the row and the second denotes the column to which this element belongs. Thus, element B_{46} belongs to the fourth row and the sixth column. Note that the *row number* is counted from the top and that the *column number* is counted from the left.

A *square matrix* is a matrix that has the same number of rows and columns (i.e., $m = n$). It should be emphasized that a square matrix is not the same thing as a determinant. For example, the following determinant, which is represented by a pair of vertical lines, has a numerical value of 10, while square matrices do not have a numerical value.

$$|A| = \begin{vmatrix} 6 & -4 \\ -2 & 3 \end{vmatrix} = (6)(3) - (-4)(-2) = 10$$

The *principal diagonal* of a square matrix $[B]$ consists of elements B_{11}, B_{22}, B_{33}, ..., B_{mm}. A *diagonal matrix* is a square matrix where all the elements are zero, except those on the principal diagonal. We shall represent a diagonal matrix by the notation $\{B\}$. A *unit matrix*, which is denoted by $[I]$, is a diagonal matrix where all of the elements on the principal diagonal equal unity. Thus, the following matrix is a three-by-three unit matrix:

$$\begin{bmatrix} 1 & 0 & 0 \\ 0 & 1 & 0 \\ 0 & 0 & 1 \end{bmatrix}$$

The above matrix is also a square matrix and a diagonal matrix. A *column matrix* has only one column and is denoted by $\{B\}$, while a *row matrix* has only one row and is denoted by $\lfloor B \rfloor$.

Two matrices are equal only if the corresponding elements of both matrices are equal. Thus, $[A] = [B]$ only if $A_{ij} = B_{ij}$ for all values of i and j. This also means that the two matrices must have the same number of rows and columns. Next we shall discuss the basic matrix arithmetic operations: addition, subtraction, multiplication, and inversion.

Two matrices can be added or subtracted only if they are of the same size. To add two matrices, add the corresponding elements. Thus, $[A] + [B] = [C]$ implies that $C_{ij} = A_{ij} + B_{ij}$ for all i and j combinations. For example,

$$\begin{bmatrix} 4 & 2 \\ -1 & 5 \end{bmatrix} + \begin{bmatrix} 1 & 7 \\ 3 & 2 \end{bmatrix} = \begin{bmatrix} 4+1 & 2+7 \\ -1+3 & 5+2 \end{bmatrix} = \begin{bmatrix} 5 & 9 \\ 2 & 7 \end{bmatrix}$$

It can be seen that $[A] + [B] = [B] + [A]$. To subtract two matrices, subtract the corresponding elements. Thus, $[A] - [B] = [C]$ implies that $C_{ij} = A_{ij} - B_{ij}$ for all values of i and j. As an example,

$$\begin{bmatrix} 4 & 2 \\ -1 & 5 \end{bmatrix} - \begin{bmatrix} 1 & 7 \\ 3 & 2 \end{bmatrix} = \begin{bmatrix} 4-1 & 2-7 \\ -1-3 & 5-2 \end{bmatrix} = \begin{bmatrix} 3 & -5 \\ -4 & 3 \end{bmatrix}$$

There are two types of multiplication. If a matrix $[A]$ is multiplied by a constant k (i.e., a scalar term), then each element in the original matrix is multiplied by that scalar. Thus, $k[A] = [B]$ implies that $B_{ij} = kA_{ij}$ for all values of i and j. For example,

$$4\begin{bmatrix} 4 & 2 \\ -1 & 5 \end{bmatrix} = \begin{bmatrix} 16 & 8 \\ -4 & 20 \end{bmatrix}$$

The second type of multiplication involves the multiplication of two matrices, and this is not always possible. If we can obtain the product $[A][B]$, then the number of columns in $[A]$ must equal the number of rows of $[B]$. Usually $[A][B]$ does not equal $[B][A]$, so the order of the two matrices is important. Now let us suppose that it is possible to obtain $[C] = [A][B]$. The element C_{ij} (which is in the ith row and jth column of the product matrix $[C]$) is obtained by taking the sum of the products of the elements of row i of $[A]$ and the corresponding elements of column j of $[B]$. If matrix $[A]$ is of size m by n and matrix $[B]$ is of size n by ℓ, this may be expressed in mathematical form by

$$C_{ij} = \sum_{k=1}^{n} A_{ik}B_{kj} \tag{3-1}$$

where k is a dummy index. Matrix $[C]$ will be of size m by ℓ. That is, the number of rows in product matrix $[C]$ equals the number of rows in matrix $[A]$, and the number of columns of $[C]$ equals the number of columns in $[B]$. As a numerical example, let us consider

$$\begin{bmatrix} 1 & 3 & 4 \\ 2 & 0 & 5 \end{bmatrix}\begin{bmatrix} 4 & 0 \\ 0 & 2 \\ 1 & 5 \end{bmatrix} = \begin{bmatrix} 8 & 26 \\ 13 & 25 \end{bmatrix}$$

Let us represent the above matrix multiplication symbolically by $[A][B] = [C]$. Multiplication is possible because the number of columns of $[A]$ equals the number of rows of $[B]$ (i.e., both equal three). To obtain element C_{11}, we use the first row of $[A]$ and the first column of $[B]$, and perform the following calculation

$$C_{11} = (1)(4) + (3)(0) + (4)(1) = 8$$

The element C_{12} is obtained using row 1 of $[A]$ and column 2 of $[B]$, and performing the following calculation

$$C_{12} = (1)(0) + (3)(2) + (4)(5) = 26$$

Elements C_{21} and C_{22} are obtained using row 2 of $[A]$ and performing the following calculations:

$$C_{21} = (2)(4) + (0)(0) + (5)(1) = 13$$
$$C_{22} = (2)(0) + (0)(2) + (5)(5) = 25$$

As special cases, it can be shown that any column matrix premultiplied by any matrix (e.g., $[A]\{B\}$) results in a column matrix, and also that

$$[A][I] = [A] \tag{3-2}$$

$$[I][A] = [A] \tag{3-3}$$

where $[A]$ represents any square matrix, and $[I]$ is a unit matrix. The previous equations are analogous to the scalar equations: $1 \cdot k = k$ and $k \cdot 1 = k$. Thus, we see an analogy between the unit matrix and the number unity.

Matrix division is never possible, and the matrix operation that is most similar in concept is *matrix inversion*. Matrix inversion is possible only with a square matrix. Another requirement is that the determinant of the square matrix (e.g., $|A|$) must not equal zero. This might be considered to be analogous to division by zero. The inverse of a matrix $[A]$ is written as $[A]^{-1}$, and the definition of this *matrix inverse* is given by the following equation

$$[A][A]^{-1} = [I] \tag{3-4}$$

That is, the multiplication of a square matrix with its inverse results in the unit matrix $[I]$. It can also be shown that $[A]^{-1}[A] = [I]$. Thus, a matrix inverse can be considered to be analogous to the reciprocal of a scalar, since $k \cdot k^{-1} = k^{-1} \cdot k = 1$ if k^{-1} is the reciprocal of scalar k. Methods for finding the inverse of a matrix, which are classified into the two broad categories of *elimination* and *iteration*, are briefly discussed in Sec. 4.8.

If $[A][X] = [B]$, then $[X] = [A]^{-1}[B]$, which is somewhat analogous to matrix division. To prove this result, if $[A][X] = [B]$, then premultiplication of both sides by $[A]^{-1}$ gives

$$[A]^{-1}[A][X] = [A]^{-1}[B]$$

Since $[A]^{-1}[A][X] = [I][X]$ and since $[I][X] = [X]$, we obtain the result that $[X] = [A]^{-1}[B]$. This result is used in Sec. 4.8 to show the usefulness of a matrix inverse for solving simultaneous, linear algebraic equations.

Subroutines to perform matrix addition, matrix subtraction, matrix multiplication, and matrix inversion are usually available at computer installations (even though the first three operations are easily programmed as shown in the illustrative examples). Two other common matrix subroutines are: (1) evaluate the determinant of a square matrix and (2) determine the eigenvalues of a square matrix. Since the reader has already learned how to evaluate determinants in a lower division mathematics course, no further discussion on this subject is furnished in this text. The **eigenvalues** (also called **characteristic values**) of a matrix are the roots of a special determinant equation. That is, the eigenvalues of a square matrix $[A]$ are the roots of the equation

$$|[A] - \lambda[I]| = 0 \tag{3-5}$$

If matrix $[A]$ is of size 3 by 3, then the above equation may be written as follows:

$$\begin{vmatrix} A_{11} - \lambda & A_{12} & A_{13} \\ A_{21} & A_{22} - \lambda & A_{23} \\ A_{31} & A_{32} & A_{33} - \lambda \end{vmatrix} = 0$$

Since the above determinant, when evaluated, results in a polynomial in λ, the above equation is a polynomial equation which is called the *characteristic equation*. The roots of this characteristic equation (i.e., polynomial) are called the *characteristic numbers* or *eigenvalues* of matrix $[A]$. Section 2.14 discusses a physical problem that requires the determination of eigenvalues in order to obtain the problem solution. Computer SUBROUTINE subprograms that calculate eigenvalues are very often used in professional practice, especially in problems that require the determination of the natural frequencies of vibration for complex structures.

As was illustrated in Sec. 2.14, an nth order square matrix has n eigenvalues. This is because the characteristic equation is a polynomial of degree n in λ, as can be shown when the previous determinant equation is expanded. Thus, the n eigenvalues may not all be distinct in value. There is also an **eigenvector** corresponding to each discrete eigenvalue. An eigenvalue that is a repeated root in the characteristic equation can have more than one eigenvector associated with it. Most subprograms that compute eigenvalues also compute the corresponding eigenvectors. The *eigenvector* associated with eigenvalue λ_i of matrix $[A]$ is defined to be the column matrix $\{x\}$ that satisfies the following equation

$$[[A] - \lambda_i[I]]\{x\} = 0 \qquad\qquad (3\text{-}6)$$

Multiplication of the two matrices in the previous equation results in a set of linear equations involving the x_i elements. Hence, the process of calculating an eigenvector involves the solution of a set of n linear algebraic equations for eigenvector elements $x_1, x_2, x_3, \ldots, x_n$. Such solution procedures are discussed in Sec. 4.8.

The procedure for determining eigenvalues consists first of determining the characteristic polynomial equation and then computing the roots of this polynomial. Complex roots or eigenvalues usually have complex eigenvectors associated with them. As an example, let us find the eigenvalues associated with the following matrix:

$$[A] = \begin{bmatrix} 3 & 4 \\ 2 & 1 \end{bmatrix}$$

The eigenvalues of matrix $[A]$ are the roots of the following determinant equation:

$$\begin{vmatrix} 3 - \lambda & 4 \\ 2 & 1 - \lambda \end{vmatrix} = 0$$

After expanding the above determinant, we obtain the following polynomial equation:

$$(3 - \lambda)(1 - \lambda) - 8 = \lambda^2 - 4\lambda - 5 = 0$$

Thus, the eigenvalues of matrix $[A]$ are 5 and -1, since they are the roots of the previous polynomial equation. For obtaining the characteristic polynomial of large matrices, which involves the expansion of a determinant, by means of a Fortran subprogram, methods such as the *Leverrier-Faddeev* method may be used. The reader is referred to numerical analysis texts for details. Methods for obtaining roots of polynomial equations were discussed in Sec. 2.15. There are also special methods for finding specific eigenvalues of a matrix (e.g., the smallest or the largest one), and there are some methods that obtain the eigenvalues from the matrix itself without first determining the characteristic equation. Illustrative Example 3.19 exemplifies how the eigenvalues of a matrix may be determined by obtaining the roots of a polynomial equation and how the corresponding eigenvectors are obtained by solving a set of simultaneous, linear algebraic equations. This example also shows how the largest eigenvalue and its eigenvector may be determined directly from the matrix itself by using a matrix iteration technique.

Illustrative Example 3.14. Suppose that a computer installation had SUBROUTINE subprograms to invert a matrix, to evaluate a determinant, and to determine the eigenvalues of a matrix. The first statements for each of these three subprograms are as follows:

SUBROUTINE MATINV(A, B, N)
SUBROUTINE MATDET(A, VAL, N)
SUBROUTINE MATEIG(A, EG, N)

where N is the size of input square matrix $[A]$, $[B] = [A]^{-1}$, VAL = $|A|$, and EG is a one-dimensional array that contains the N eigenvalues. Write Fortran statements to calculate $[R] = [T]^{-1}$, $D = |T|$, and the eigenvalues for square matrix $[T]$, whose size is 16, in a main Fortran program that uses these three subprograms.

Solution. We shall utilize the following three CALL statements to do the three desired calculations by use of these three SUBROUTINE subprograms, where CHAR is the array that contains the eigenvalues.

CALL MATINV(T, R, 16)
CALL MATDET(T, D, 16)
CALL MATEIG(T, CHAR, 16)

Illustrative Example 3.15. Write subroutines to perform matrix addition, matrix subtraction, and the multiplication of a matrix by a constant.

Solution. The following subroutine is for matrix addition. It performs the operation $[A] + [B] = [C]$, where NROW is the number of rows in $[A]$ and $[B]$ and NCOL is the number of columns in $[A]$ and $[B]$. Each element of $[C]$ is obtained using the equation $C_{ij} = A_{ij} + B_{ij}$. The second DO statement causes the calculation of C_{ij} for all column elements in a row. The first DO statement causes all of the rows to be included. Thus all elements of $[C]$ are calculated.

```
    SUBROUTINE MATADD(A, B, C, NROW, NCOL)
    DIMENSION A(20, 20), B(20, 20), C(20, 20)
    DO 4 I = 1, NROW
    DO 4 J = 1, NCOL
  4 C(I, J) = A(I, J) + B(I, J)
    RETURN
    END
```

The following subroutine for matrix subtraction is very similar. It calculates $[C] = [A] - [B]$ by means of the equation $C_{ij} = A_{ij} - B_{ij}$ for all values of i and j.

```
    SUBROUTINE MATSUB(A, B, C, NROW, NCOL)
    DIMENSION A(20, 20), B(20, 20), C(20, 20)
    DO 4 I = 1, NROW
    DO 4 J = 1, NCOL
  4 C(I, J) = A(I, J) - B(I, J)
    RETURN
    END
```

The following subroutine multiplies matrix $[A]$ by the scalar $CNST$, and the result is denoted by matrix $[C]$. Thus, $C_{ij} = (CNST)A_{ij}$ for all values of i and j.

```
    SUBROUTINE MATCON(A, C, CNST, NROW, NCOL)
    DIMENSION A(20, 20), C(20, 20)
    DO 4 I = 1, NROW
    DO 4 J = 1, NCOL
  4 C(I, J) = CNST * A(I, J)
    RETURN
    END
```

Illustrative Example 3.16. Write a matrix multiplication subroutine.

Solution. The following subroutine performs the operation $[A][B] = [C]$, where MA and NA are the number of rows and columns, respectively, of matrix $[A]$ and MB and NB are the number of rows and columns, respectively, of matrix $[B]$. If NA does not equal MB, the subroutine prints a statement to say that this matrix operation is not possible. The first two DO statements cause the element C_{ij} to be calculated for every row and column, respectively, since matrix $[C]$ will consist of MA rows and NB columns. The C(I, J) = 0.0 statement, the last DO statement, and statement 5 calculate each element C_{ij} according to the equation

$$C_{ij} = \sum_{k=1}^{NA} A_{ik}B_{kj}$$

```
     SUBROUTINE MATMUL(A, B, C, MA, NA, MB, NB)
     DIMENSION A(20, 20), B(20, 20), C(20, 20)
     IF(NA − MB)3, 4, 3
  3  PRINT 11
 11  FORMAT (35HAN IMPOSSIBLE MATRIX MULTIPLICATION)
     GO TO 6
  4  DO 5 I = 1, MA
     DO 5 J = 1, NB
     C(I, J) = 0.0
     DO 5 K = 1, NA
  5  C(I, J) = C(I, J) + A(I, K) * B(K, J)
  6  RETURN
     END
```

Illustrative Example 3.17. Write a subroutine to read a matrix into the computer and, then, print this input matrix.

Solution. The following subroutine reads matrix $[A]$ into the computer and then prints this input matrix, which is of size NROW by NCOL. One row of matrix $[A]$ is read and printed during each cycle of the DO loop.

```
     SUBROUTINE MATRED(A, NROW, NCOL)
     DIMENSION A(20, 20)
     READ 11, NROW, NCOL
 11  FORMAT (2I5)
 12  FORMAT (5F8.2)
 13  FORMAT (5F12.2)
     DO 5 I = 1, NROW
     READ 12, (A(I, J), J = 1, NCOL)
  5  PRINT 13, (A(I, J), J = 1, NCOL)
     RETURN
     END
```

We could have chosen to print "INPUT MATRIX" as a title for this matrix (along with the values of NROW and NCOL) inside this subroutine. It was decided here to print the title outside the subroutine and in the calling program, as is demonstrated in Ill. Ex. 3.18. The subprogram in Ill. Ex. 3.11 (which reads and prints input curves) could also be changed so that the input curve can be printed with a special title.

Illustrative Example 3.18. Write a main Fortran program, using the subprograms of Ill. Exs. 3.15 to 3.17, to perform the following matrix calculations:

$$[R] = b[D]$$
$$[V] = [E][F] − [R]$$

Solution. The following Fortran program reads and prints scalar B and the input matrices $[D]$, $[E]$, and $[F]$, and then calculates $[R] = B[D]$, $[G] = [E][F]$, and $[V] = [G] - [R]$. This program prints output matrices $[R]$ and $[V]$ before it goes to statement 1 for the next case. In order that this program will fit the IBM 1620 computer, the maximum size of each matrix is 10 by 10. Thus, the DIMENSION statements in each SUBROUTINE subprogram that is used must be changed so that the maximum size of each matrix is also 10 by 10.

```
      DIMENSION D(10, 10), E(10, 10), F(10, 10), G(10, 10), R(10, 10),
     V(10, 10)
  1   READ 11, B
 11   FORMAT (F8.3)
      PRINT 12, B
 12   FORMAT (///8HSCALAR B/F12.3///14HINPUT MATRIX D)
      CALL MATRED(D, ND, MD)
      PRINT 13
 13   FORMAT (///14HINPUT MATRIX E)
      CALL MATRED(E, NE, ME)
      PRINT 14
 14   FORMAT (///14HINPUT MATRIX F)
      CALL MATRED(F, NF, MF)
      CALL MATCON(D, R, B, ND, MD)
      CALL MATMUL(E, F, G, NE, ME, NF, MF)
      CALL MATSUB(G, R, V, ND, MD)
      PRINT 15
 15   FORMAT (///15HOUTPUT MATRIX R)
 16   FORMAT (5F12.4)
      DO 4 I = 1, ND
  4   PRINT 16, (R(I, J), J = 1, MD)
      PRINT 17
 17   FORMAT (///15HOUTPUT MATRIX V)
      DO 5 I = 1, ND
  5   PRINT 16, (V(I, J), J = 1, MD)
      GO TO 1
      END
```

Illustrative Example 3.19. Find the eigenvalues and the eigenvectors of the following matrix:

$$\begin{bmatrix} 1.0 & 0.2 & 0.5 \\ 0.2 & 1.0 & 0.3 \\ 0.5 & 0.3 & 1.0 \end{bmatrix}$$

Solution. The three eigenvalues for this matrix may be obtained by solving the following determinant equation:

$$\begin{vmatrix} 1.0 - \lambda & 0.2 & 0.5 \\ 0.2 & 1.0 - \lambda & 0.3 \\ 0.5 & 0.3 & 1.0 - \lambda \end{vmatrix} = 0$$

Expansion of the determinant gives the following third-degree polynomial equation:

$$f(\lambda) = \lambda^3 - 3\lambda^2 + 2.62\lambda + 0.68 = 0$$

We shall solve for one root using the Newton-Raphson method, which is

$$\lambda_{n+1} = \lambda_n - \frac{f(\lambda)}{f'(\lambda)}$$

Assuming that $\lambda_1 = 1.000$, we find

$$\lambda_2 = 1.000 - \frac{f(1.000)}{f'(1.000)} = 1.000 - \frac{(-0.060)}{(-0.380)} = 0.842$$

$$\lambda_3 = 0.842 - \frac{f(0.842)}{f'(0.842)} = 0.842 - \frac{(-0.050)}{(-0.305)} = 0.828$$

Another calculation gives $\lambda_4 = 0.828$, which means that one root of $f(\lambda)$ is 0.828. Division of $f(\lambda)$ by $(\lambda - 0.828)$ gives

$$g(\lambda) = \lambda^2 - 2.172\lambda + 0.8216$$

The roots of $g(\lambda)$ can be easily obtained by use of the quadratic formula. The results are $\lambda = 1.685$ and $\lambda = 0.488$. The three eigenvalues are, thus, equal to 0.488, 0.828, and 1.685.

An eigenvector is defined to be the set of x_i values that satisfy the following matrix equation for a specific value of eigenvalue λ_i.

$$[[A] - \lambda_i[I]]\{x\} = 0$$

The previous equation can be rewritten in the following form:

$$[A]\{x\} = \lambda_i\{x\}$$

Insertion of the a_{ij} elements for matrix $[A]$ and performing a matrix multiplication gives

$$x_1 + 0.2x_2 + 0.5x_3 = \lambda_i x_1$$
$$0.2x_1 + x_2 + 0.3x_3 = \lambda_i x_2$$
$$0.5x_1 + 0.3x_2 + x_3 = \lambda_i x_3$$

For $\lambda_i = 1.685$, these equations become

$$x_1 + 0.2x_2 + 0.5x_3 = 1.685x_1$$
$$0.2x_1 + x_2 + 0.3x_3 = 1.685x_2$$
$$0.5x_1 + 0.3x_2 + x_3 = 1.685x_3$$

Solution of these three algebraic equations, after setting $x_1 = 1.000$, gives $x_2 = 0.757$ and $x_3 = 1.064$. Thus, we have the eigenvector that is associated with an eigenvalue of 1.685. Repeating this procedure for $\lambda_i = 0.828$ gives $x_1 = 1.00$, $x_2 = -1.91$, and $x_3 = 0.420$. For $\lambda_i = 0.487$, we obtain $x_1 = 1.00$, $x_2 = 0.274$, and $x_3 = -1.14$.

Let us now illustrate how we may solve for the eigenvalues and eigenvectors by use of a relatively simple iteration procedure. This method, in a modified form, is very commonly used in vibration analysis to find the natural frequencies of spring-mass, disk-shaft, and complex elastic structures. The details may be found in vibration analysis textbooks. Since an eigenvector can be defined to be the $\{x\}$ matrix that satisfies the following equation, where λ is an eigenvalue for matrix $[A]$

$$\{r\} \equiv [A]\{x\} = \lambda\{x\}$$

we can use the following iteration equation, where $\{x\}_{n+1}$ is the next approximation for $\{x\}$ and is calculated from the previous approximation $\{x\}_n$.

$$\{x\}_{n+1} = [A]\{x\}_n$$

The iteration is completed when we come to a condition where

$$\{x\}_{n+1} = k\{x\}_n$$

When this condition occurs, k is an eigenvalue for matrix $[A]$ and $\{x\}_{n+1}$ is its eigenvector. To apply this iteration technique to this problem, let us first assume that $x_1 = x_2 = x_3 = 1$. Thus, the first iteration gives

$$\{x\}_1 = \begin{bmatrix} 1.0 & 0.2 & 0.5 \\ 0.2 & 1.0 & 0.3 \\ 0.5 & 0.3 & 1.0 \end{bmatrix} \begin{Bmatrix} 1.00 \\ 1.00 \\ 1.00 \end{Bmatrix} = \begin{Bmatrix} 1.70 \\ 1.50 \\ 1.80 \end{Bmatrix} = 1.70 \begin{Bmatrix} 1.00 \\ 0.88 \\ 1.06 \end{Bmatrix}$$

The values of $\{x\}_{n+1}$ are normalized so that one x_i element equals unity before it is utilized in the next iteration. This is done to prevent large magnitudes. The second iteration gives

$$\{x\}_2 = \begin{bmatrix} 1.0 & 0.2 & 0.5 \\ 0.2 & 1.0 & 0.3 \\ 0.5 & 0.3 & 1.0 \end{bmatrix} \begin{Bmatrix} 1.00 \\ 0.88 \\ 1.06 \end{Bmatrix} = \begin{Bmatrix} 1.72 \\ 1.40 \\ 1.82 \end{Bmatrix} = 1.72 \begin{Bmatrix} 1.00 \\ 0.817 \\ 1.06 \end{Bmatrix}$$

The ninth iteration gives

$$\{x\}_9 = [A] \begin{Bmatrix} 1.00 \\ 0.755 \\ 1.06 \end{Bmatrix} = \begin{Bmatrix} 1.68 \\ 1.27 \\ 1.79 \end{Bmatrix} = 1.68 \begin{Bmatrix} 1.00 \\ 0.760 \\ 1.06 \end{Bmatrix}$$

Since the tenth iteration gives

$$\{x\}_{10} = [A] \begin{Bmatrix} 1.00 \\ 0.760 \\ 1.06 \end{Bmatrix} = \begin{Bmatrix} 1.68 \\ 1.27 \\ 1.79 \end{Bmatrix} = 1.68 \begin{Bmatrix} 1.00 \\ 0.760 \\ 1.06 \end{Bmatrix}$$

one eigenvalue for matrix $[A]$ equals 1.68, and its corresponding eigenvector is given by $x_1 = 1.00$, $x_2 = 0.760$, and $x_3 = 1.06$. This method produces the largest eigenvalue, which for some problems is all that is desired. For some problems, however, we only desire to find the smallest eigenvalue. This can be done by devising an iteration procedure to solve the following matrix equation for $(\lambda - f)$

$$[[A] - f[\mathrm{I}]]\{x\} = (\lambda - f)\{x\}$$

where constant f equals the largest eigenvalue, or approximately so. Thus, $|\lambda - f|$ becomes a maximum when λ equals the smallest eigenvalue. Another iteration technique is the **Jacobi method,** whose details may be found in numerical analysis references.

PROBLEMS

3.1. Write a complete Fortran program to do the calculations of Ill. Ex. 3.5. Assume that array A consists of at most fifty elements.

3.2. Write a complete Fortran program to do the calculations of Ill. Ex. 3.7. Assume that each array consists of at most forty elements.

3.3. Write enough Fortran instructions to perform the following calculations:

$$R = \left[\sum_{i=1}^{N} (A_i - B_i^2) \right]^{0.282}$$

3.4. Write a complete Fortran program to do the calculations of Prob. 3.3. Assume that each array consists of at most seventy elements.

3.5. Write enough Fortran instructions to perform the following calculations:

$$X_i = A_i B_i^2 \qquad \text{if } A_i < B_i$$
$$X_i = 0 \qquad \text{if } A_i = B_i$$
$$X_i = A_i^2 B_i \qquad \text{if } A_i > B_i$$

$$R = \sum_{i=1}^{N} X_i e^{B_i}$$

3.6. Write enough Fortran instructions to perform the following calculations:

$$\sum_{j=1}^{30} \sum_{i=1}^{40} (Y_{ij} \sin X_i + R_{ij})$$

3.7. Write a complete Fortran program to do the calculations of Prob. 3.6.

3.8. Write a complete Fortran program that will determine and print the maximum and minimum values of array A, which contains 200 elements.

3.9. Write six arithmetic statement functions to do the following:

(a) Calculate $\log_{10} x$ using the LOGF(X) library function.
(b) Calculate $\sinh x$ using the EXPF(X) library function.
(c) Calculate $\cosh x$ using the EXPF(X) library function.
(d) Calculate $\tanh x$ using the EXPF(X) library function.
(e) Calculate $\cos x$ using the SINF(X) and SQRTF(X) library functions.
(f) Calculate $\sin^{-1} x$ using the ATANF(X) and SQRTF(X) library functions.

3.10. Write a complete Fortran program to perform the following calculations using an arithmetic statement function.

$$X = A^2 - B^{0.86}/A$$
$$Y = C^2 - D^{0.86}/C$$
$$Z = E^2 - F^{0.86}/E$$

3.11. Write a Fortran program and a FUNCTION subprogram that will perform the calculations in Prob. 3.10.

3.12. Same as Prob. 3.11, except use a SUBROUTINE subprogram.

3.13. Consider an electrical circuit consisting of a current source and a linear resistor of resistance R. The output of the current source is plotted and tabulated versus time t. Represent this curve in a Fortran program by the arrays CUR and TIME. Write a Fortran program to do the following:

 (a) Read and print the current-source output curve using the subprogram in Ill. Ex. 3.11.
 (b) Read a specific time T into the computer.
 (c) Interpolate the current-source output curve for the current at time T. Represent this current as CT, and use the subprogram in Ill. Ex. 3.13.
 (d) Calculate the voltage drop at time T using Ohm's Law (i.e., $E = CT * R$).
 (e) Print time T and voltage drop E.
 (f) Go to (b) for the next value of time T.

3.14. Check out the Fortran program in Ill. Ex. 3.18 using the following input matrices, where $b = 6.20$:

$$[D] = \begin{bmatrix} 6 & 1 & -9 & 5 \\ -4 & 0 & 3 & 8 \\ 7 & 2 & 6 & 4 \end{bmatrix}, \quad [E] = \begin{bmatrix} 3 & 6 \\ -5 & 9 \\ 8 & -7 \end{bmatrix},$$

$$[F] = \begin{bmatrix} -2 & 7 & 4 & 9 \\ 8 & 0 & 3 & -8 \end{bmatrix}$$

3.15. Write a complete Fortran program to perform the following matrix calculations and print the results. Make use of the subprograms in Sec. 3.7. All input matrices are square matrices of size N.

$$[T] = d[E] - [F]^{-1} - [D][F]$$
$$[P] = [D][T][F] + |T|[E]$$

CHAPTER 4

Engineering Problems That Use Arrays

4.1 Solution of an Electrical Circuit with an Arbitrary Voltage Source

Consider the nonlinear electrical circuit in Sec. 2.6 which consisted of a voltage source, a linear inductor, and a nonlinear resistor connected in series. Let us replace that voltage source (whose output was $E_0 \sin \omega t$) with one whose output is not easy to describe mathematically. In order to describe this voltage source variation, we have plotted the voltage output versus time as a curve, and we wish to use this curve as input for a Fortran program. Let us assume that this voltage output curve can be approximated by a series of straight lines as shown in Fig. 4-1. To approximate a curve by a series of straight lines, take a ruler (or some other straight-edge) and line this ruler along the curve. Mark the straight-line segments such that there is very little daylight between the curve and these segments. Thus, the points do not have to be equally spaced.

Fig. 4-1

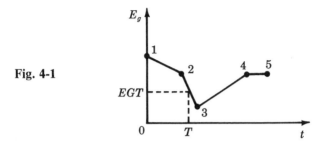

In Ill. Ex. 3.2, we found that a curve can be represented in a Fortran program by two one-dimensional arrays. Let us represent the previous curve by arrays EG and TE, and let each array consist of NE points. That is, $E_g = f(t)$ is represented by EG = f(TE), or EG(I) is the voltage output at time TE(I). Thus, in Fig. 4-1 point 1 is represented by EG(1) and TE(1), point 2 is represented by EG(2) and TE(2), etc. (i.e., the array TE is arranged in ascending values of time). It is wise to tabulate the values of these NE points in a table. In Sec. 3.4, we found that this curve can be read into the computer by a statement such as

READ 11, NE, (TE(I), EG(I), I = 1, NE)

The calculations to be performed for this problem are:

$$E_{g_t} = f(t) \text{ by a curve}$$
$$E_{R_t} = F|i_t|^a i_t$$
$$\left(\frac{di}{dt}\right)_t = \frac{1}{L}(E_{g_t} - E_{R_t})$$
$$t_{t+\Delta t} = t_t + \Delta t$$
$$i_{t+\Delta t} = i_t + (\Delta t)\left(\frac{di}{dt}\right)_t$$

and the only difference in these calculations from those of Sec. 2.6 is that here E_{g_t} is obtained from a graph instead of being calculated by an equation. Thus, we want to compute, at each time interval, the value of E_g for a specific value of time t. We can do it in the program by *linear interpolation*, because we have tabulated points from the graph so that this is valid. Before we can interpolate, we must find the straight-line segment in which time t lies (e.g., look at the dotted lines in Fig. 4-1). The following Fortran instructions can be used to calculate voltage E_{g_t}, which is represented by the symbol EGT, at time t, which is represented by the symbol T.

```
8   DO 2 I = 1, NE
    IF (T − TE(I))3, 2, 2
2   CONTINUE
    I = NE
3   SLPE = (EG(I) − EG(I−1))/(TE(I) − TE(I−1))
    EGT = EG(I−1) + SLPE ∗ (T − TE(I−1))
```

The first three statements of these Fortran instructions (i.e., the DO loop) scan the TE array to find the interval in which time T (i.e., t) lies. This is explained in detail in Ill. Ex. 3.6 in Sec. 3.3. Thus, at statement 3 we know that time T lies between (or equals) TE(I−1) and TE(I) in value. The I = NE statement takes care of the situation when T $\geq$ TE(NE) (i.e., the last point on the curve). Statement 3 calculates the slope m (represented by the symbol SLPE) of the straight-line segment using the equation

$$m = \frac{E_{g_i} - E_{g_{i-1}}}{t_i - t_{i-1}}$$

The last statement calculates the voltage E_{g_t} using the equation

$$E_{g_t} = E_{g_{i-1}} + m(t - t_{i-1})$$

Note that the previous equations are valid if time T equals TE(I−1) or TE(I). If time T exceeds the last time point TE(NE), then extrapolation (instead of interpolation) results. This extrapolation might be a valid approximation. *Extrapolation* is the evaluation of a function $f(x)$ for $x = x_k$ when the interpolated x_k point lies outside the range of the x-data points for $f(x)$. If time T is less in value than the first point TE(1), then an erroneous result will occur. The engineer should be notified if either condition occurs, and this can be done by the following Fortran instructions which print a warning message along with the values of T, TE(1), and TE(NE). Statement 8 is the first statement of the linear interpolation.

```
    IF (T − TE(1))5, 8, 6
6   IF (T − TE(NE))8, 8, 5
5   PRINT 15, T, TE(1), TE(NE)
15  FORMAT (30HTIME IS OUTSIDE RANGE OF
    CURVE/3F11.3)
```

A complete Fortran program to solve this problem is given next. It is very similar to the Fortran program in Sec. 2.6 (with the modification of Sec. 2.7), except that this program reads in and prints an E_g-versus-t curve and obtains the value of E_{g_t} by linear interpolation (instead of by an equation). The calculation sequence for this program is given in Ill. Ex. 4.1.

```
     DIMENSION TE(20), EG(20)
 1   READ 11, NE, (TE(I), EG(I), I = 1, NE)
11   FORMAT (I5/(8F8.3))
     PRINT 12, NE, (TE(I), EG(I), I = 1, NE)
12   FORMAT (///20HVOLTAGE SOURCE CURVE/I6/(6F11.3))
     READ 13, KODE, AL, F, A, T, CUR, TMAX, DT, DTPRT
13   FORMAT (I5, 8F8.3)
     PRINT 14, KODE, AL, F, A, T, CUR, TMAX, DT, DTPRT
14   FORMAT (///6HINPUTS/I5/4F11.3/4F11.3///7X4HTIME,
         4X7HCURRENT)
     TPRT = T
 4   IF (T − TE(1))5, 8, 6
 6   IF (T − TE(NE))8, 8, 5
 5   PRINT 15, T, TE(1), TE(NE)
15   FORMAT (30HTIME IS OUTSIDE RANGE OF CURVE/3F11.3)
 8   DO 2 I = 1, NE
     IF (T − TE(I))3, 2, 2
 2   CONTINUE
     I = NE
 3   SLPE = (EG(I) − EG(I−1))/(TE(I) − TE(I−1))
     EGT = EG(I−1) + SLPE * (T − TE(I − 1))
     ER = F * CUR * (ABSF(CUR) ** A)
     DIDT = (EGT − ER)/AL
     IF (T − TPRT)23, 9, 9
 9   TPRT = TPRT + DTPRT
     IF (KODE)21, 22, 22
21   PRINT 16, T, CUR, EGT, ER, DIDT, TE(I), EG(I)
16   FORMAT (2F11.4, 5F10.2)
     GO TO 23
22   PRINT 16, T, CUR
23   T = T + DT
     CUR = CUR + DT * DIDT
     IF (T − TMAX)4, 4, 1
     END
```

Illustrative Example 4.1.   Write a calculation sequence for the Fortran program in this section. It had been mentioned previously in this text that a good preliminary check (i.e., before a computer run) of a Fortran program is to write a calculation sequence from the program itself, and then determine whether the program does what was intended.

Solution. A calculation sequence for this program is as follows. The reader should check to see how this calculation sequence differs from that in Sec. 2.6.

(1) Load and print the $E_g = f(t)$ curve.

(2) Load and print the single-term inputs: $KODE$, L, F, a, t_0, i_0, t_{max}, Δt, and $(\Delta t)_{print}$.

(3) Set the first value of print-time t_{print} equal to t_0.

(4) Calculate $E_{g_t} = f(t_t)$ by linear interpolation.

(5) $E_{R_t} = F|i_t|^a i_t$.

(6) $\left(\dfrac{di}{dt}\right)_t = \dfrac{1}{L}(E_{g_t} - E_{R_t})$

(7) Test $(t_t - t_{print})$: If <0, go to (13).
    If ≥ 0, go to (8).

(8) Add $(\Delta t)_{print}$ to t_{print}.

(9) Test $KODE$: If <0, go to (10).
    If ≥ 0, go to (12).

(10) Print t_t, i_t, E_{g_t}, E_{R_t}, $(di/dt)_t$, and the TE(I) and EG(I) terms in the interpolation.

(11) Go to (13).

(12) Print t_t and i_t.

(13) $t_{t+\Delta t} = t_t + \Delta t$

(14) $i_{t+\Delta t} = i_t + (\Delta t)\left(\dfrac{di}{dt}\right)_t$

(15) Test $(t_{t+\Delta t} - t_{max})$: If ≤ 0, go to (4) for next time cycle.
     If >0, go to (1) for next case.

4.2 Use of a Linear Interpolation Subroutine to Generalize Previous Engineering Problems

Some of the problems that we had programmed in Chapter 2 would be more general, and sometimes much more useful, if we had read in some of the inputs as curves (instead of treating them as constant-value terms). For example, in the heat transfer problem in Sec. 2.10, the specific heat c varies with wall temperature T_w. Thus, specific heat should be read in as a $c = f(T_w)$ curve. Also convection coefficient h varies with *film temperature* T_m, the average of surface temperature T_w and fluid temperature T_f. That is,

$$T_m = \tfrac{1}{2}(T_w + T_f)$$

and the convection coefficient should be read in as an $h = f(T_m)$ curve. The fluid flow problem in Sec. 2.12 would be more general if flow rate Q were read in as a function of time (i.e., as a $Q = f(t)$ curve). Also the pressures p_1 and p_2 should be read in as functions of time t or as functions of flow rate Q. Thus, the problem now becomes one that involves trial-and-error solutions at specific values of time t. The nonlinear mechanical vibration problem in Sec. 2.9 would be more general if we used a $c = f(\dot{x})$ curve for the damping coefficient c and a $k = f(x)$ curve for the spring constant k. The latter curve could account for the nonlinear ranges of the spring. The applied force could be represented by a $F_E = f(t)$ curve, instead of by $F_0 \cos \omega t$. This would make the problem much more general, since external force F_E can now have any specified variation with time t (e.g., F_E can be a pulse force or a random force).

So far in this section, we have discussed three physical problems, where each problem requires reading several input curves into the computer and where each curve must be interpolated to obtain a value. Problems in this category are very often encountered in the engineering profession. Input curves for such problems are often the results of test data. Let us modify the nonlinear electrical circuit problem of Sec. 4.1 so that it also requires the reading of several curves and requires several interpolations. For this modified problem, we shall assume that we have a voltage source (of the same type as in Sec. 4.1), a nonlinear inductor, and a nonlinear resistor connected in series. Thus, $E_g = L(di/dt) + Ri$, as before, and is the equation from which we calculate di/dt. We shall assume that both the nonlinear inductance L and the nonlinear resistance R are plotted as functions of current i. Thus, the calculations to be performed for this problem are:

$$E_{g_t} = f(t_t) \text{ by a curve}$$
$$L_t = f(i_t) \text{ by a curve}$$
$$R_t = f(i_t) \text{ by a curve}$$

$$\left(\frac{di}{dt}\right)_t = \frac{1}{L_t}(E_{g_t} - R_t i_t)$$

$$t_{t+\Delta t} = t_t + \Delta t$$

$$i_{t+\Delta t} = i_t + (\Delta t)\left(\frac{di}{dt}\right)_t$$

Since this problem requires the reading of three curves and requires three interpolations per time cycle, it would be wise to have SUBROUTINE subprograms for doing this. A subprogram to read in and print an input curve is furnished in Ill. Ex. 3.11 in Sec. 3.6. A SUBROUTINE subprogram to perform a linear interpolation is given next. The details of this subroutine, which calculates $YA = f(XA)$ from the N points for a $Y = f(X)$ curve, has already been described in Sec. 4.1.

```
SUBROUTINE LINTRP (X, Y, XA, N, YA)
DIMENSION X(20), Y(20)
IF (XA − X(1))3, 7, 6
```

```
6   IF (XA − X(N))7, 7, 3
3   PRINT 4, XA, X(1), X(N)
4   FORMAT (31HPOINT IS OUTSIDE RANGE OF
        CURVE/3F11.3)
7   DO 8 I = 1, N
    IF (XA − X(I))9, 8, 8
8   CONTINUE
    I = N
9   SLPE = (Y(I) − Y(I−1))/(X(I) − X(I−1))
    YA = Y(I−1) + SLPE * (XA − X(I−1))
    RETURN
    END
```

The following is a calculation sequence for a Fortran program to solve this nonlinear electrical circuit problem.

(1)   Load and print the E_g-versus-t curve.

(2)   Load and print the L-versus-i curve.

(3)   Load and print the R-versus-i curve.

(4)   Load and print the single-term inputs: $KODE$, t_0, i_0, t_{max}, Δt, and $(\Delta t)_{print}$.

(5)   Set the first value of t_{print} equal to t_0.

(6)   Calculate $E_{g_t} = f(t_t)$ by the linear interpolation subprogram.

(7)   Calculate $L_t = f(i_t)$ by the linear interpolation subprogram.

(8)   Calculate $R_t = f(i_t)$ by the linear interpolation subprogram.

(9) $\left(\dfrac{di}{dt}\right)_t = \dfrac{1}{L_t}(E_{g_t} - R_t i_t)$

(10) Test $(t_t - t_{print})$: If <0, go to (16).
                          If ≥ 0, go to (11).

(11) Add $(\Delta t)_{print}$ to t_{print}.

(12) Test $KODE$: If <0, go to (13).
                   If ≥ 0, go to (15).

(13) Print t_t, i_t, E_{g_t}, L_t, R_t, and $\left(\dfrac{di}{dt}\right)_t$.

(14) Go to (16).

(15) Print t_t and i_t.

(16) $t_{t+\Delta t} = t_t + \Delta t$

(17) $i_{t+\Delta t} = i_t + (\Delta t)\left(\dfrac{di}{dt}\right)_t$

(18) Test $(t_{t+\Delta t} - t_{max})$: If >0, go to (1) for next case.
                               If ≤ 0, go to (6) for next time cycle.

The following Fortran program was written using the previous calculation sequence, and it utilizes the curve-reading and linear-interpolation subprograms mentioned in this section. The $E_g = f(t)$ curve is represented by arrays EG and TE (which have NE elements); the $L = f(i)$ curve is represented by arrays AL and AI (which have NL elements); and the $R = f(i)$ curve is represented by arrays RC and RI (which have NR elements). The symbol EGT represents E_{g_i}, the symbol ALT represents L_i, and the symbol RT represents R_i.

```
      DIMENSION AL(20), AI(20), RC(20), RI(20), EG(20), TE(20)
    1 CALL CURVRD(TE, EG, NE)
      CALL CURVRD(AI, AL, NL)
      CALL CURVRD(RI, RC, NR)
      READ 12, KODE, T, CUR, TMAX, DT, DTPRT
   12 FORMAT (I5, 5F8.3)
      PRINT 13, KODE, T, CUR, TMAX, DT, DTPRT
   13 FORMAT (///6HINPUTS/I6, 5F11.3///7X4HTIME,
         4X7HCURRENT)
      TPRT = T
    5 CALL LINTRP(TE, EG, T, NE, EGT)
      CALL LINTRP(AI, AL, CUR, NL, ALT)
      CALL LINTRP(RI, RC, CUR, NR, RT)
      DIDT = (EGT − RT * CUR)/ALT
      IF (T − TPRT)9, 6, 6
    6 TPRT = TPRT + DTPRT
      IF (KODE)7, 8, 8
    7 PRINT 14, T, CUR, EGT, ALT, RT, DIDT
   14 FORMAT (6F11.4)
      GO TO 9
    8 PRINT 14, T, CUR
    9 T = T + DT
      CUR = CUR + DT * DIDT
      IF (T − TMAX)5, 5, 1
      END
```

Illustrative Example 4.2. Suppose for the heat transfer problem in Sec. 2.10, a curve of convection coefficient h versus film temperature T_m and a curve of specific heat c versus wall temperature T_w are furnished. Write the calculation sequence for computing the convection coefficients h_1, h_2, h_3, and h_4 and the specific heats c_A and c_B for each time cycle.

Solution. The calculation sequence is as follows, where $h_i = f(T_{mi})$ denotes that convection coefficient h_i is obtained from the h-versus-T_m curve, and where $c_j = g(T_j)$ denotes the use of the c-versus-T_w curve to compute specific heat c_j.

(1) $T_{m1_t} = \frac{1}{2}(T_{A_t} + T_{f1})$
(2) $h_{1_t} = f(T_{m1_t})$
(3) $T_{m2_t} = \frac{1}{2}(T_{A_t} + T_{f2})$
(4) $h_{2_t} = f(T_{m2_t})$
(5) $T_{m3_t} = \frac{1}{2}(T_{B_t} + T_{f2})$
(6) $h_{3_t} = f(T_{m3_t})$
(7) $T_{m4_t} = \frac{1}{2}(T_{B_t} + T_{f3})$
(8) $h_{4_t} = f(T_{m4_t})$
(9) $c_{A_t} = g(T_{A_t})$
(10) $c_{B_t} = g(T_{B_t})$

This new heat transfer program would require the loading of two curves, and six interpolations would be required per time cycle. Thus, a curve-reading subprogram and an interpolation subprogram could be advantageously used in this program.

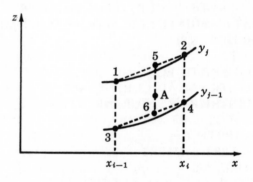

Fig. 4-2

Illustrative Example 4.3. Write the calculation sequence for linearly interpolating a $z = f(x, y)$ curve.

Solution. Let x_A and y_A be the coordinates of the interpolated point, which is represented as point A in Fig. 4-2. Thus, we wish to find $z_A = f(x_A, y_A)$. The curve $z = f(x, y)$ can be loaded as a two-dimensional array $Z(I, J)$. For example, the column $Z(I, 3)$ can represent a $z = f(x)$ curve for the case when $y = y_3$ (i.e., y is constant in value). Thus, for this array $Z(4, 2)$ is the value of z when $x = x_4$ and $y = y_2$. The tabulated x and y values can be represented by arrays X and Y, respectively. A calculation sequence to perform this interpolation is as follows, where points 1 to 6 are denoted in Fig. 4-2 and where three linear interpolations are required.

(1) Use a DO loop to find the x-interval in which point A lies. Call these two x-points, x_{i-1} and x_i.
(2) Use a DO loop to find the y-interval in which point A lies. Call these two y-points, y_{j-1} and y_j.

(3) Calculate $z_5 \approx z(x_A, y_j)$ by linear interpolation. That is,

$$z_5 = z_1 + \left(\frac{z_2 - z_1}{x_i - x_{i-1}} \right)(x_A - x_{i-1})$$

where $z_1 = z(x_{i-1}, y_j)$ and $z_2 = z(x_i, y_j)$.

(4) Calculate $z_6 \approx z(x_A, y_{j-1})$ by linear interpolation between points 3 and 4.

(5) Calculate z_A by the following linear interpolation equation between points 5 and 6 in the y-direction

$$z_A = z_6 + \left(\frac{z_5 - z_6}{y_j - y_{j-1}} \right)(y_A - y_{j-1})$$

4.3 Discussion of Interpolation Methods

Oftentimes, the approximation of a curve by straight-line segments, as was done in Sec. 4.1, will not be a very accurate representation, especially in regions where the curvature is large. That is, it is not always easy to approximate all portions of a curve with straight-line segments. There are several interpolation methods available which represent $(n + 1)$ successive points on a curve by a polynomial of degree n and which interpolate along this polynomial curve. Thus, this means that the interpolated curve should be smooth along these $(n + 1)$ points, and therefore caution must be exercised when a polynomial interpolation subroutine is utilized. For example, we cannot accurately solve Problems 4.1 or 4.2 at the end of this chapter by using a polynomial interpolation of degree 2 or greater. That is, three successive points in Fig. 4-13 should not be represented by a quadratic polynomial. Note in Fig. 4-3 that quadratic $P(x)$ fits the three points, but does not fit the curve. The reader will find many SUBROUTINE subprograms available that can perform polynomial interpolations of plotted curves and calculated or tabulated data (e.g., test results).

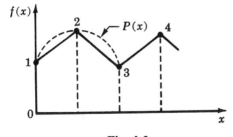

Fig. 4-3

Since most curves that have regions of fairly large curvature can be adequately represented by successive quadratic polynomials, we shall be very interested in interpolation methods that represent three successive points on the curve by a quadratic polynomial. For this type of interpolation, the curve must be smooth along three successive points, and, thus, the choice of these three points can be important, as was shown in Fig. 4-3. In this figure, the curve is smooth between Points 1 and 2, but not between Points 1 and 3. This example serves to illustrate the important fact that because numerical methods are approximations, judgment should be utilized whenever they are applied. There are several methods for the polynomial interpolation of data where these data points are equally spaced. Some of these equal-interval, polynomial-interpolation methods, which are often applied by using finite-difference tables, are the *Newton-Gregory*, *Newton-Gauss*, *Bessel*, *Stirling*, and *Everett* methods. Space does not allow us to discuss these methods in much detail. Besides, engineers will usually find much more value in interpolation methods where the tabulated points do not have to be equally spaced. For example, test data is often tabulated at unequal intervals. The details of these methods can be found in numerical analysis textbooks.

Suppose that we wish to find the value of $f(x)$ for $x = x_A$ and that we have found that x_A is located between the tabulated points x_i and x_{i+n}. The *forward Newton-Gregory formula* can be written as follows

$$f(x_A) \equiv f(x_i + rh) = f_i + r\Delta f_i + \frac{r(r-1)}{2!}\Delta^2 f_i + \frac{r(r-1)(r-2)}{3!}\Delta^3 f_i$$

$$+ \ldots + \frac{r(r-1)\ldots(r-n+1)}{n!}\Delta^n f_i \quad \text{(4-1)}$$

where the previous interpolation formula was derived by approximating $(n + 1)$ successive, equally spaced points, located at x_i to x_{i+n}, by a polynomial of degree n. In the previous formula, $f_i \equiv f(x_i)$, $f_{i+1} \equiv f(x_{i+1})$, h is the size of the equal interval (e.g., $x_{i+1} - x_i$), $r = (x_A - x_i)/h$, and

$$\Delta f_i = f_{i+1} - f_i$$
$$\Delta^2 f_i = \Delta f_{i+1} - \Delta f_i = (f_{i+2} - f_{i+1}) - (f_{i+1} - f_i) = f_{i+2} - 2f_{i+1} + f_i$$
$$\Delta^3 f_i = \Delta^2 f_{i+1} - \Delta^2 f_i = f_{i+3} - 3f_{i+2} + 3f_{i+1} - f_i$$
$$\Delta^n f_i = \Delta^{n-1} f_{i+1} - \Delta^{n-1} f_i$$

where the term $\Delta^k f_i$ is called the kth *forward difference* for the function $f(x)$. These forward difference terms are often represented in tabular form. It might be noted that for $n = 1$, the following linear interpolation equation results from Eq. (4-1):

$$f(x_A) = f_i + r(f_{i+1} - f_i)$$

To derive Eq. (4-1), we must show that a polynomial $P(x)$ of degree n, and which passes through the given set of $(n + 1)$ equally spaced points, can be written in the form of Eq. (4-1). To simplify matters, let us call the x-values of these equally spaced points $x_0, x_1, x_2, \ldots, x_n$ and the corresponding $f(x)$ values $f_0, f_1, f_2, \ldots, f_n$. Let us write this nth degree polynomial in the form

$$P(x) = a_0 + a_1(x - x_0) + a_2(x - x_0)(x - x_1)$$
$$+ a_3(x - x_0)(x - x_1)(x - x_2)$$
$$+ \ldots + a_n(x - x_0)(x - x_1) \ldots (x - x_{n-1})$$

We wish to solve for coefficients a_0 to a_n such that $P(x_0) = f_0$, $P(x_1) = f_1$, $\ldots$, and $P(x_n) = f_n$. Successive substitution of $x = x_0$, $x = x_1$, $\ldots$, $x = x_n$ (along with the relations $P(x_0) = f_0$, $P(x_1) = f_1$, etc.) give us n equations for solving for the n unknowns a_0 to a_n. For example, the first three substitutions give us the following three equations, where h is the interval size:

$$P(x_0) = f_0 = a_0$$
$$P(x_1) = f_1 = a_0 + a_1(x_1 - x_0) = a_0 + a_1h$$
$$P(x_2) = f_2 = a_0 + a_1(x_2 - x_0) + a_2(x_2 - x_0)(x_2 - x_1)$$
$$= a_0 + 2a_1h + 2a_2h^2$$

Solving for these coefficients gives $a_0 = f_0$, $a_1 = (f_1 - f_0)/h = \Delta f_0/h$, $a_2 = (f_2 - 2f_1 + f_0)/2h^2 = \Delta^2 f_0/2h^2$, etc. In general form, the kth coefficient, a_k, equals $(\Delta^k f_0)/(k!h^k)$. Substitution of these results, along with $r = (x - x_0)/h$, into the equation for polynomial $P(x)$ gives us the following equation:

$$P(x) = f_0 + r\Delta f_0 + \frac{r(r-1)}{2!}\Delta^2 f_0 + \ldots + \frac{r(r-1)\ldots(r-n+1)}{n!}\Delta^n f_0$$

which has the same form as Eq. (4-1).

The **backward Newton-Gregory formula** is a modification of Eq. (4-1) for the interpolation of points near the end of a table. That is, it is more convenient to apply than Eq. (4-1) when at the last portion of the tabulated points. This backward interpolation formula can be written as follows:

$$f(x_A) = f_i + r\nabla f_i + \frac{r(r+1)}{2!}\nabla^2 f_i$$
$$+ \ldots + \frac{r(r+1)\ldots(r+n-1)}{n!}\nabla^n f_i \quad \textbf{(4-2)}$$

where the previous equation employs *backward difference* terms of the form $\nabla^k f_i$ and where $\nabla f_i = f_i - f_{i-1}$ and $\nabla^k f_i = \nabla^{k-1}f_i - \nabla^{k-1}f_{i-1}$.

The *forward Newton-Gauss interpolation formula* may be written as follows:

$$f(x_A) \equiv f(x_i + rh) = f_i + r\Delta f_i + \frac{r(r-1)}{2!}\Delta^2 f_{i-1}$$

$$+ \frac{r(r-1)(r+1)}{3!}\Delta^3 f_{i-1} + \frac{r(r-1)(r+1)(r-2)}{4!}\Delta^4 f_{i-2} + \cdots \tag{4-3}$$

The equation for the **Everett method** can be obtained from the forward Newton-Gauss formula [i.e., Eq. (4-3)] by replacing the forward differences of odd order in Eq. (4-3) with even forward differences of lower order. The Everett and the **Bessel** methods both require an even number of successive points. *Stirling's interpolation formula* may be obtained by taking the average of the forward and the backward Newton-Gauss formulae, and this method requires an odd number of successive points. The formulae for the Everett, Bessel, and Stirling methods may be found in numerical analysis texts.

It should be mentioned again that each of the previous polynomial interpolation formulae passes a polynomial of degree n through $(n + 1)$ equally spaced points. Thus, although the appearance of these formulae are quite different, application of any of these methods will give the same result *if* the same tabulated points are used for each interpolation. This is because each of these interpolation formulae would use the same polynomial approximation equation, but each is written in a different way to denote a different sequence of calculations.

Because $\Delta^2 f_{i-1} = \Delta f_i - \Delta f_{i-1} = (f_{i+1} - f_i) - (f_i - f_{i-1})$, the first three terms of the forward Newton-Gauss formula can be expressed as

$$f(x_A) = f_i + r(f_{i+1} - f_i) + \left(\frac{r^2 - r}{2}\right)(f_{i+1} - 2f_i + f_{i-1}) \tag{4-4}$$

which can be rewritten as

$$f(x_A) = f_i + \frac{r}{2}(f_{i+1} - f_{i-1}) + \frac{r^2}{2}(f_{i+1} - 2f_i + f_{i-1}) \tag{4-5}$$

Since Eq. (4-5) is a very useful formula for interpolation along three equally spaced points, let us derive this equation in another manner. The value of $f(x_A)$ can be calculated by Taylor series as follows:

$$f(x_A) = f_i + f_i'(x_A - x_i) + f_i'' \frac{(x_A - x_i)^2}{2!} + \cdots$$

Let us approximate $f(x_A)$ by using only the first three terms of this Taylor series. Eq. (4-14) in Sec. 4.4 shows that we can approximate the derivative f_i' by

$$f_i' \equiv \frac{df_i}{dx} = \frac{f_{i+1} - f_{i-1}}{2h} \tag{4-6}$$

where h is the size of the constant x-interval. Eq. (4-16) in Sec. 4.4 shows that we can approximate the second derivative f_i'' by the equation

$$f_i'' = \frac{f_{i+1} - 2f_i + f_{i-1}}{h^2} \qquad (4\text{-}7)$$

Substitution of Eqs. (4-6) and (4-7), along with the equation

$$r = \frac{(x_A - x_i)}{h}$$

into the first three terms of the Taylor series will give us Eq. (4-5).

For data whose points are unequally spaced, we could use linear interpolation (as was done in Secs. 4.1 and 4.2), Newton's divided-difference method, Aitken's method, or Lagrange's interpolation method. *Newton's divided-difference method* applies a fundamental interpolation formula which becomes the forward Newton-Gregory formula when the points x_0, x_1, x_2, ..., x_n are equally spaced an interval h apart. The *Aitken method* utilizes successive linear interpolations and extrapolations in order to achieve a polynomial interpolation. *Lagrange's interpolation formula,* which is very frequently used for interpolating unequally spaced data, is given by the following equation, where the x-coordinates are x_0, x_1, x_2, ..., and x_n.

$$
\begin{aligned}
f(x_A) = {} & \frac{(x_A - x_1)(x_A - x_2)\ldots(x_A - x_n)}{(x_0 - x_1)(x_0 - x_2)\ldots(x_0 - x_n)} f(x_0) \\
& + \frac{(x_A - x_0)(x_A - x_2)\ldots(x_A - x_n)}{(x_1 - x_0)(x_1 - x_2)\ldots(x_1 - x_n)} f(x_1) + \ldots \qquad \textbf{(4-8)} \\
& + \frac{(x_A - x_0)(x_A - x_1)\ldots(x_A - x_{n-1})}{(x_n - x_0)(x_n - x_1)\ldots(x_n - x_{n-1})} f(x_n)
\end{aligned}
$$

This Lagrange formula passes a polynomial of degree n through $(n + 1)$ successive points. Point x_A can be located anywhere in the interval from x_0 to x_n. Equation (4-8) can be used for extrapolation if point x_A lies outside this range. When $n = 2$, Eq. (4-8) becomes

$$
\begin{aligned}
f(x) = {} & \frac{(x - x_1)(x - x_2)}{(x_0 - x_1)(x_0 - x_2)} f(x_0) + \frac{(x - x_0)(x - x_2)}{(x_1 - x_0)(x_1 - x_2)} f(x_1) \\
& + \frac{(x - x_0)(x - x_1)}{(x_2 - x_0)(x_2 - x_1)} f(x_2)
\end{aligned} \qquad \textbf{(4-9)}
$$

where a quadratic polynomial is provided along the three successive points x_0, x_1, and x_2, and where we replaced $f(x_A)$ by $f(x)$ and x_A by x. We could derive Eq. (4-9), but instead let us just verify it. It can be seen that Eq.

(4-9) is a polynomial of degree 2 in x since each of the three terms is a polynomial of degree 2 in x. That is,

$$f(x) = f(x_0)P_0(x) + f(x_1)P_1(x) + f(x_2)P_2(x)$$

where $P_0(x)$, $P_1(x)$, and $P_2(x)$ are all polynomials of degree 2. For example, $P_0(x) = (x - x_1)(x - x_2)/(x_0 - x_1)(x_0 - x_2)$. Illustrative Example 4.4 verifies this in a more complete manner. Also when $x = x_0$, it can be seen that the first term in Eq. (4-9) equals $f(x_0)$ and the other two terms equal zero. Simiiarly, it can be shown that Eq. (4-9) gives $f(x) = f(x_1)$ when $x = x_1$ and $f(x) = f(x_2)$ when $x = x_2$. Equation (4-8) can be verified in the same manner that we verified Eq. (4-9).

Since Eq. (4-9) represents a polynomial of degree 2, it is possible to rewrite it in the following form, as verified in Ill. Ex. 4.4,

$$f(x) = a_0 + a_1x + a_2x^2$$

where this equation satisfies the following equations

$$f(x_0) = a_0 + a_1x_0 + a_2x_0^2 = y_0$$
$$f(x_1) = a_0 + a_1x_1 + a_2x_1^2 = y_1$$
$$f(x_2) = a_0 + a_1x_2 + a_2x_2^2 = y_2$$

where y_0, y_1, and y_2 are values of the tabulated function. Thus, this polynomial agrees with the tabulated function at points x_0, x_1, and x_2; but could differ from this function for other values of x, as was shown in Fig. 4-3. We could solve the previous three equations for coefficients a_0, a_1, and a_2 by methods such as Cramer's rule.

Another advantage of the Lagrange formula [i.e., Eq. (4-8)] for digital computer calculations is that it directly uses the values of the tabulated points. Most of the other methods that were presented used finite differences, and these methods have more of a historical interest since they are seldom used in today's computer programs. This is another reason why they are very briefly discussed in this text. In the days when most interpolations were hand-calculated, however, these finite-difference methods were widely used, and they were computed by first tabulating finite-difference tables.

We can also polynomially interpolate a $z = f(x, y)$ curve. Suppose that we wish to use quadratic interpolation polynomials. We can locate the x- and the y-intervals about the z point by the manner given in Ill. Ex. 4.3. Then we find the desired value of z using four quadratic interpolations (e.g., by the three-point Lagrange formula) in a manner similar to the way three linear interpolations were applied in Ill. Ex. 4.3. For some tabulated data or curves, a *logarithmic interpolation* may be more desirable than a polynomial interpolation. Some physical problems require the interpolation of curves which are periodic, nonsinusoidal functions. Examples of such curves might be the applied force in a mechanical vibration and the current or voltage source output in an electrical circuit. For such curves **trigonometric interpolation** can be useful, but a three-point Lagrange interpolation would suffice if the three points were properly chosen in a close-together fashion. A trigonometric interpolation can be performed by using **Hermite's formula,** which is as follows:

$$f(x_A) = f_0 T_0(x_A) + f_1 T_1(x_A) + \ldots + f_n T_n(x_A) \qquad (4\text{-}10)$$

where the $T_i(x_A)$ function in the $(i + 1)$th term is given by

$$T_i(x_A) = \frac{\sin(x_A - x_0) \ldots \sin(x_A - x_{i-1}) \sin(x_A - x_{i+1}) \ldots \sin(x_A - x_n)}{\sin(x_i - x_0) \ldots \sin(x_i - x_{i-1}) \sin(x_i - x_{i+1}) \ldots \sin(x_i - x_n)}$$

It can be seen that Eq. (4-10) is a periodic function, and that substitution of $x_A = x_i$ results in the tabulated value f_i. That is, if $x_A = x_i$, then all terms vanish except the $f_i T_i(x_A)$ term, and $T_i(x_A) = 1$ when $x_A = x_i$. Sometimes it is desirable to smooth the tabulated data first before an interpolation is done. There are SUBROUTINE subprograms available that smooth the data and provide a function or equation for the smoothed-data. Such curve-fitting methods are briefly discussed in Sec. 4.11. The interpolation is then obtained by substitution in the evaluated function. For example, if the quadratic polynomial $ax^2 + bx + c$ is fitted among n tabulated points, then $f(x_A) = ax_A^2 + bx_A + c$.

Illustrative Example 4.4.   Write the three-point Lagrange interpolation formula in the quadratic form

$$f(x) = a_0 + a_1 x + a_2 x^2$$

Solution.   Rewrite Eq. (4-9) as follows

$$f(x) = e(x - x_1)(x - x_2) + g(x - x_0)(x - x_2) + h(x - x_0)(x - x_1)$$

where constant $e = f(x_0)/(x_0 - x_1)(x_0 - x_2)$,

$$\text{constant } g = f(x_1)/(x_1 - x_0)(x_1 - x_2),$$

and constant $h = f(x_2)/(x_2 - x_0)(x_2 - x_1)$. Multiplication of the factors in the terms of the $f(x)$ equation gives

$$f(x) = [ex^2 - e(x_1 + x_2)x + ex_1 x_2] + [gx^2 - g(x_0 + x_2)x + gx_0 x_2]$$
$$+ [hx^2 - h(x_0 + x_1)x + hx_0 x_1]$$

which can be rewritten in the following quadratic form:

$$f(x) = (e + g + h)x^2 + (-ex_1 - ex_2 - gx_0 - gx_2 - hx_0 - hx_1)x$$
$$+ (ex_1 x_2 + gx_0 x_2 + hx_0 x_1)$$

Illustrative Example 4.5.   Using an interval of $\pi/4$, approximate the value of $\cos(\pi/8)$ using the three-point, forward Newton-Gauss formula.

Solution. We shall choose the three tabulated (i.e., known) points to be: $x_{i-1} = 0$, $x_i = \pi/4$, and $x_{i+1} = \pi/2$. Thus, $f_{i-1} \equiv \cos 0 = 1.000$, $f_i \equiv \cos(\pi/4) = 0.707$, and $f_{i+1} \equiv \cos(\pi/2) = 0$. The value of r is given by

$$r = \frac{x - x_i}{h} = \frac{\pi/8 - \pi/4}{\pi/4} = -\frac{1}{2}$$

Application of Eq. (4-5) gives

$$f(\pi/8) \equiv \cos(\pi/8) = 0.707 + (-0.250)(0 - 1.000)$$
$$+ (0.125)(0 - 1.414 + 1.000) = 0.906$$

Since the correct value of $\cos(\pi/8)$ or $\cos 22.5°$ is 0.924, the error of this polynomial approximation is 0.018.

Illustrative Example 4.6. Solve Ill. Ex. 4.5 using the three-point forward Newton-Gregory formula.

Solution. The first three terms of Eq. (4-1) can be written as

$$f(x_A) = f_i + r(f_{i+1} - f_i) + \left(\frac{r^2 - r}{2}\right)(f_{i+2} - 2f_{i+1} + f_i)$$

If we choose the same three tabulated points as in Ill. Ex. 4.5, $x_i = 0$, $x_{i+1} = \pi/4$, and $x_{i+2} = \pi/2$. Thus, $f_i = 1.000$, $f_{i+1} = 0.707$, $f_{i+2} = 0$, and

$$r = (\pi/8 - 0)/(\pi/4) = 0.500$$

Substitution in the equation for $f(x_A)$ gives

$$f\left(\frac{\pi}{8}\right) \equiv \cos\left(\frac{\pi}{8}\right) = 1.000 + (0.500)(0.707 - 1.000)$$
$$+ \left(\frac{0.250 - 0.500}{2}\right)(0 - 1.414 + 1.000) = 0.906$$

which is the same result as Ill. Ex. 4.5. This is to be expected since both polynomial-approximation methods were applied over the same three tabulated points.

Illustrative Example 4.7. Solve Ill. Ex. 4.5 using the three-point Lagrange interpolation formula. Use the same three tabulated points.

Solution. For equal intervals, Eq. (4-9) (i.e., Lagrange's three-point formula) may be rewritten as follows:

$$f(x) = (1/2h^2)[(x - x_1)(x - x_2)f_0 - 2(x - x_0)(x - x_2)f_1 + (x - x_0)(x - x_1)f_2]$$

Since $x_0 = 0$, $x_1 = \pi/4$, and $x_2 = \pi/2$; $f_0 = 1.000$, $f_1 = 0.707$, and $f_2 = 0$. Substitution in the previous $f(x)$ equation gives

$$f\left(\frac{\pi}{8}\right) \equiv \cos\left(\frac{\pi}{8}\right) = \frac{1}{2\left(\frac{\pi}{4}\right)^2}\left[\left(-\frac{\pi}{8}\right)\left(-\frac{3\pi}{8}\right)(1.000)\right.$$
$$\left. - 2\left(\frac{\pi}{8}\right)\left(-\frac{3\pi}{8}\right)(0.707) + \left(\frac{\pi}{8}\right)\left(-\frac{\pi}{8}\right)(0)\right] = 0.906$$

which is the same result as that in Ill. Exs. 4.5 and 4.6. This is to be expected since all three quadratic-approximation formulae were applied over the same three tabulated points.

Illustrative Example 4.8.   Write a SUBROUTINE subprogram that will perform a three-point Lagrange interpolation.

Solution.   The subprogram that follows is exactly the same as the linear interpolation subprogram of Sec. 4.2, except for the first statement (which contains the title of the subprogram) and for some statements that follow statement 8. Thus, Sec. 4.2 furnishes the details of how the subprogram locates the interval (i.e., the three points x_{i-1}, x_i, and x_{i+1}) in which to perform the Lagrange interpolation. The four statements that start with statement 9 apply Eq. (4-9), where $X(I - 1) = x_0$, $X(I) = x_1$, $X(I + 1) = x_2$, and array Y represents the tabulated $f(x_i)$ values. The $I = N - 1$ statement insures that there is an x_{i+1} point in array X if the DO loop goes through N cycles [i.e., it sets $X(I + 1) = X(N)$].

```
   SUBROUTINE LAGTRP (X, Y, XA, N, YA)
   DIMENSION X(20), Y(20)
   IF (XA − X(1))3, 7, 6
 6 IF (XA − X(N))7, 7, 3
 3 PRINT 4, XA, X(1), X(N)
 4 FORMAT (31HPOINT IS OUTSIDE RANGE OF CURVE/3F11.3)
 7 DO 8 I = 1, N
   IF (XA − X(I))9, 8, 8
 8 CONTINUE
   I = N − 1
 9 TERM 1 = (XA−X(I)) * (XA−X(I+1)) * Y(I−1)/((X(I−1)−X(I)) *
     (X(I−1)−X(I+1)))
   TERM 2 = (XA−X(I−1)) * (XA−X(I+1)) * Y(I)/((X(I)−X(I−1)) *
     (X(I)−X(I+1)))
   TERM 3 = (XA−X(I−1)) * (XA−X(I)) * Y(I+1)/((X(I+1)−X(I−1)) *
     (X(I+1)−X(I)))
   YA = TERM 1 + TERM 2 + TERM 3
   RETURN
   END
```

4.4   Differentiation of Tabulated Data

Sometimes when solving engineering problems, it is desired to obtain the derivatives of tabulated or plotted data. It should be forewarned that numerical differentiation formulas contain enough inherent inaccuracies so that their use should be avoided whenever possible in a problem. Thus, use these approximation formulae only when absolutely necessary.

As an elementary example of a physical problem where differentiation is useful, consider the motion of a concentrated mass in a frictionless mechanical system, and let this motion be complex. If we can measure its instantaneous velocity continuously during its motion, we can also determine the work W_k done by this mass throughout this motion, since there is no frictional energy loss. From our dynamics course, we know that the work done at time t and displacement s equals the final kinetic energy minus the initial kinetic energy. That is, $W_k = (m/2)(v^2 - v_0^2)$, where v_0 is the initial velocity and v is the velocity at time t and displacement s.

Since the work W_k is defined to equal $\int F \cos \theta \, ds$, where θ is the angle between the applied force F and displacement s, we can compute the force component $F_s \equiv F \cos \theta$ (where the magnitudes of F and θ can vary with s) from the equation $F_s = dW_k/ds$. Also since power P is the rate of doing work, $P = dW_k/dt$. Thus, if we measure and tabulate the values of t, s, and v during the motion of this mass, then we can also compute the values of W_k, F_s, and P at these tabulated values of time t. The calculation of F_s and P would require numerical differentiation. As another physical example, consider a loaded elastic beam, of uniform material and cross-section, where we know the vertical deflection $y(x)$ along the length of the beam and where x is the distance from the left end of the beam. From our strength of materials course, we know that $d^2y(x)/dx^2 = M(x)/EI$, where $M(x)$ is the bending moment at location x of the beam, E is the beam modulus of elasticity, and I is the beam moment of inertia. Thus, we could obtain the bending moment distribution $M(x)$ by two differentiations of the tabulated beam deflections in order to obtain $d^2y(x)/dx^2$.

If we are given a function of one variable $f(x)$, we know from calculus that its first derivative is defined by

$$\frac{df}{dx} = f'(x) = \lim_{\Delta x \to 0} \frac{f(x + \Delta x) - f(x)}{\Delta x}$$

Thus, if the tabulated points (x_i, f_i) and (x_{i+1}, f_{i+1}) are close together (i.e., $x_{i+1} - x_i$ is very small), we may approximate $f'(x_i)$ by the *forward-slope* equation

$$f_i' \equiv f'(x_i) = \frac{f_{i+1} - f_i}{x_{i+1} - x_i} \tag{4-11}$$

If a derivative exists at a point, then the forward slope must equal the backward slope. Thus, we may also approximate $f'(x_i)$ using the *backward-slope* equation

$$f_i' \equiv f'(x_i) = \frac{f_i - f_{i-1}}{x_i - x_{i-1}} \tag{4-12}$$

A better approximation would be to use the average of these two slopes to obtain

$$f'_i = \frac{1}{2}\left[\frac{f_{i+1} - f_i}{x_{i+1} - x_i} + \frac{f_i - f_{i-1}}{x_i - x_{i-1}}\right] \qquad (4\text{-}13)$$

which is the mean of Eqs. (4-11) and (4-12). If the tabulated data are equally spaced an interval h apart (i.e., $x_{i+1} - x_i = x_i - x_{i-1} = h$), then the previous equation can be rewritten in the following *central-difference* form

$$f'_i = \frac{f_{i+1} - f_{i-1}}{2h} \qquad (4\text{-}14)$$

From the previous equation, it is seen that we can approximate the derivative $f'(x)$ at the center of an interval by dividing the length of the interval into the difference of the $f(x)$ values at the end-points of this interval. Applying this principle, we can approximate the second derivative f''_i (for equally spaced, tabulated data) by the central-difference equation

$$f''_i = \frac{f'_{i+\frac{1}{2}} - f'_{i-\frac{1}{2}}}{h} \qquad (4\text{-}15)$$

Also from the principle of Eq. (4-14), we can obtain the central-difference approximations

$$f'_{i+\frac{1}{2}} = \frac{f_{i+1} - f_i}{h}$$

$$f'_{i-\frac{1}{2}} = \frac{f_i - f_{i-1}}{h}$$

Substitution of the previous two equations into Eq. (4-15) gives us the following approximation for f''_i

$$f''_i = \frac{f_{i+1} - 2f_i + f_{i-1}}{h^2} \qquad (4\text{-}16)$$

The previous equation can also be derived by approximating f_{i+1} and f_{i-1} by the first four terms of a Taylor series as follows, and then adding these two equations to get Eq. (4-16).

$$f_{i+1} = f_i + hf'_i + \frac{h^2}{2!}f''_i + \frac{h^3}{3!}f'''_i$$

$$f_{i-1} = f_i - hf'_i + \frac{h^2}{2!}f''_i - \frac{h^3}{3!}f'''_i$$

Let us show how we may apply these differentiation formulae. Suppose that we had a set of N unequally spaced points and that we wished to compute their derivatives. We could use Eq. (4-13) to approximate the derivatives of all the tabulated points, except for the first point and the last point. For the first point, we can use Eq. (4-11) to obtain

$f_1' = (f_2 - f_1)/(x_2 - x_1)$; and for the last point, we can use Eq. (4-12) to obtain $f_N' = (f_N - f_{N-1})/(x_N - x_{N-1})$.

In order to obtain more accurate results, we want to obtain better formulae for differentiating tabulated data. One method (which is discussed in Sec. 4.11) might be to fit a curve through the tabulated data points and then differentiate the equation for the fitted curve. This method can give good results if it properly smooths this tabulated data. For example, if the quadratic polynomial $ax^2 + bx + c$ is fitted through N points, then the derivatives can be computed by the equation $f_i' \equiv f'(x_i) = 2ax_i + b$.

From Sec. 4.3, we obtained polynomial interpolation formulae which fit a polynomial of degree N through $(N + 1)$ successive, tabulated points. Thus, we can compute derivatives by *differentiating interpolation formulae.* For example, if we differentiate the forward Newton-Gregory formula [i.e., Eq. (4-1)], which requires equally spaced data-points, we can obtain the formula

$$f_i' \equiv f'(x_i) = \frac{1}{h}\left[\Delta f_i - \frac{\Delta^2 f_i}{2} + \frac{\Delta^3 f_i}{3} - \ldots + (-1)^{N-1}\frac{\Delta^N f_i}{N} \right] \quad \textbf{(4-17)}$$

and differentiation of the previous equation gives

$$f_i'' \equiv f''(x_i) = \frac{1}{h^2}\left[\Delta^2 f_i - \Delta^3 f_i + \ldots \right] \quad \textbf{(4-18)}$$

We can also obtain an N-point differentiation formula by taking the derivative of the N-point Lagrange interpolation formula (which does not require equally spaced points). The following numerical differentiation formulae may be verified by using finite-difference methods or by differentiating the Lagrange interpolation formula. These formulae assume that we have a set of N equally spaced, tabulated points (x_1, f_1) to (x_N, f_N), and that we wish to calculate the derivatives f_i' at these same x_i locations. These equations can be reapplied to approximate second- and higher-order derivatives, or the reader can look up more accurate high-order derivative formulae in numerical analysis references. Since these formulae require equally spaced points, it might be stated that it is possible to use an interpolation subprogram to obtain a set of equally spaced points from a set of unequally spaced data. This is exemplified in Ill. Ex. 4.11. The reader is referred to numerical analysis references for other numerical differentiation formulae. When any numerical differentiation formula is applied, the error decreases when the interval size is reduced. Thus, it is wise to apply such a formula for two different interval sizes, if possible, and compare results. Equations (4-19) to (4-23) calculate the derivatives at specified, equally spaced values of the independent variable x. We may approximate the derivatives at in-between points by the use of one of the interpolation formulae discussed in Sec. 4.3.

$$f_1' = (1/2h)(-3f_1 + 4f_2 - f_3) \qquad \textbf{(4-19)}$$

$$f_2' = (1/6h)(-2f_1 - 3f_2 + 6f_3 - f_4) \qquad \textbf{(4-20)}$$

$$f_{N-1}' = (1/6h)(f_{N-3} - 6f_{N-2} + 3f_{N-1} + 2f_N) \qquad \textbf{(4-21)}$$

$$f_N' = (1/2h)(f_{N-2} - 4f_{N-1} + 3f_N) \qquad \textbf{(4-22)}$$

For $3 \leq i \leq N - 2$, use:

$$f_i' = (1/12h)(f_{i-2} - 8f_{i-1} + 8f_{i+1} - f_{i+2}) \qquad \textbf{(4-23)}$$

Illustrative Example 4.9. Write a SUBROUTINE subprogram that utilizes Eqs. (4-11) through (4-13) to differentiate unequally spaced tabulated data.

Solution. In the following subprogram, there are NF points. In other words, there are NF tabulated values of (x_i, f_i). Array X contains the x_i values, array F contains the f_i values, and array DF consists of the computed f_i' values. The third and fourth statements compute f_1' and f_N' using Eqs. (4-11) and (4-12), respectively, while statement 10 computes the other values of f_i' by using Eq. (4-13).

```
       SUBROUTINE DIFF(X, F, DF, NF)
       DIMENSION X(50), F(50), DF(50)
       DF(1) = (F(2) − F(1))/(X(2) − X(1))
       DF(NF) = (F(NF) − F(NF − 1))/(X(NF) − X(NF − 1))
       NFA = NF − 1
       DO 10 I = 2, NFA
   10  DF(I) = 0.5 * (F(I + 1) − F(I))/(X(I + 1) − X(I))
            + 0.5 * (F(I) − F(I − 1))/(X(I) − X(I − 1))
       RETURN
       END
```

Illustrative Example 4.10. Write a SUBROUTINE subprogram that utilizes Eqs. (4-19) to (4-23) to differentiate equally spaced tabulated data.

Solution. In the following subprogram, there are NF equally spaced points, X1 is the value of x_1, and DX is the interval size h. Array F contains the given f_i values, array X contains the computed values of x_i, and array DF contains the computed values of f_i'. The third to fifth statements compute the x_i values using the equation $x_i = x_{i-1} + h$. The sixth to ninth statements of the subprogram compute f_1', f_2', f_{N-1}', and f_N' using Eqs. (4-19) through (4-22). Statement 10 computes the other values of f_i' by using Eq. (4-23).

```
       SUBROUTINE DIFATE(F, DF, X, X1, DX, NF)
       DIMENSION F(50), DF(50), X(50)
       X(1) = X1
       DO 8 I = 2, NF
    8  X(I) = X(I − 1) + DX
```

DF(1) = (−3.0 ∗ F(1) + 4.0 ∗ F(2) − F(3))/(2.0 ∗ DX)
DF(2) = (−2.0 ∗ F(1) − 3.0 ∗ F(2) + 6.0 ∗ F(3) − F(4))/(6.0 ∗ DX)
DF(NF − 1) = (F(NF − 3) − 6.0 ∗ F(NF − 2) + 3.0 ∗ F(NF − 1)
                 + 2.0 ∗ F(NF))/(6.0 ∗ DX)
DF(NF) = (F(NF − 2) − 4.0 ∗ F(NF − 1) + 3.0 ∗ F(NF))/(2.0 ∗ DX)
NFA = NF − 2
DO 10 I = 3, NFA
10   DF(I) = (F(I − 2) − 8.0 ∗ F(I − 1) + 8.0 ∗ F(I + 1)
                 − F(I + 2))/(12.0 ∗ DX)
RETURN
END

Illustrative Example 4.11. Suppose that we are given a set of N unequally spaced points. Write a SUBROUTINE subprogram that uses a three-point Lagrange interpolation formula to obtain a set of equally spaced points with interval Δx represented by DX.

Solution. Let arrays XX and FF represent the given set of N unequally spaced points, and let arrays X and F contain the computed set of equally spaced points. The third statement in the subprogram computes NF, the number of equally spaced points, and the sixth statement uses the Lagrange interpolation subroutine of Ill. Ex. 4.8 to compute F(I) for a given value of X(I). The DIMENSION statement of the Lagrange interpolation subprogram must be modified to accommodate this subprogram.

```
SUBROUTINE EQSPAC (XX, FF, N, X, F, DX, NF)
DIMENSION XX(50), FF(50), X(50), F(50)
NF = 1.0 + (XX(N) − XX(1))/DX
X(1) = XX(1)
DO 10 I = 1, NF
CALL LAGTRP (XX, FF, X(I), N, F(I))
10    X(I + 1) = X(I) + DX
RETURN
END
```

4.5 Numerical Integration of Curves and Tabulated Data

Sometimes in engineering problems, it is desired to integrate tabulated, calculated, or plotted data. As an elementary example from the reader's course in dynamics, we know that work W_k is defined to equal $\int F \cos \theta \, ds$, where θ is the angle between the applied force F and displacement s. Thus, if F and θ both vary with displacement s, we can calculate work W_k by plotting $F \cos \theta$ versus s and then measuring the area under this curve. We can also calculate work W_k by tabulating values of $F \cos \theta$ versus s, and then apply numerical integration or quadrature formulae. The accuracy, when applying a numerical integration formula, increases when the interval size is reduced. Thus, it is wise to apply such a formula for two different interval sizes, if possible, and compare results. As another physical example, consider a loaded elastic beam of uniform material and cross-section, where we know the bending moment distribution $M(x)$ along the length of the beam. Since we know from our strength of materials course that $d^2y(x)/dx^2 = M(x)/EI$, we can calculate the vertical deflection $y(x)$ along the length of the beam by two integrations of $M(x)$. That is, integration of $M(x)/EI$ gives us the slope $y'(x)$ along the beam, and integration of this slope gives us deflection $y(x)$. The beam support at $x = 0$ furnishes the two necessary boundary conditions. As an example, a rigid support gives us $y(0) = 0$ and $y'(0) = 0$.

We can derive some approximation formulae for $\int f(x)\,dx$ by use of the fact that this integral equals the area under an $f(x)$ versus x curve. In Fig. 4-4, the area under the curve is represented by a series of rectangles.

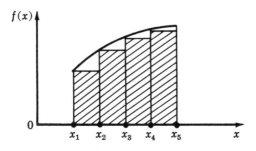

Fig. 4-4

The error of this method, which is called **rectangular integration,** is equal to the unshaded area under the curve in this figure, and it is clear that this error decreases when the interval size is reduced. If we let subscript i denote the number of the tabulated point [i.e., the ith point is (x_i, f_i)] then the rectangular integration method can be expressed by the following formula

$$\int_{x_i}^{x_{i+1}} f(x)\,dx = f_i(x_{i+1} - x_i) \qquad (4\text{-}24)$$

which considers $f(x)$ to equal f_i and, thus, to be constant in the interval from x_i to x_{i+1}. The **midpoint method** assumes that $f(x)$ equals f_{i+1} in the interval from x_i to x_{i+2}, which consists of three equally spaced points. Thus, if we let h denote the interval size, then this method can be expressed by the following formula:

$$\int_{x_i}^{x_{i+2}} f(x)\, dx = f_{i+1}(x_{i+2} - x_i) = f_{i+1}(2h) \qquad \textbf{(4-25)}$$

Formulae (4-24) and (4-25) are two examples of *open* numerical-integration formulae, because these two formulae do not utilize all of the tabulated $f(x)$ values in the interval. Let us now derive some *closed* numerical-integration formulae, which are more accurate and which utilize all tabulated $f(x)$ values in the specified interval. In Fig. 4-5 the area under

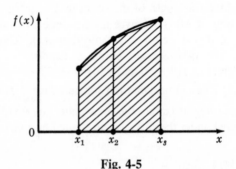

Fig. 4-5

the curve is represented by a series of trapezoids, and comparison with Fig. 4-4 shows that this **trapezoidal integration method** is more accurate than the rectangular integration method. If we denote the ith tabulated point by (x_i, f_i), then the trapezoidal method can be expressed by the following formula, which assumes that the average value of $f(x)$ in the interval from x_i to x_{i+1} equals $(f_i + f_{i+1})/2$.

$$\int_{x_i}^{x_{i+1}} f(x)\, dx = \tfrac{1}{2}(f_i + f_{i+1})(x_{i+1} - x_i) \qquad \textbf{(4-26)}$$

It should be noted that neither Eq. (4-24) or Eq. (4-26) requires equally spaced points for its application. Also note that the trapezoidal method passes a first-degree polynomial (i.e., a straight line) through two successive points, and then finds the area under this straight-line segment.

The **Simpson one-third method** passes a quadratic (i.e., second-degree) polynomial through three equally spaced points, and then finds the area under this curve-segment. Thus, if the interval size is h, the quadratic polynomial $P(x)$ that passes through the three equally spaced points (x_i, f_i), (x_{i+1}, f_{i+1}), and (x_{i+2}, f_{i+2}) can be written in the following form:

$$P(x) = (1/2h^2)[(x - x_{i+1})(x - x_{i+2})f_i - 2(x - x_i)(x - x_{i+2})f_{i+1} + (x - x_i)(x - x_{i+1})f_{i+2}] \qquad \textbf{(4-27)}$$

Since each of the three terms in the previous equation is of the second-degree in x, we know that $P(x)$ is a quadratic polynomial. Since $P(x) = f_i$ when $x = x_i$, since $P(x) = f_{i+1}$ when $x = x_{i+1}$, and since $P(x) = f_{i+2}$ when $x = x_{i+2}$; we know that Eq. (4-27) is the desired polynomial. Since $x_{i+2} = x_i + 2h$, it can be shown that

$$\int_{x_i}^{x_{i+2}} (x - x_{i+1})(x - x_{i+2})f_i \, dx = \tfrac{2}{3} f_i h^3$$

$$\int_{x_i}^{x_{i+2}} -2(x - x_i)(x - x_{i+2})f_{i+1} \, dx = \tfrac{8}{3} f_{i+1} h^3$$

$$\int_{x_i}^{x_{i+2}} (x - x_i)(x - x_{i+1})f_{i+2} \, dx = \tfrac{2}{3} f_{i+2} h^3$$

The Simpson one-third method approximates $\int_{x_i}^{x_{i+2}} f(x) \, dx$ by $\int_{x_i}^{x_{i+2}} P(x) \, dx$. Thus, application of the previous three results gives us the following equation which is Simpson's one-third formula.

$$\int_{x_i}^{x_{i+2}} f(x) \, dx = (h/3)(f_i + 4f_{i+1} + f_{i+2}) \qquad \textbf{(4-28)}$$

If we pass a third-degree (i.e., cubic) polynomial through four equally spaced points and integrate the result, we will obtain the *Simpson three-eighths formula,* which is

$$\int_{x_i}^{x_{i+3}} f(x) \, dx = (3h/8)(f_i + 3f_{i+1} + 3f_{i+2} + f_{i+3}) \qquad \textbf{(4-29)}$$

The derivation of Eq. (4-29) is very similar to that for Eq. (4-28). *Boole's formula* uses five successive, equally spaced points, and it is given by

$$\int_{x_i}^{x_{i+4}} f(x) \, dx = (2h/45)(7f_i + 32f_{i+1} + 12f_{i+2} + 32f_{i+3} + 7f_{i+4}) \qquad \textbf{(4-30)}$$

Weddle's formula is obtained by use of a fifth-degree polynomial and seven successive, equally spaced points, and it is given by

$$\int_{x_i}^{x_{i+6}} f(x) \, dx$$
$$= (3h/10)(f_i + 5f_{i+1} + f_{i+2} + 6f_{i+3} + f_{i+4} + 5f_{i+5} + f_{i+6}) \qquad \textbf{(4-31)}$$

It should be noted that Eqs. (4-30) and (4-31), which use a high degree polynomial and which use five and seven successive points, should be used with care, since they approximate the shape of $f(x)$ over a wide interval. Figure 4-3 in Sec. 4.3 and Fig. 4-9 in Sec. 4.11 both illustrate how a polynomial $P(x)$ can fit the tabulated points and yet be a poor approximation of $f(x)$. High degree polynomials can oscillate between the fitted points, as shown in Fig. 4-9. Simpson's one-third method, which uses a quadratic approximation over three successive points, should furnish reasonable results if interval h is sufficiently small and if function $f(x)$ has no discontinuities and does not vary too rapidly in the three-point interval.

The **Gauss quadrature method,** whose description can be found in numerical analysis references, has accuracy advantages, but it has limitations in applicability because it can be used only if the x-values for the tabulated $f(x)$ data are properly selected. Besides open and closed numerical-integration formulae, we also have *partial-range* formulae which utilize $f(x)$ values that lie outside the interval. The following equation is a four-point partial range formula.

$$\int_{x_i}^{x_{i+1}} f(x)\,dx = (h/24)(-f_{i-1} + 13f_i + 13f_{i+1} - f_{i+2}) \tag{4-32}$$

Let us now apply some of the previous integration formulae to calculate $\int_a^b f(x)\,dx$, where we have N equally spaced tabulated points. For this case $x_1 = a$, $x_N = b$, and interval-size h equals $(b - a)/(N - 1)$. Since

$$\int_{x_1}^{x_N} f(x)\,dx = \int_{x_1}^{x_2} f(x)\,dx + \int_{x_2}^{x_3} f(x)\,dx + \ldots + \int_{x_{N-1}}^{x_N} f(x)\,dx$$

application of Eq. (4-24), the rectangular integration method, gives

$$\int_a^b f(x)\,dx = h \sum_{i=1}^{N-1} f_i = [(b - a)/(N - 1)] \sum_{i=1}^{N-1} f_i \tag{4-33}$$

and application of Eq. (4-26), the trapezoidal method, gives

$$\int_a^b f(x)\,dx = (h/2) \sum_{i=1}^{N-1} (f_i + f_{i+1})$$

$$= [(b - a)/(N - 1)]\left[\tfrac{1}{2}(f_1 + f_N) + \sum_{i=2}^{N-1} f_i \right] \tag{4-34}$$

Figures 4-4 and 4-5 verify these two previous results. If the data were not equally spaced, then application of Eq. (4-26) gives

$$\int_a^b f(x)\,dx = \sum_{i=1}^{N-1} \tfrac{1}{2}(f_i + f_{i+1})(x_{i+1} - x_i) \tag{4-35}$$

If N, the number of tabulated points, is an odd number, then

$$\int_{x_1}^{x_N} f(x)\,dx = \int_{x_1}^{x_3} f(x)\,dx + \int_{x_3}^{x_5} f(x)\,dx + \ldots + \int_{x_{N-2}}^{x_N} f(x)\,dx$$

and application of Eq. (4-25) gives

$$\int_a^b f(x)\,dx = 2h(f_2 + f_4 + f_6 + \ldots + f_{N-1}) \tag{4-36}$$

and application of Eq. (4-28), Simpson's one-third formula, gives

$$\int_a^b f(x)\,dx = (h/3)[(f_1 + 4f_2 + f_3) + (f_3 + 4f_4 + f_5) + \ldots$$
$$+ (f_{N-2} + 4f_{N-1} + f_N)] \quad \textbf{(4-37)}$$
$$= (h/3)(f_1 + 4f_2 + 2f_3 + 4f_4 + 2f_5 + \ldots$$
$$+ 2f_{N-2} + 4f_{N-1} + f_N)$$

Thus, application of Eqs. (4-25) and (4-28) requires an even number of equal-size intervals or an odd number of equally spaced points. In Eq. (4-37), note that the coefficients of f_1 and f_N equal unity and that the other coefficients alternate between 4 and 2. In a similar manner, we may also write the equations to calculate $\int_a^b f(x)\,dx$ by the other numerical integration formulae given in this section. If the number of intervals is odd (i.e., an even number of N points), we can apply Eq. (4-29), Simpson's three-eighths formula, over the first four or the last four points; and then we can use Eq. (4-28), Simpson's one-third formula, for the other integrations, if we do not wish to apply Eq. (4-29), Simpson's three-eighths formula, throughout.

A numerical integration formula can be applied twice to approximate the double integral $\iint f(x)\,dx$, or the reader can look up special formulae in numerical analysis references for doing this operation. Since most of the numerical integration formulae given in this section require equally spaced points, it might be stated that it is possible to use an interpolation subprogram to obtain a set of equally spaced points from a set of unequally spaced data. This is exemplified in Ill. Ex. 4.11.

Illustrative Example 4.12. Suppose that we had N tabulated values of $f(x)$ versus x. Write a SUBROUTINE subprogram that utilizes the trapezoidal method to calculate the N integrals $\int_{x_1}^{x_i} f(x)\,dx$, where $i = 1$ to N.

Solution. In the following subprogram, arrays X and F contain the given x_i and $f(x_i)$ data, respectively, each of which contain NF points. Array SF contains the calculated values of $\int_{x_1}^{x_i} f(x)\,dx$. Thus, X(4) = x_4, F(4) = f_4, and SF(4) = $\int_{x_1}^{x_4} f(x)\,dx$. The third statement calculates SF(1) $\equiv \int_{x_1}^{x_1} f(x)\,dx = 0$, while statement 10 utilizes Eq. (4-26) to employ the trapezoidal method.

```
      SUBROUTINE TRPINT(X, F, SF, NF)
      DIMENSION X(50), F(50), SF(50)
      SF(1) = 0.0
      NFA = NF − 1
      DO 10 I = 1, NFA
   10 SF(I + 1) = SF(I) + 0.50 * (F(I) + F(I + 1)) * (X(I + 1) − X(I))
      RETURN
      END
```

Illustrative Example 4.13. Suppose in Ill. Ex. 4.12 that the tabulated values are equally spaced. Write two SUBROUTINE subprograms that utilize Eqs. (4-28) and (4-29) (i.e., both Simpson methods) to calculate $\int_{x_1}^{x_i} f(x)\,dx$.

Solution. In the following Simpson's one-third formula subprogram, array FF contains the given $f(x_i)$ data, array SF contains the calculated values of $\int_{x_1}^{x_i} f(x)\,dx$, X1 is the value of x_1, DX is the value of the interval-size h, and NF is the number of tabulated $f(x_i)$ values. Arrays X and F are the values of x_i and $f(x_i)$ that correspond to array SF. This was done because the size of array SF will be about half the size of array FF. The third, fourth, and fifth statements calculate the first elements in arrays X, SF, and F, respectively. The DO loop calculates the rest of the values for these three arrays. The statement that calculates SF(J + 1) is based on the following equation:

$$\int_{x_1}^{x_{i+2}} f(x)\,dx = \int_{x_1}^{x_i} f(x)\,dx + \int_{x_i}^{x_{i+2}} f(x)\,dx$$

This statement uses Eq. (4-28), which is Simpson's one-third formula, to approximate the last integral in the previous equation.

```
      SUBROUTINE SIMINT(FF,SF,X,F,X1,DX,NF)
      DIMENSION FF(50),SF(30),X(30),F(30)
      X(1) = X1
      SF(1) = 0.0
      F(1) = FF(1)
      J = 1
      NFA = NF − 2
      DO 10 I = 1,NFA,2
      X(J + 1) = X(J) + 2.0 * DX
      SF(J + 1) = SF(J) + (DX/3.0) * (FF(I) + 4.0 * FF(I + 1) + FF(I + 2))
      F(J + 1) = FF(I + 2)
   10 J = J + 1
      RETURN
      END
```

The following subprogram, which utilizes Eq. (4-29) or Simpson's three-eighths formula, is written in a manner that is very similar to the previous subprogram.

```
      SUBROUTINE THRATE(FF,SF,X,F,X1,DX,NF)
      DIMENSION FF(50),SF(20),X(20),F(20)
      X(1) = X1
      SF(1) = 0.0
      F(1) = FF(1)
      J = 1
      NFA = NF − 3
      DO 10 I = 1,NFA,3
      X(J + 1) = X(J) + 3.0 * DX
```

```
      SF(J + 1) = SF(J) + (3.0 * DX/8.0) * (FF(I) + 3.0 * FF(I + 1)
     + 3.0 * FF(I + 2) + FF(I + 3))
      F(J + 1) = FF(I + 3)
10  J = J + 1
      RETURN
      END
```

4.6   Steady-State Temperatures in a Rectangular Plate

Several physical engineering problems may be expressed mathematically by the following partial differential equation

$$\frac{\partial^2\phi}{\partial x^2} + \frac{\partial^2\phi}{\partial y^2} + \frac{\partial^2\phi}{\partial z^2} = 0 \qquad (4\text{-}38)$$

which is called *Laplace's equation*. This equation may also be written in the form $\nabla^2\phi = 0$, since $\nabla^2\phi$ may be defined as follows for a Cartesian (i.e., *x-y-z*) coordinate system.

$$\nabla^2\phi = \frac{\partial^2\phi}{\partial x^2} + \frac{\partial^2\phi}{\partial y^2} + \frac{\partial^2\phi}{\partial z^2} \qquad (4\text{-}39)$$

Some of the physical problems that are satisfied by Eq. (4-38) are:

(a) Steady-state heat conduction, where the symbol ϕ represents temperature.
(b) Gravitational attraction, where ϕ represents gravitational potential.
(c) Ideal fluid flow, where ϕ can represent the stream function and also the velocity potential.
(d) Electrostatics, where ϕ represents the electrostatic potential.
(e) Electromagnetics, where ϕ represents the magnetic potential.
(f) Steady electrical flow in a metallic conductor, where ϕ is the current density.
(g) Stretched, non-vibrating elastic membrane, where ϕ is the displacement of any point from a reference plane.

Before we can solve a partial differential equation numerically, we must first learn how to write partial derivatives in finite-difference form. Let us assume here that quantity ϕ varies with location x, y, z and time t. Since the partial derivative $\partial\phi/\partial y$ is defined to be

$$\frac{\partial\phi}{\partial y} = \lim_{\Delta y \to 0} \frac{\phi(x, y + \Delta y, z, t) - \phi(x, y, z, t)}{\Delta y}$$

use of Eq. (4-11) or the previous definition shows that we can use the following finite-difference approximation if Δy is sufficiently small

$$\frac{\partial \phi}{\partial y} = \frac{\phi(x, y + \Delta y, z, t) - \phi(x, y, z, t)}{\Delta y} \tag{4-40}$$

In a similar manner, we can use Eq. (4-16) to obtain the following finite-difference approximation for the indicated, second partial-derivative:

$$\frac{\partial^2 \phi}{\partial y^2} = \frac{\phi(x, y + \Delta y, z, t) - 2\phi(x, y, z, t) + \phi(x, y - \Delta y, z, t)}{(\Delta y)^2} \tag{4-41}$$

Thus, the following two-dimensional Laplace equation, which could represent the steady-state temperatures for all points within a rectangular plate

$$\frac{\partial^2 \phi}{\partial x^2} + \frac{\partial^2 \phi}{\partial y^2} = 0$$

can be written in numerical, finite-difference form as follows

$$\frac{\phi(x + \Delta x, y) - 2\phi(x, y) + \phi(x - \Delta x, y)}{(\Delta x)^2}$$
$$+ \frac{\phi(x, y + \Delta y) - 2\phi(x, y) + \phi(x, y - \Delta y)}{(\Delta y)^2} = 0$$

where Eq. (4-41) was applied twice and where quantity ϕ varies only with x and y. If we let $\Delta x = \Delta y = k$, we obtain the equation

$$\phi(x, y) = \tfrac{1}{4}[\phi(x + k, y) + \phi(x - k, y) \\ + \phi(x, y + k) + \phi(x, y - k)] \tag{4-42}$$

which tells us that the value of $\phi(x, y)$ is the average of the ϕ-values at the four adjacent points. If we write the three-dimensional Laplace equation (i.e., Eq. (4-38)) in finite-difference form and let $\Delta x = \Delta y = \Delta z = k$, we will obtain

$$\phi(x, y, z) = \tfrac{1}{6}[\phi(x + k, y, z) + \phi(x - k, y, z) + \phi(x, y + k, z) \\ + \phi(x, y - k, z) + \phi(x, y, z + k) + \phi(x, y, z - k)] \tag{4-43}$$

Let us now consider how Eq. (4-42) may be applied to determine the ϕ-values along a plane surface, where the ϕ-values are known around the external boundary. The surface is divided into small squares, so that $\Delta x = \Delta y = k$, and the values of ϕ at each node (i.e., corner of a square) are assumed. If ϕ satisfies the two-dimensional Laplace equation, as does temperature in a steady heat conduction problem, then Eq. (4-42) can be used to improve the values that were guessed. This is an iteration procedure that is repeated until Eq. (4-42) is satisfied at all points. Since Eq. (4-42) is based on a finite-difference approximation of partial derivatives, the accuracy of the results increases as interval-size k is reduced. We can apply this procedure by using the *relaxation method*. To utilize this method for solving Laplace's equation, consider point 1 and its four adjacent points 2, 3, 4, and 5. The *residual* R_1 at point 1 is defined by the equation

$$R_1 = \phi_2 + \phi_3 + \phi_4 + \phi_5 - 4\phi_1 \tag{4-44}$$

From Eq. (4-42), we see that the value of ϕ_1 should satisfy the equation

$$\phi_1 = \tfrac{1}{4}(\phi_2 + \phi_3 + \phi_4 + \phi_5)$$

Since the previous equation is satisfied if $R_1 = 0$, the assumed values of ϕ should be iteratively recalculated until the value of the residual at point 1, and at all other points, equals zero. That is, the procedure is to calculate the residuals for all of the non-boundary points for a given set of ϕ-values. The values of ϕ are recalculated by adding approximately one-fourth of the residual values to the previous ϕ-values. The residuals are recalculated, and the process is repeated until all residuals are as close to zero as desired. For example, a residual equal to two means an error of one-half, which may be within the required accuracy. Illustrative Example 4.14 should better exemplify this procedure. Analogous statements can be made about the use of Eq. (4-43) and the relaxation method to solve a problem that satisfies the three-dimensional Laplace equation or the two- or three-dimensional Poisson equation. *Poisson's equation* states that $\nabla^2\phi = b$, where b varies with location (x, y, z) or is a constant.

The Fortran program in this section uses the relaxation method to calculate the steady-state temperatures (or the electrostatic potential values or any other physical quantity that satisfies Laplace's equation) in a rectangular plate. Its calculation sequence may be written briefly as follows, where the symbol NX represents the number of x-points for the problem, NY is the number of y-points, ITMAX is the maximum number of iterations to perform when the problem converges very slowly, RMAX is the maximum absolute value within which all residuals must be when the problem is solved, V is the array that contains the values of the temperatures at the internal and the boundary points, and array R contains the values of the residuals at the internal points. The reader is referred at this point to Ill. Ex. 4.14 in order to make the details of this calculation sequence more clear.

(1)   Load and print the single-term inputs: KODE, NX, NY, ITMAX, and RMAX.

(2)   Load and print input array V, which contains the initially guessed values of temperature. The first and last rows and columns of this array are the given boundary values.

(3)   Set NITN, the number of iterations, equal to zero.

(4)   Add 1 to NITN, the iteration count.

(5)   Calculate the residuals at all of the internal points using the equation

$$R(I, J) = V(I+1, J) + V(I-1, J) + V(I, J+1)$$
$$+ V(I, J-1) - 4V(I, J)$$

(6) If NITN (the number of iterations) is less than ITMAX, go to step (7). If NITN = ITMAX, go to step (10).

(7) Test the residual values. If all values of $|R(I, J)|$ are less than RMAX, go to step (10). Otherwise, go to step (8).

(8) Calculate the new values of V(I, J) at the internal points of array V by adding R(I, J)/4 to the old values.

(9) Go to step (4) for the next iteration.

(10) Print the number of iterations, temperature array V, and residual array R.

(11) Go to step (1) for the next case.

The corresponding Fortran program is as follows:

```
    DIMENSION V(20, 20), R(20, 20)
1   READ 10, KODE, NX, NY, ITMAX, RMAX
10  FORMAT (4I4, F8.3)
    PRINT 11, KODE, NX, NY, ITMAX, RMAX
11  FORMAT (///6HINPUTS/4I5, F11.3///27HBOUNDARY
      AND INITIAL VALUES)
    DO 2 I = 1, NY
    READ 12, (V(I, J), J = 1, NX)
2   PRINT 15, (V(I, J), J = 1, NX)
12  FORMAT (10F7.2)
15  FORMAT (7F10.2)
    NITN = 0
    NYA = NY - 1
    NXA = NX - 1
3   NITN = NITN + 1
    DO 4 I = 2, NYA
    DO 4 J = 2, NXA
4   R(I, J) = V(I+1, J) + V(I-1, J) + V(I, J+1) + V(I, J-1)
      - 4.0 * V(I, J)
    IF (NITN - ITMAX)5, 9, 9
5   DO 6 I = 2, NYA
    DO 6 J = 2, NXA
    IF (ABSF(R(I, J)) - RMAX)6, 6, 7
6   CONTINUE
    GO TO 9
7   DO 8 I = 2, NYA
    DO 8 J = 2, NXA
```

```
 8   V(I, J) = V(I, J) + R(I, J)/4.0
     GO TO 3
 9   PRINT 13, NITN
13   FORMAT (///10HITERATIONS/I10///14HRELAXED
     VALUES)
     DO 21 I = 1, NY
21   PRINT 15, (V(I, J), J = 1, NX)
     PRINT 14
14   FORMAT (///9HRESIDUALS)
     DO 22 I = 2, NYA
22   PRINT 15, (R(I, J), J = 2, NXA)
     GO TO 1
     END
```

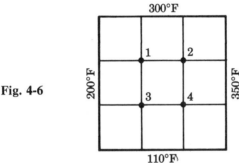

Fig. 4-6

Illustrative Example 4.14. Consider a thin square plate whose side dimension is 1.50 ft. The temperatures at its four sides are 200 °F, 300 °F, 350 °F, and 110 °F, as shown in Fig. 4-6. Find the steady-state temperature distribution along the surface of this plate.

Solution. This problem satisfies the two-dimensional Laplace equation. Let us divide this plate into nine equal sub-squares, as shown in Fig. 4-6, and calculate the steady-state temperatures at the four nodal points 1, 2, 3, and 4. A more accurate solution would require a finer network than one with nine sub-squares and four internal points. Since this problem satisfies the two-dimensional Laplace equation, we shall calculate these four temperatures using the relaxation technique. The residuals at the four internal points may be calculated by the following four equations:

$$R_1 = 200 + 300 + T_2 + T_3 - 4T_1$$
$$R_2 = 300 + 350 + T_1 + T_4 - 4T_2$$
$$R_3 = 200 + 110 + T_1 + T_4 - 4T_3$$
$$R_4 = 350 + 110 + T_2 + T_3 - 4T_4$$

As a first approximation, let us guess that $T_1 = 250\,°F$, $T_2 = 300\,°F$, $T_3 = 200\,°F$, and $T_4 = 250\,°F$. Calculation of residual R_1 gives

$$R_1 = 200 + 300 + 300 + 200 - 4(250) = 0$$

and calculation of the other residuals give $R_2 = -50$, $R_3 = 10$, and $R_4 = -40$. Thus, the new temperature values are

$$T_1 = 250 + (R_1/4) = 250\,°F$$
$$T_2 = 300 + (-50/4) = 287.5\,°F$$
$$T_3 = 200 + (10/4) = 202.5\,°F$$
$$T_4 = 250 + (-40/4) = 240\,°F$$

This procedure is repeated until the absolute values of the residuals are all as small as desired. If we iterate to a step where $T_1 = 245\,°F$, $T_2 = 283\,°F$, $T_3 = 198\,°F$, and $T_4 = 235\,°F$, the residual values are $R_1 = 1$, $R_2 = -2$, $R_3 = -2$, and $R_4 = 1$. Since none of these four residuals has an absolute value larger than two, these temperatures have been iterated to the nearest 1 °F. It may be noted that a similar procedure would be used to calculate the electrostatic or magnetic potential distribution in a rectangular plate when the values are known along the boundary of this plate.

4.7 Solution of Other Types of Partial Differential Equations

It should be mentioned that there is no general approach for the numerical solution of nonlinear partial differential equations. Methods have been developed, however, for the numerical solution of linear partial differential equations, especially those that arise in engineering. In Sec. 4.6, we discussed the numerical solution of the Laplace and the Poisson equations, neither of which had time as an independent variable. In this section, we shall discuss the numerical solutions of the diffusion and the wave equations, both of which have time and the location coordinates as their independent variables. These four types of linear partial differential equations can be solved analytically for some simple shapes by using such means as the separation of variables and the Laplace transform techniques. These analytical solutions can be plotted or tabulated for future reference. Solution by analytical techniques can become rather involved when the problem conditions are not simple. Worse yet, the geometric boundaries must be of a regular shape; however, many problems of practical interest have irregular geometric shapes and thus do not permit an analytical solution. The advantages of numerical techniques are that they can be employed to solve problems that have irregularly shaped boundaries and boundary conditions that vary with both time and location, without adding much complication when these techniques are applied. Numerical solution techniques are also easy to program for a digital computer solution. As was previously shown in Sec. 4.6, the first step in the numerical solution of a partial differential equation is to write each partial derivative in the given equation in finite-difference form. That is, the partial differential equation is rewritten as a finite-difference equation, and this will be further exemplified in this section.

It might be worthwhile to mention that partial derivatives and partial differential equations are often written in subscript form. For example, ϕ_t is the subscript form of $\partial\phi/\partial t$, ϕ_{yy} is the subscript form of $\partial^2\phi/\partial y^2$. We may write the most general equation-form for a linear, second-order partial differential equation in two variables x and y, in subscript form, as follows

$$A\phi_{xx} + B\phi_{xy} + C\phi_{yy} + D\phi_x + E\phi_y + F\phi + G = 0$$

where the coefficients A, B, C, D, E, F, and G must be either constant or a function of x and y only. The previous two-independent-variable equation may be classified as follows:

If $(B^2 - 4AC)$ is negative, the equation is elliptic.
If $(B^2 - 4AC)$ equals zero, the equation is parabolic.
If $(B^2 - 4AC)$ is positive, the equation is hyperbolic.

Using this previous classification criteria, it is seen that the two-dimensional Laplace and Poisson equations are both elliptic. The three-dimensional forms of these equations are also elliptic.

The *wave equation*, which is hyperbolic, may be written in the following form

$$\nabla^2\phi = \frac{1}{a^2}\frac{\partial^2\phi}{\partial t^2} \qquad (4\text{-}45)$$

where $\nabla^2\phi$ is defined by Eq. (4-39). Some of the physical problems that are satisfied by Eq. (4-45) are as follows. The number of location coordinates (i.e., dimensions) that may be involved are listed within the parentheses (e.g., the vibrating membrane problem satisfies the two-dimensional wave equation).

(a) Vibration of an elastic string, where ϕ is the transverse displacement from the equilibrium position, a^2 equals T/m, T is the string tension, and m is the mass per unit length (1).

(b) Vibration of an elastic membrane, where ϕ is the transverse displacement from the equilibrium position, a^2 equals T/m, T is the tension per unit length, and m is the mass per unit area (2).

(c) Torsional vibration of an elastic shaft, where ϕ is the angle of twist of the shaft as referenced to the equilibrium position, a^2 equals G/m, G is the shear modulus, and m is the mass per unit volume (1).

(d) Vibration of an elastic bar, where ϕ is the longitudinal displacement from the equilibrium position, a^2 equals E/m, E is the modulus of elasticity, and m is the mass per unit volume (1).

(e) Plane sound waves in a horn of circular cross-section, where ϕ is the velocity potential and a is the speed of the sound wave (1).

(f) Sound waves in space, where ϕ is the velocity potential and a is the speed of the sound wave (1, 2, 3).

(g) Electromagnetic field in empty space, where ϕ can represent the electric field strength and also the magnetic field strength (1, 2, 3).

(h) Lossless electric transmission line, where ϕ can represent the voltage and also the current in the line, $a^2 = 1/LC$, L is the inductance per unit length, and C is the capacitance per unit length (1).

(i) Tidal waves in a long channel, where ϕ is the longitudinal displacement of the fluid, a equals $\sqrt{gh}$ and is the speed at which the tidal waves are propagated, g is the gravitational acceleration, and h is the depth of the fluid in the channel before it was disturbed.

Applying Eq. (4-41) to write the one-dimensional wave equation $\phi_{xx} = \phi_{tt}/a^2$ in finite-difference form, we have

$$\frac{\phi(x + \Delta x, t) - 2\phi(x, t) + \phi(x - \Delta x, t)}{(\Delta x)^2}$$
$$= \frac{\phi(x, t + \Delta t) - 2\phi(x, t) + \phi(x, t - \Delta t)}{a^2(\Delta t)^2}$$

If we let Δx equal $a(\Delta t)$, we obtain the following approximation equation for $\phi(x, t + \Delta t)$:

$$\phi(x, t + \Delta t) = \phi(x + \Delta x, t) + \phi(x - \Delta x, t) - \phi(x, t - \Delta t) \quad \textbf{(4-46)}$$

In a similar manner, if we write the two-dimensional wave equation $\phi_{xx} + \phi_{yy} = \phi_{tt}/a^2$ in finite difference form and let $\Delta x = \Delta y = a(\Delta t)$, we will obtain the following approximation equation for $\phi(x, y, t + \Delta t)$

$$\phi(x, y, t + \Delta t) = \phi(x + \Delta x, y, t) + \phi(x - \Delta x, y, t) + \phi(x, y + \Delta y, t)$$
$$+ \phi(x, y - \Delta y, t) - 2\phi(x, y, t) - \phi(x, y, t - \Delta t) \quad \textbf{(4-47)}$$

Illustrative Example 4.15 illustrates the use of Eq. (4-46) in obtaining the numerical solution of an elastic-string vibration problem. The string displacement is tabulated in Table 4-1 as a function of location x along the string and time t.

The *diffusion equation*, which is parabolic, may be written in the following form

$$\nabla^2 \phi = \frac{1}{a^2} \frac{\partial \phi}{\partial t} \quad \textbf{(4-48)}$$

where $\nabla^2\phi$ is defined by Eq. (4-39). Some of the physical problems that are satisfied by Eq. (4-48) are as follows:

(a) Unsteady heat conduction, where the symbol ϕ represents temperature, thermal diffusivity a^2 equals $k/c\rho g$, k is the thermal conductivity of the material, c is the specific heat of the material, g is the gravitational acceleration, and ρ is the density of the material.

(b) Diffusion of a liquid in a slab of porous material, where ϕ is the liquid concentration at a point in the slab.

(c) Well-insulated, noninductive transmission line, where ϕ can represent the voltage and also the current in the line, $a^2 = 1/RC$, R is the resistance per unit length, C is the capacitance per unit length, and x is the only location coordinate (which is directed along the cable).

(d) Current density in a metallic conductor, where ϕ is the current density.

(e) Viscous fluid flow started from rest, where ϕ is the fluid vorticity, a^2 equals μ/ρ, μ is the fluid viscosity, and ρ is the density of the fluid.

(f) Slowing down of neutrons in matter when no neutrons are being produced, where ϕ is the number of neutrons per unit time within reach of age t, $a^2 = 1$, and x is the only location coordinate.

(g) Soil consolidation, where ϕ is the excess hydrostatic pressure and a^2 is the soil consolidation coefficient.

Applying Eqs. (4-40) and (4-41) to write the one-dimensional diffusion equation $\phi_{xx} = \phi_t/a^2$ in finite-difference form, we have

$$\frac{\phi(x + \Delta x, t) - 2\phi(x, t) + \phi(x - \Delta x, t)}{(\Delta x)^2} = \frac{\phi(x, t + \Delta t) - \phi(x, t)}{a^2(\Delta t)}$$

Solving the above equation for $\phi(x, t + \Delta t)$, we obtain

$$\phi(x, t + \Delta t) = a^2 \frac{\Delta t}{(\Delta x)^2} \phi(x + \Delta x, t) + \left(1 - 2a^2 \frac{\Delta t}{(\Delta x)^2}\right) \phi(x, t)$$

$$+ a^2 \frac{\Delta t}{(\Delta x)^2} \phi(x - \Delta x, t)$$

The above equation shows that if we let Δt approach zero as Δx is held constant, then $\phi(x, t + \Delta t)$ approaches $\phi(x, t)$. If Δt were held constant as Δx approaches zero, then $\phi(x, t + \Delta t)$ would approach infinity. Thus, we want the ratio $(\Delta t)/(\Delta x)^2$ to be constant. Let us denote the term $a^2(\Delta t)/(\Delta x)^2$ by b. Since Δt equals $b(\Delta x/a)^2$, the time interval sharply decreases as the Δx interval is made smaller. For accuracy considerations, it is recommended that $b \leq 1/2$. The numerical error will be a minimum if we set $b = 1/6$. Thus, if we desire the highest accuracy, the following approximation equation is recommended:

$$\phi(x, t + \Delta t) = \tfrac{1}{6}[\phi(x + \Delta x, t) + \phi(x - \Delta x, t)] + \tfrac{2}{3}\phi(x, t) \quad \textbf{(4-49)}$$

If we set $b = 1/2$, we will obtain the following very simple form of the diffusion difference equation, which is called the ***Bender-Schmidt*** equation.

$$\phi(x, t + \Delta t) = \tfrac{1}{2}[\phi(x + \Delta x, t) + \phi(x - \Delta x, t)] \quad \textbf{(4-50)}$$

The above equation states that the value of ϕ at location x and time $(t + \Delta t)$ equals the average of the ϕ-values of the neighboring points at time t. These neighboring points are located at $(x - \Delta x)$ and $(x + \Delta x)$.

If we write the two-dimensional diffusion equation $\phi_{xx} + \phi_{yy} = \phi_t/a^2$ in finite-difference form and let $4a^2(\Delta t) = (\Delta x)^2 = (\Delta y)^2$, we will obtain the following approximation equation

$$\phi(x, y, t + \Delta t) = \tfrac{1}{4}[\phi(x + \Delta x, y, t) + \phi(x - \Delta x, y, t) \\ + \phi(x, y + \Delta y, t) + \phi(x, y - \Delta y, t)] \quad \textbf{(4-51)}$$

which states that the value of ϕ at point (x, y) and time $(t + \Delta t)$ equals the average of the four neighboring point values at the previous time t. Illustrative Examples 4.16 and 4.17 exemplify the use of Eqs. (4-50) and (4-51) in obtaining the numerical solution of two unsteady, heat-transfer problems.

As stated previously, numerical methods can be applied, without adding much complication to solve certain linear, partial differential equations with rather flexible boundary and initial conditions. Initial conditions that vary with location and boundary conditions that vary with time are rather easily handled, and this is illustrated in Ill. Ex. 4.16. If an initial condition differs from the boundary condition at an instant later (e.g., a step input at the boundary), then it is recommended that the average of these two values be used as the initial boundary value, in order to obtain the best results when solving partial differential equations by numerical techniques. In more general terms, it may be stated that if at time t there is a sudden change in a boundary value at a specified point, then the average of the two discontinuous values should be chosen as the boundary value at time t for that point. This is exemplified in Ill. Ex. 4.17.

For certain types of boundary conditions, it is desirable to add a fictitious surface. Suppose, in a heat transfer application, that we are given a wall where one of the wall surfaces is insulated. At that surface $\partial T/\partial x = 0$, where T is the surface temperature, since no heat is conducted across that surface. If the wall is divided into slabs that are Δx units thick, then we can add a fictitious slab adjacent to the insulated surface that is also Δx units thick. Let T_i be the temperature of the insulated surface and let T_{i+1} be the temperature of the fictitious surface. Since the finite-difference approximation for $\partial T/\partial x$ at the insulated surface is $(T_{i+1} - T_i)/\Delta x$, we set T_{i+1} equal to T_i so that $\partial T/\partial x = 0$ at that surface. Illustrative Example 4.16 will more clearly exemplify this procedure. If we had a homogeneous-material wall that was heated in the same manner on both external surfaces, the symmetry of the temperature distribution would allow the problem to be treated as a wall insulated at the center. This is because the symmetrical conditions cause $\partial T/\partial x$ to equal zero at the center plane of the wall.

For problems involving the torsional vibration of an elastic shaft, the boundary condition at a free or unsupported end is $\partial\theta/\partial x = 0$, where θ is the twist angle. For problems involving the longitudinal vibration of an elastic bar, the boundary condition at a free end is $\partial h/\partial x = 0$, where h is the longitudinal displacement. These two boundary conditions can be handled by use of a fictitious surface in the same manner as that given in the previous paragraph for an insulated surface. Other types of boundary conditions can also be handled in numerical solutions by special treatment. For example, convection and other types of surface heating can be handled, and the reader is referred to heat transfer texts if he is interested in the details.

Illustrative Example 4.15. Consider an elastic string 10 ft long and fixed at both ends. Its value of a^2 or T/m is 16 ft^2/sec^2. The string is held in the position shown in Fig. 4-7 for one second and then released. Find the time variation

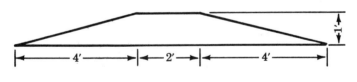

Fig. 4-7

of the string displacement up to 5 seconds after the string is released from this initial position.

Solution. It is known that this problem satisfies the one-dimensional wave equation. We shall calculate the displacement at five evenly spaced intervals. Thus, $\Delta x = 2$ ft. The choice of the Δx interval specifies the size of the Δt interval. Since $a = 4$ ft/sec, $\Delta t = \Delta x/a = 0.500$ sec. Since the string is fixed at both ends, its displacement equals zero at $x = 0$ and at $x = 10$ ft for all values of time t. This result is shown in Table 4-1. The initial displacement, as given by Fig. 4-7, is also inserted in Table 4-1 for $t = 0$ and for $t = -0.500$ sec, since this displacement was maintained for one second. Since the initial and boundary conditions have now been inserted in Table 4-1, we can now apply Eq. (4-46) to calculate the other values of the string displacement $\bar{y}(x, t)$. For example

$$\bar{y}(2.00, 0.500) = \bar{y}(4.00, 0) + \bar{y}(0, 0) - \bar{y}(2.00, -0.500)$$
$$= 1.000 + 0 - 0.500 = 0.500$$

The results of these calculations are shown in Table 4-1 and from this table, it can be seen that an oscillation results. The accuracy of these results could be improved by using a smaller value for Δx.

Table 4-1

t (sec) \ x (ft)	0	2.00	4.00	6.00	8.00	10.00
-0.500	0	0.500	1.000	1.000	0.500	0
0	0	0.500	1.000	1.000	0.500	0
0.500	0	0.500	0.500	0.500	0.500	0
1.000	0	0	0	0	0	0
1.500	0	-0.500	-0.500	-0.500	-0.500	0
2.000	0	-0.500	-1.000	-1.000	-0.500	0
2.500	0	-0.500	-1.000	-1.000	-0.500	0
3.000	0	-0.500	-0.500	-0.500	-0.500	0
3.500	0	0	0	0	0	0
4.000	0	0.500	0.500	0.500	0.500	0
4.500	0	0.500	1.000	1.000	0.500	0
5.000	0	0.500	1.000	1.000	0.500	0

Illustrative Example 4.16. Consider a plane wall, one foot thick and insulated on the right side. Initially, the wall temperature varies linearly from 400 °F to 100 °F. The temperature of the heated left side varies with time t and equals $(400 + 3.2t)$ °F, where t is measured in seconds. The thermal diffusivity a^2 of the wall is 25 ft²/hr. Find the timewise variation of the wall temperature distribution for the next 27 seconds using the Bender-Schmidt equation.

Solution. This problem satisfies the one-dimensional diffusion equation, $T_{xx} = T_t/a^2$. If the wall is divided into four equal-size slabs, Δx equals 0.250 ft. The time interval Δt equals $(0.25/5.0)^2/2$ hr. Thus, $\Delta t = 0.00125$ hr or 4.50 sec. The tabular solution is shown in Table 4-2. T_1 and T_5 are the wall surface temperatures, while T_I is the temperature of the fictitious insulation surface. Wall locations 1 to 5 are spaced 0.250 ft apart. The temperatures are all known at $t = 0$. Temperatures T_2 to T_5 for the next time interval, and all subsequent time intervals, were obtained by using Eq. (4-50). Temperature T_I is obtained by setting T_I equal to T_5, since that surface is insulated. Temperature T_1 equals $(400 + 3.2t)$ °F. We would get a more accurate solution if we used Eq. (4-49), instead of Eq. (4-50), and if we used a smaller value for Δx.

Table 4-2

Time (sec)	$T_1(°F)$	$T_2(°F)$	$T_3(°F)$	$T_4(°F)$	$T_5(°F)$	$T_I(°F)$
0	400.0	325.0	250.0	175.0	100.0	100.0
4.50	414.4	325.0	250.0	175.0	137.5	137.5
9.00	428.8	332.2	250.0	193.8	156.3	156.3
13.50	443.2	339.4	263.0	203.2	175.1	175.1
18.00	457.6	353.1	271.3	219.0	189.1	189.1
22.50	472.0	364.5	286.0	230.2	204.0	204.0
27.00	486.4	379.0	297.4	245.0	217.1	217.1

Illustrative Example 4.17. Consider a thin square plate, whose side dimension is 1.50 ft. The plate is initially at 200 °F, but suddenly the temperatures at its four sides are changed to and maintained at 200 °F, 300 °F, 350 °F, and 110 °F, as shown in Fig. 4-6 in Sec. 4.6. Find the plate temperature distribution when time t equals 18 sec, if the thermal diffusivity a^2 is 25.0 ft²/hr.

Solution. This problem satisfies the two-dimensional diffusion equation. Let us divide this plate into nine equal sub-squares, as shown in Fig. 4-6, and calculate the temperatures at the four nodal points 1, 2, 3, and 4. Since $\Delta x = \Delta y = 0.50$ ft, time interval Δt equals $(0.500)^2/4(25.0)$ hr. Thus, Δt equals 0.00250 hr or 9.00 sec. Since there were three step-input temperatures, the temperatures of the four sides at $t = 0$ are 200 °F, 250 °F, 275 °F, and 155 °F. Application of Eq. (4-51) gives the following values for the four internal temperatures at $t = 9.0$ sec

$$T_1 = \tfrac{1}{4}(200 + 200 + 250 + 200) = 212.50 \ °F$$
$$T_2 = \tfrac{1}{4}(275 + 200 + 250 + 200) = 231.25 \ °F$$
$$T_3 = \tfrac{1}{4}(200 + 200 + 200 + 155) = 188.75 \ °F$$
$$T_4 = \tfrac{1}{4}(275 + 200 + 200 + 155) = 207.50 \ °F$$

Since for $t > 0$ the temperatures of the four sides are 200 °F, 300 °F, 350 °F, and 110 °F, as given, we may use the following equations, which are obtained from Eq. (4-51), for subsequent calculations

$$T_{1,t+\Delta t} = \tfrac{1}{4}(T_{2,t} + 200 + 300 + T_{3,t})$$
$$T_{2,t+\Delta t} = \tfrac{1}{4}(350 + T_{1,t} + 300 + T_{4,t})$$
$$T_{3,t+\Delta t} = \tfrac{1}{4}(T_{4,t} + 200 + T_{1,t} + 110)$$
$$T_{4,t+\Delta t} = \tfrac{1}{4}(350 + T_{3,t} + T_{2,t} + 110)$$

It may be noted that the steady-state temperatures for this problem were calculated in Ill. Ex. 4.14. Applying the above equations to calculate these four internal temperatures at $t = 18.0$ sec, we obtain

$$T_1 = \tfrac{1}{4}(231.25 + 200 + 300 + 188.75) = 230.00 \ °F$$
$$T_2 = \tfrac{1}{4}(350 + 212.50 + 300 + 207.50) = 267.50 \ °F$$
$$T_3 = \tfrac{1}{4}(207.50 + 200 + 212.50 + 110) = 182.50 \ °F$$
$$T_4 = \tfrac{1}{4}(350 + 188.75 + 231.25 + 110) = 220.00 \ °F$$

4.8 Solution of Simultaneous, Linear Algebraic Equations and Matrix Inversion

Both the professional and the student engineer often are encountered with the necessity of solving a set of simultaneous, linear algebraic equations. Such a set of equations occurs in certain types of electrical circuit, elastic structure, mechanical vibration, etc. problems. Solution of such a set of algebraic equations is also required when a set of linear ordinary differential equations are to be solved analytically by classical or Laplace transform means to obtain exact solutions. It has also been shown in Sec. 2.11 that such a solution is required for certain types of numerical solutions of differential equations of the two-point boundary-value type. Section 4.11 shows its need when a least squares curve-fit is desired. When the numerical approximation for Laplace's partial differential equation, as given by Eq. (4-42) or (4-43), is applied at different (x, y) or (x, y, z) locations, then a set of simultaneous, linear algebraic equations results. In fact, the relaxation method described in Sec. 4.6 was devised originally for the purpose of iteratively solving a set of simultaneous, linear algebraic equations. Section 3.7 shows that the corresponding eigenvectors can be determined by solving a set of linear algebraic equations when the eigenvalues of a matrix are known. A set of simultaneous, linear algebraic equations can be expressed in the matrix form of $[A]\{x\} = \{d\}$. As a simplified example, the following three linear algebraic equations

$$a_{11}x_1 + a_{12}x_2 + a_{13}x_3 = d_1 \tag{4-52a}$$

$$a_{21}x_1 + a_{22}x_2 + a_{23}x_3 = d_2 \tag{4-52b}$$

$$a_{31}x_1 + a_{32}x_2 + a_{33}x_3 = d_3 \tag{4-52c}$$

can be expressed by the following matrix equation, which can be verified by matrix multiplication

$$\begin{bmatrix} a_{11} & a_{12} & a_{13} \\ a_{21} & a_{22} & a_{23} \\ a_{31} & a_{32} & a_{33} \end{bmatrix} \begin{Bmatrix} x_1 \\ x_2 \\ x_3 \end{Bmatrix} = \begin{Bmatrix} d_1 \\ d_2 \\ d_3 \end{Bmatrix}$$

The reader has already learned in a previous algebra course how to solve a set of simultaneous, linear algebraic equations by use of *Cramer's rule.* When only two or three equations need to be solved, this is a very good means of solution, especially when the calculations are to be done by hand. In professional engineering problems, however, we will have to solve many more than three simultaneous algebraic equations. For example, a fifteen-loop electrical circuit problem may require the solution of fifteen simultaneous algebraic equations, and the use of fifty stations in an elastic structure may require the solution of fifty simultaneous, linear algebraic equations. For such problems, Cramer's rule should not be used, because it requires the evaluation of determinants. Though determinant-evaluation subprograms are available, Cramer's rule is very inefficient for large problems because the evaluation of a large determinant requires very many multiplication and other computer operations. For example, the solution of only three simultaneous equations can involve twenty addition-subtraction operations and 36 multiplication-division operations if Cramer's rule is used, while the use of an algebraic elimination method could be programmed to require only eleven addition-subtraction operations and nineteen multiplication-division operations.

We shall classify the techniques for solving simultaneous, linear algebraic equations into three general types: direct methods, iterative methods, and matrix inverse methods. *Direct methods* obtain a solution in a direct manner and in a finite number of steps that can be determined from the number of equations to be solved. Thus, they always furnish an answer in a specific number of steps. Examples are Cramer's rule and elimination methods, which use specific algebraic operations to eliminate the unknown variables. The reader has already learned some methods for eliminating unknowns in a previous algebra course. *Iterative methods* assume a solution and then iteratively apply an equation or equations to compute better solutions, until the results are the same for two successive iterations. From Sec. 3.7 we know that since a set of linear algebraic equations can be expressed in the matrix form of $[A]\{x\} = \{d\}$, then the x_i values may be computed from the equation $\{x\} = [A]^{-1}\{d\}$, where $[A]^{-1}$ is the inverse of matrix $[A]$. Thus, a *matrix inverse method* first inverts a square matrix and then obtains the x_i values by matrix multiplication. It should be mentioned that many SUBROUTINE subprograms that solve a set of linear algebraic equations or invert a matrix are available, so that an engineer can incorporate them into his Fortran programs when such a solution is required. Before a solution of a set of linear algebraic equations is attempted, they should be first inspected to see if it would be worthwhile. This is done to be sure that a unique solution exists. From our course in algebra, we know that there is no solution for the equations

$$5x_1 + 8x_2 = 11$$
$$5x_1 + 8x_2 = 46$$

and that there is no solution for

$$5x_1 + 8x_2 = 11$$
$$10x_1 + 16x_2 = 51$$

We also know that there is an infinite number of solutions for the following set of equations because two of the equations are proportional to each other

$$5x_1 + 8x_2 + 4x_3 = 11$$
$$7x_1 + 19x_2 + 8x_3 = 58$$
$$15x_1 + 24x_2 + 12x_3 = 33$$

If the last equation in the previous set of equations was $501x_1 + 802x_2 + 400x_3 = 1105$, then the equations are *ill-conditioned* since the first and third equations are nearly proportional and since an accurate solution will be difficult to obtain. If we have n unknown x_i values, we need n independent equations to solve for these n unknowns. If we have more than n independent equations for the n unknowns, we have an *overdetermined system* which in general does not have a unique solution.

The **Gaussian elimination method** uses algebraic methods to eliminate the unknowns. For a simplified example, let us consider the three linear algebraic equations given by Eqs. (4-52a, b, c). The first step of this method is to eliminate the term x_1 from all of the equations but the first equation. We can eliminate x_1 in the ith equation by multiplying the first equation by (a_{i1}/a_{11}) and subtracting the result from the ith equation. Thus, the new elements a'_{ij} and d'_i in the ith equation are given by

$$a'_{ij} = a_{ij} - \left(\frac{a_{i1}}{a_{11}}\right) a_{1j} \tag{4-53}$$

$$d'_i = d_i - \left(\frac{a_{i1}}{a_{11}}\right) d_1 \tag{4-54}$$

and the new equations are as follows:

$$a_{11}x_1 + a_{12}x_2 + a_{13}x_3 = d_1$$
$$a'_{22}x_2 + a'_{23}x_3 = d'_2$$
$$a'_{32}x_2 + a'_{33}x_3 = d'_3$$

We can now eliminate x_2 algebraically from the third of the new set of equations by multiplying the second equation by (a'_{32}/a'_{22}) and subtracting this result from the third equation. Thus, the new elements in the third equation are given by

$$a''_{33} = a'_{33} - \left(\frac{a'_{32}}{a'_{22}}\right) a'_{23}$$

$$d''_3 = d'_3 - \left(\frac{a'_{32}}{a'_{22}}\right) d'_2$$

and the new equations will be of the following triangular form.

$$a_{11}x_1 + a_{12}x_2 + a_{13}x_3 = d_1$$
$$a'_{22}x_2 + a'_{23}x_3 = d'_2$$
$$a''_{33}x_3 = d''_3$$

Now we can solve the third of the previous set of equations for x_3, then solve the second equation for x_2, and then solve the first equation for x_1. Since they were involved in divisions, we do not want coefficients a_{11} or a'_{22} to equal zero. We can always rearrange the set of equations so that this does not happen because switching the order of a pair of equations will not affect the solutions for x_1, x_2, and x_3. The **Gauss-Jordan method** is a procedure that goes a few steps further by eliminating all variables but x_1 in the first equation, eliminating all variables but x_2 in the second equation, etc., so that we end up with the solutions for the x_i unknowns. Other commonly used elimination methods are the **Crout** and **Choleski** methods. To permit the Gaussian or the Gauss-Jordan methods to be performed by a digital computer, we can form a matrix composed of the a_{ij} and d_i elements as follows. It is an augmented matrix for $[A]$ because we added an extra column composed of the d_i elements to matrix $[A]$.

$$\begin{bmatrix} a_{11} & a_{12} & a_{13} & d_1 \\ a_{21} & a_{22} & a_{23} & d_2 \\ a_{31} & a_{32} & a_{33} & d_3 \end{bmatrix}$$

Since the equations that compute the new elements are of a set form, they can be programmed to compute the matrix

$$\begin{bmatrix} a_{11} & a_{12} & a_{13} & d_1 \\ 0 & a'_{22} & a'_{23} & d'_2 \\ 0 & a'_{32} & a'_{33} & d'_3 \end{bmatrix}$$

and finally the matrix

$$\begin{bmatrix} a_{11} & a_{12} & a_{13} & d_1 \\ 0 & a'_{22} & a'_{23} & d'_2 \\ 0 & 0 & a''_{33} & d''_3 \end{bmatrix}$$

from which x_1, x_2, and x_3 may be obtained. If necessary, matrix rows may be rearranged just as the algebraic equations can also be rearranged. It is also possible to compute the successive matrices by multiplication by specific matrices if desired, instead of programming generalized formulae. The Gauss-Jordan method, which can also be programmed by use of generalized equations as shown in Ill. Ex. 4.19, ends up with a matrix of the following form, where the solutions are $x_1 = d'''_1$, $x_2 = d'''_2$, and $x_3 = d'''_3$. The Gaussian elimination method and the Gauss-Jordan method are exemplified in Ill. Exs. 4.18 and 4.19.

$$\begin{bmatrix} 1 & 0 & 0 & d'''_1 \\ 0 & 1 & 0 & d'''_2 \\ 0 & 0 & 1 & d'''_3 \end{bmatrix}$$

Elimination methods are the most commonly used type of direct methods because they are comparatively efficient, but they have a disadvantage in that they involve numerous arithmetic operations when a large number of equations are involved. For such cases, the additive effect of roundoff errors can cause slight errors in the results. Thus, for a large number of equations, it is wise to correct (i.e., improve) the results of an elimination method by use of an iteration technique. For this reason, the better SUBROUTINE subprograms that solve this type of problem combine an elimination method and an iteration method. That is, they start with elimination and follow this by an iteration method in order to attain more accuracy.

The *Gauss iteration method* first assumes values for the x_i unknowns. Using these assumed values, the method calculates x_1 from the first equation, calculates x_2 from the second equation, calculates x_3 from the third equation, etc. The method then uses these calculated x_i values for the next set of assumed values and repeats the process. A solution occurs when two successive sets of x_i values are equal. This method is exemplified in Ill. Ex. 4.20. It is a very easy method to program, but it does not always converge to a solution. For this method the matrix of the a_{ij} coefficients should be symmetric about the main diagonal (i.e., $a_{ji} = a_{ij}$) which might be attained by rearranging the equations. Elastic structure problems often satisfy this symmetrical condition.

The *Gauss-Seidel method* is a slight modification of the previous method, but it has a better convergence, as shown by Ill. Exs. 4.20 and 4.21. This method first assumes x_2 to x_n and solves for x_1 in the first algebraic equation. Next it uses this value of x_1, assumes x_3 to x_n, and solves for x_2 in the second algebraic equation. Then it uses these values of x_1 and x_2, assumes x_4 to x_n, and solves for x_3 in the third algebraic equation. After x_n is calculated from the nth and last algebraic equation, the procedure is repeated. A solution occurs when two successive sets of x_i values are in agreement, and the procedure for this method is exemplified in Ill. Ex. 4.21. An advantage of this method is that it is simple and easy to program. It will not always converge to a solution or it may converge very slowly, but this method will converge to a solution if, for the matrix of the a_{ij} coefficients, each major diagonal element (i.e., a_{11} to a_{nn}) is significantly large in absolute value when compared to the off-diagonal elements (i.e., a_{ij} where $i \neq j$) in its row or equation. We know that this method will converge if for each equation, the coefficient a_{ii} in the ith equation is larger in absolute value than the sum of the absolute values of the other a_{ij} coefficients in that equation. This condition is seldom met, and experience shows that this method converges for much less stringent cases. Sometimes this condition can be attained by a rearrangement of the given algebraic equations. As mentioned previously, such a rearrangement will not affect the solutions for the unknowns x_1 to x_n. Thus, we will converge faster if we arrange the given algebraic equations so that the largest a_{ij} coefficients in absolute value will lie along the major diagonal, if possible. Many practical engineering problems involve simultaneous, linear algebraic equations which can be arranged such that, for each equation, the a_{ij} coefficient of x_i in the ith equation (i.e., a_{ii}) is large in absolute value when compared to the other a_{ij} coefficients in that equation. Such problems are well-suited for a Gauss-Seidel solution of the x_i unknowns.

The details of the *conjugate gradient method* are described and exemplified in Ill. Ex. 4.22. It is an iterative method which requires that a solution be assumed, but it will converge to a solution in exactly n steps, where n is the number of linear algebraic equations that must be simultaneously solved. The basic method requires that the matrix of a_{ij} coefficients be symmetric about the major diagonal (i.e., $a_{ij} = a_{ji}$), but this method can be modified to handle non-symmetrical arrangements. Its major disadvantage is that very many arithmetic operations (e.g., multiplication and divisions) are required, and the resultant roundoff errors, when applied to a large number of equations, cause the solutions by this method to be usually less accurate than those obtained by elimination methods. As has been mentioned previously, the *relaxation method,* that was described in Sec. 4.6, is basically an iterative method for solving simultaneous, linear algebraic equations. Another iterative technique is the *Hotelling method* which is exemplified in Ill. Ex. 4.23. It iterates a matrix equation which is stated in this illustrative example. It is a relatively easy method to program, but there is no assurance that it will converge to a solution. The matrix of the a_{ij} coefficients should be symmetric about the major diagonal.

Suppose for Eqs. (4-52a, b, c), we had a physical problem where the a_{ij} coefficients of the x_i terms never changed, but we had to determine the values of x_1, x_2, and x_3 for several sets of d_1, d_2, and d_3 values. Many professional engineering problems fall within this category, except that many more than three equations are usually involved. Thus, let us express Eqs. (4-52a, b, c) in the matrix form $[A]\{x\} = \{d\}$, where the size of square matrix $[A]$ equals the number of equations to be solved. *Matrix inversion methods* are very advantageous for such problems because we only have to invert matrix $[A]$ once, since its a_{ij} elements do not change. Thus, for each set of d_i values, we can calculate the x_i values by matrix multiplication. That is, we use the equation $\{x\} = [A]^{-1}\{d\}$ to calculate several sets of x_i values. The reader had learned a matrix inversion method in a previous algebra course where the first step in the procedure was to replace each element of the matrix with its co-factor. This method is a good hand-calculation method when we want to invert a square matrix of size 2 or 3, but it is a very inefficient method for large matrices because each calculation of a co-factor requires the evaluation of a determinant. The determinant of the whole matrix must also be evaluated. Thus, if this method is used to invert a matrix of size n, then $(n^2 + 1)$ determinants must be evaluated. There are many other methods that calculate an inverse by direct means, and which are more efficient in comparison. Some of these better known methods are the **Gauss, Gauss-Jordan, Crout, Choleski,** and **Doolittle** matrix-inversion methods. Matrices have also been statistically inverted using Monte Carlo methods. For small computers with an auxiliary memory (e.g., magnetic tape or disk), large matrices can be inverted by first partitioning them into smaller square submatrices. The procedures for doing this may be found in numerical analysis references. The **Gauss-Jordan matrix inversion method** is an elimination method that uses the same mathematical operations as those for the Gauss-Jordan method for solving simultaneous, linear algebraic equations. The difference is that they start with a different augmented matrix. A matrix is augmented when additional columns are added to it. If we wanted to invert a matrix $[A]$ of size 3 by the Gauss-Jordan method, the initial augmented matrix would be as follows, where the nine a_{ij} terms are the nine elements of matrix $[A]$.

$$\begin{bmatrix} a_{11} & a_{12} & a_{13} & 1 & 0 & 0 \\ a_{21} & a_{22} & a_{23} & 0 & 1 & 0 \\ a_{31} & a_{32} & a_{33} & 0 & 0 & 1 \end{bmatrix}$$

This method performs specific operations to calculate successive augmented matrices. The details for this method are exemplified in Ill. Ex. 4.24. When the method is completed, the last augmented matrix will be of the form

$$\begin{bmatrix} 1 & 0 & 0 & e_{11} & e_{12} & e_{13} \\ 0 & 1 & 0 & e_{21} & e_{22} & e_{23} \\ 0 & 0 & 1 & e_{31} & e_{32} & e_{33} \end{bmatrix}$$

and the inverse matrix is

$$\begin{bmatrix} e_{11} & e_{12} & e_{13} \\ e_{21} & e_{22} & e_{23} \\ e_{31} & e_{32} & e_{33} \end{bmatrix}$$

That is, this method, in effect, ends at a condition where the first three columns of the *initial* augmented matrix is multiplied by its inverse and where the last three columns are also multiplied by this inverse. A comparison of the initial and the final augmented matrices should show this effect. The equations used to calculate the successive augmented matrices are the same as those used to calculate the successive matrices when the

Gauss-Jordan method is used to solve a set of linear algebraic equations. These equations are given and are verified in Ill. Ex. 4.19, which solves a set of linear algebraic equations. These equations are applied in Ill. Ex. 4.24 to invert a matrix. To summarize the calculation procedure, this method obtains the inverse of a square matrix of size n in n steps or reductions. For the kth step, the elements in the kth row, for the next augmented matrix, are calculated from the equation

$$a'_{kj} = a_{kj}/a_{kk} \qquad (4\text{-}55)$$

and the other elements for the next augmented matrix are calculated from the equation

$$a'_{ij} = a_{ij} - a_{ik}a'_{kj} \qquad (4\text{-}56)$$

where a_{ij}, a_{kj}, a_{ik}, and a_{kk} are elements of the previous matrix and where a'_{ij} and a'_{kj} are computed elements for the next augmented matrix. As can be verified from Ill. Ex. 4.24, when a matrix of size 3 is inverted by the Gauss-Jordan method, the first step obtains an augmented matrix of the following form, when Eqs. (4-55) and (4-56) are applied

$$\begin{bmatrix} 1 & b_{12} & b_{13} & b_{14} & 0 & 0 \\ 0 & b_{22} & b_{23} & b_{24} & 1 & 0 \\ 0 & b_{32} & b_{33} & b_{34} & 0 & 1 \end{bmatrix}$$

and the second step obtains an augmented matrix of the following form when these two equations are applied

$$\begin{bmatrix} 1 & 0 & d_{13} & d_{14} & d_{15} & 0 \\ 0 & 1 & d_{23} & d_{24} & d_{25} & 0 \\ 0 & 0 & d_{33} & d_{34} & d_{35} & 1 \end{bmatrix}$$

The inverse matrix is obtained in the third step by these two equations, as is shown in Ill. Ex. 4.24. The numerous arithmetic operations that are required when a large matrix is inverted by a direct method can cause significant roundoff errors in the results. These errors can be corrected by following a direct-method solution with an iterative type of solution. Thus, the better matrix inverse SUBROUTINE subprograms combine a direct solution method with an iterative method. One iterative method applies the following equation to successively compute a new inverse $[A^{-1}]_{i+1}$ from a previously computed inverse $[A^{-1}]_i$, until these two matrices are equal and where $[I]$ is a unit matrix.

$$[A^{-1}]_{i+1} = [A^{-1}]_i[2[I] - [A][A^{-1}]_i] \qquad (4\text{-}57)$$

Illustrative Example 4.18. Solve the following three algebraic equations for x_1, x_2, and x_3 using the Gaussian elimination method.

$$x_1 + 0.20x_2 + 0.50x_3 = 2.00$$
$$0.20x_1 + \quad x_2 + 0.30x_3 = 1.00$$
$$0.50x_1 + 0.30x_2 + \quad x_3 = 3.00$$

Solution.   The initial augmented matrix for this problem is as follows

$$\begin{bmatrix} 1.00 & 0.20 & 0.50 & 2.00 \\ 0.20 & 1.00 & 0.30 & 1.00 \\ 0.50 & 0.30 & 1.00 & 3.00 \end{bmatrix}$$

Using Eqs. (4-53) and (4-54), we obtain

$$a'_{21} = 0.20 - (0.20/1.00)(1.00) = 0$$
$$a'_{22} = 1.00 - (0.20/1.00)(0.20) = 0.96$$
$$a'_{23} = 0.30 - (0.20/1.00)(0.50) = 0.20$$
$$d'_2 = 1.00 - (0.20/1.00)(2.00) = 0.60$$
$$a'_{31} = 0.50 - (0.50/1.00)(1.00) = 0$$
$$a'_{32} = 0.30 - (0.50/1.00)(0.20) = 0.20$$
$$a'_{33} = 1.00 - (0.50/1.00)(0.50) = 0.75$$
$$d'_3 = 3.00 - (0.50/1.00)(2.00) = 2.00$$

Thus, the second augmented matrix is

$$\begin{bmatrix} 1.00 & 0.20 & 0.50 & 2.00 \\ 0 & 0.96 & 0.20 & 0.60 \\ 0 & 0.20 & 0.75 & 2.00 \end{bmatrix}$$

Since calculation shows that $a''_{32} = 0$, $a''_{33} = 0.708$, and $d''_{33} = 1.875$, the third augmented matrix is

$$\begin{bmatrix} 1.000 & 0.200 & 0.500 & 2.000 \\ 0 & 0.960 & 0.200 & 0.600 \\ 0 & 0 & 0.708 & 1.875 \end{bmatrix}$$

Thus, $x_3 = 1.875/0.708 = 2.65$. The other two solutions are

$$x_2 = [0.600 - 0.200(2.65)]/0.960 = 0.0720$$
$$x_1 = [2.000 - 0.500(2.65) - 0.200(0.072)] = 0.661$$

Illustrative Example 4.19.   Solve the problem in Ill. Ex. 4.18 using the Gauss-Jordan elimination method.

Solution.   Since both procedures start out the same, the first two augmented matrices will be the same as that obtained by Gaussian elimination. In this method, we also divide the first row by a_{11} so that a'_{11} will always equal unity. To calculate the third augmented matrix, we use the following equations, where it should be noted that we first divided the second row by a'_{22} so that a''_{22} will equal unity. For convenience, we have now represented elements d_1, d_2, and d_3 by a_{14}, a_{24}, and a_{34}, respectively.

$$a''_{2j} = a'_{2j}/a'_{22}$$
$$a''_{1j} = a'_{1j} - a_{12}a''_{2j}$$
$$a''_{3j} = a'_{3j} - a_{32}a''_{2j}$$

Use of the previous equations gives us the following third augmented matrix.

$$\begin{bmatrix} 1.000 & 0 & 0.458 & 1.875 \\ 0 & 1.000 & 0.208 & 0.625 \\ 0 & 0 & 0.708 & 1.875 \end{bmatrix}$$

To calculate the fourth augmented matrix, we use the following equations, where it should be noted that we first divided the third row by a_{33}'' so that a_{33}''' will equal unity.

$$a_{3j}''' = a_{3j}''/a_{33}''$$
$$a_{1j}''' = a_{1j}'' - a_{13}'' a_{3j}'''$$
$$a_{2j}''' = a_{2j}'' - a_{23}'' a_{3j}'''$$

Use of the previous equations gives us the following fourth augmented matrix.

$$\begin{bmatrix} 1.000 & 0 & 0 & 0.666 \\ 0 & 1.000 & 0 & 0.073 \\ 0 & 0 & 1.000 & 2.648 \end{bmatrix}$$

Thus the solutions are $x_1 = 0.666$, $x_2 = 0.073$, and $x_3 = 2.648$. It would not be too difficult to program this procedure to solve n linear algebraic equations. From this example, it can be seen that the operations for calculating the $(k + 1)$th augmented matrix are to first divide the kth row by element a_{kk} so that the next value of a_{kk} will equal unity. That is, $a_{kj}' = a_{kj}/a_{kk}$. The other elements can then be calculated from the following equation, where a_{ij}' now denotes elements of the $(k + 1)$th matrix, and a_{ij} now denotes elements of the kth augmented matrix.

$$a_{ij}' = a_{ij} - a_{ik}a_{kj}' = a_{ij} - a_{ik}(a_{kj}/a_{kk})$$

Illustrative Example 4.20. Solve the problem in Ill. Ex. 4.18 using the Gauss iteration method.

Solution. If we solve the first algebraic equation for x_1, solve the second algebraic equation for x_2, and solve the third algebraic equation for x_3, we obtain

$$x_1 = 2.00 - 0.20x_2 - 0.50x_3$$
$$x_2 = 1.00 - 0.20x_1 - 0.30x_3$$
$$x_3 = 3.00 - 0.50x_1 - 0.30x_2$$

For a first approximation, let us assume that $x_1 = x_2 = x_3 = 1.00$. Substitution of these values in the previous three equations gives us the following second approximations:

$$x_1 = 2.00 - 0.20 - 0.50 = 1.30$$
$$x_2 = 1.00 - 0.20 - 0.30 = 0.50$$
$$x_3 = 3.00 - 0.50 - 0.30 = 2.20$$

Substitution of these second approximations in the three equations for x_1, x_2, and x_3 gives us the following third approximations:

$$x_1 = 2.00 - 0.20(0.50) - 0.50(2.20) = 0.80$$
$$x_2 = 1.00 - 0.20(1.30) - 0.30(2.20) = 0.08$$
$$x_3 = 3.00 - 0.50(1.30) - 0.30(0.50) = 2.20$$

The third iteration gives $x_1 = 0.88$, $x_2 = 0.18$, and $x_3 = 2.58$. The ninth iteration gives $x_1 = 0.67$, $x_2 = 0.08$, and $x_3 = 2.65$. Substitution of these results into the three equations for x_1, x_2, and x_3 gives us the following results for the tenth iteration:

$$x_1 = 2.00 - 0.20(0.08) - 0.50(2.65) = 0.66$$
$$x_2 = 1.00 - 0.20(0.67) - 0.30(2.65) = 0.07$$
$$x_3 = 3.00 - 0.50(0.67) - 0.30(0.08) = 2.65$$

Illustrative Example 4.21. Solve the problem in Ill. Ex. 4.18 using the Gauss-Seidel iteration method.

Solution. We shall first assume that $x_2 = x_3 = 1.00$ and solve for x_1 in the first algebraic equation to obtain

$$x_1 = 2.00 - 0.20x_2 - 0.50x_3 = 2.00 - 0.20(1) - 0.50(1) = 1.30$$

Next we use $x_1 = 1.30$ and $x_3 = 1.00$ and solve for x_2 in the second algebraic equation to obtain

$$x_2 = 1.00 - 0.20x_1 - 0.30x_3 = 1.00 - 0.20(1.3) - 0.30(1.0) = 0.44$$

Using $x_1 = 1.30$ and $x_2 = 0.44$ and solving for x_3 in the third algebraic equation, we obtain

$$x_3 = 3.00 - 0.50x_1 - 0.30x_2 = 3.00 - 0.50(1.30) - 0.30(0.44) = 2.22$$

The second iteration gives

$$x_1 = 2.00 - 0.20(0.44) - 0.50(2.22) = 0.80$$
$$x_2 = 1.00 - 0.20(0.80) - 0.30(2.22) = 0.17$$
$$x_3 = 3.00 - 0.50(0.80) - 0.30(0.17) = 2.55$$

The third iteration gives $x_1 = 0.69$, $x_2 = 0.10$, and $x_3 = 2.62$; and the fourth iteration gives $x_1 = 0.69$, $x_2 = 0.076$, and $x_3 = 2.63$. Since the fifth iteration gives $x_1 = 0.67$, $x_2 = 0.077$, and $x_3 = 2.64$, we have the following results for the sixth iteration:

$$x_1 = 2.00 - 0.20(0.077) - 0.50(2.64) = 0.67$$
$$x_2 = 1.00 - 0.20(0.67) - 0.30(2.64) = 0.074$$
$$x_3 = 3.00 - 0.50(0.67) - 0.30(0.074) = 2.64$$

Illustrative Example 4.22. Solve the problem in Ill. Ex. 4.18 using the conjugate-gradient method.

Solution. This method can be applied by iteratively performing the following matrix calculations, where subscript n denotes the result of the nth iteration and where (p_n, Ap_n) denotes the multiplication of row matrix $\lfloor p_n \rfloor$ by column matrix $\{Ap_n\}$.

$$\{Ap_n\} = [A]\{p_n\} \tag{4-58}$$

$$g_{n+1} = \frac{(r_n, r_n)}{(p_n, Ap_n)} \tag{4-59}$$

$$\{x^{n+1}\} = \{x^n\} + g_{n+1}\{p_n\} \tag{4-60}$$

$$\{r^{n+1}\} = \{r_n\} - g_{n+1}\{Ap_n\} \tag{4-61}$$

$$b_{n+1} = \frac{(r_{n+1}, r_{n+1})}{(r_n, r_n)} \tag{4-62}$$

$$\{p_{n+1}\} = \{r_{n+1}\} + b_{n+1}\{p_n\} \tag{4-63}$$

To start this method, we have to assume values for x_1, x_2, and x_3, and we shall represent these assumed values by the matrix $\{x_0\}$. The initial p_i and r_i values are calculated from the equation

$$\{p_0\} = \{r_0\} = \{d\} - [A]\{x_0\}$$

where the A_{ij} elements are the coefficients of x_i in the given algebraic equations and the d_i elements are the constant terms in these same equations. Thus, the assumption that $x_1 = x_2 = x_3 = 1.00$ gives

$$\{p_0\} = \{r_0\} = \begin{Bmatrix} 2 \\ 1 \\ 3 \end{Bmatrix} - \begin{bmatrix} 1.0 & 0.2 & 0.5 \\ 0.2 & 1.0 & 0.3 \\ 0.5 & 0.3 & 1.0 \end{bmatrix} \begin{Bmatrix} 1 \\ 1 \\ 1 \end{Bmatrix} = \begin{Bmatrix} 0.3 \\ -0.5 \\ 1.2 \end{Bmatrix}$$

Application of the previous iteration formulae gives the following results.

$$\{Ap_0\} = [A]\{p_0\} = \begin{bmatrix} 1.0 & 0.2 & 0.5 \\ 0.2 & 1.0 & 0.3 \\ 0.5 & 0.3 & 1.0 \end{bmatrix} \begin{Bmatrix} 0.3 \\ -0.5 \\ 1.2 \end{Bmatrix} = \begin{Bmatrix} 0.80 \\ -0.08 \\ 1.20 \end{Bmatrix}$$

$$g_1 = \frac{(0.3)^2 + (-0.5)^2 + (1.2)^2}{(0.3)(0.8) + (-0.5)(-0.08) + (1.2)(1.2)} = 1.035$$

$$\{x_1\} = \begin{Bmatrix} 1 \\ 1 \\ 1 \end{Bmatrix} + 1.035 \begin{Bmatrix} 0.30 \\ -0.50 \\ 1.20 \end{Bmatrix} = \begin{Bmatrix} 1.3105 \\ 0.4825 \\ 2.2420 \end{Bmatrix}$$

$$\{r_1\} = \begin{Bmatrix} 0.3 \\ -0.5 \\ 1.2 \end{Bmatrix} - 1.035 \begin{Bmatrix} 0.80 \\ -0.08 \\ 1.20 \end{Bmatrix} = \begin{Bmatrix} -0.528 \\ -0.417 \\ -0.042 \end{Bmatrix}$$

$$b_1 = \frac{(-0.528)^2 + (-0.417)^2 + (-0.042)^2}{(0.3)^2 + (-0.5)^2 + (1.2)^2} = 0.2553$$

$$\{p_1\} = \begin{Bmatrix} -0.528 \\ -0.417 \\ -0.042 \end{Bmatrix} + 0.2553 \begin{Bmatrix} 0.30 \\ -0.50 \\ 1.20 \end{Bmatrix} = \begin{Bmatrix} -0.451 \\ -0.545 \\ 0.264 \end{Bmatrix}$$

For the second iteration, we calculate g_2 to equal 0.982, so that

$$\{x_2\} = \begin{Bmatrix} 1.3105 \\ 0.4825 \\ 2.240 \end{Bmatrix} + 0.982 \begin{Bmatrix} -0.451 \\ -0.545 \\ 0.264 \end{Bmatrix} = \begin{Bmatrix} 0.8681 \\ -0.0531 \\ 2.5010 \end{Bmatrix}$$

The elements of $\{r_2\}$ are -0.108, 0.129, and 0.081, and b_2 is calculated as 0.0762, so that

$$\{p_2\} = \begin{Bmatrix} -0.108 \\ 0.129 \\ 0.081 \end{Bmatrix} + 0.0762 \begin{Bmatrix} -0.451 \\ -0.545 \\ 0.264 \end{Bmatrix} = \begin{Bmatrix} -0.143 \\ 0.088 \\ 0.101 \end{Bmatrix}$$

For the third iteration, we calculate g_3 to equal 1.455, so that

$$\{x_3\} = \left\{\begin{array}{r} 0.8681 \\ -0.0531 \\ 2.5010 \end{array}\right\} + 1.455 \left\{\begin{array}{r} -0.143 \\ 0.088 \\ 0.101 \end{array}\right\} = \left\{\begin{array}{r} 0.660 \\ 0.075 \\ 2.648 \end{array}\right\}$$

The elements of $\{r_3\}$ and of $\{p_3\}$ all equal zero. Thus, the iteration converges in three cycles as predicted, since

$$\{x_4\} = \{x_3\} + a_3\{p_3\} = \{x_3\}$$

Thus, our solutions are $x_1 = 0.660$, $x_2 = 0.075$, and $x_3 = 2.648$.

Illustrative Example 4.23. Solve the problem in Ill. Ex. 4.18 using Hotelling's method.

Solution. The formula for Hotelling's method is given by the following matrix equation, where subscript n denotes the result of the nth iteration, where the A_{ij} elements are the coefficients of x_i in the given algebraic equations, and where the d_i elements are the constant terms in these same equations. The value of the scalar h must be assumed.

$$\{x_{n+1}\} = h\{d\} + [I - hA]\{x_n\} \tag{4-64}$$

Use of $h = 1$ gives the following results.

$$h\{d\} = \{d\} = \left\{\begin{array}{c} 2 \\ 1 \\ 3 \end{array}\right\}$$

$$[I - hA] = [I] - h[A] = [I] - [A]$$

$$= \begin{bmatrix} 1 & 0 & 0 \\ 0 & 1 & 0 \\ 0 & 0 & 1 \end{bmatrix} - \begin{bmatrix} 1.0 & 0.2 & 0.5 \\ 0.2 & 1.0 & 0.3 \\ 0.5 & 0.3 & 1.0 \end{bmatrix} = \begin{bmatrix} 0 & 0.2 & 0.5 \\ 0.2 & 0 & 0.3 \\ 0.5 & 0.3 & 0 \end{bmatrix}$$

where the choice of $h = 1$ caused the major diagonal elements of matrix $[I - hA]$ to equal zero for this problem. If we assume for a first guess that $x_1 = x_2 = x_3 = 1.00$, then the three elements of matrix $\{x_0\}$ all equal unity and the iterations are as follows:

$$\{x_1\} = \left\{\begin{array}{c} 2.00 \\ 1.00 \\ 3.00 \end{array}\right\} - [I - hA]\left\{\begin{array}{c} 1.00 \\ 1.00 \\ 1.00 \end{array}\right\} = \left\{\begin{array}{c} 1.30 \\ 0.50 \\ 2.20 \end{array}\right\}$$

$$\{x_2\} = \left\{\begin{array}{c} 2.00 \\ 1.00 \\ 3.00 \end{array}\right\} - [I - hA]\left\{\begin{array}{c} 1.30 \\ 0.50 \\ 2.20 \end{array}\right\} = \left\{\begin{array}{c} 0.80 \\ 0.08 \\ 2.20 \end{array}\right\}$$

$$\{x_3\} = \left\{\begin{array}{c} 2.00 \\ 1.00 \\ 3.00 \end{array}\right\} - [I - hA]\left\{\begin{array}{c} 0.80 \\ 0.08 \\ 2.20 \end{array}\right\} = \left\{\begin{array}{c} 0.88 \\ 0.18 \\ 2.58 \end{array}\right\}$$

$$\{x_4\} = \begin{Bmatrix} 2.00 \\ 1.00 \\ 3.00 \end{Bmatrix} - [I - hA]\begin{Bmatrix} 0.88 \\ 0.18 \\ 2.58 \end{Bmatrix} = \begin{Bmatrix} 0.67 \\ 0.05 \\ 2.51 \end{Bmatrix}$$

$$
\begin{array}{ccccc}
\cdot & \cdot & \cdot & \cdot & \cdot \\
\cdot & \cdot & \cdot & \cdot & \cdot \\
\cdot & \cdot & \cdot & \cdot & \cdot \\
\end{array}
$$

$$\{x_{10}\} = \begin{Bmatrix} 2.00 \\ 1.00 \\ 3.00 \end{Bmatrix} - [I - hA]\begin{Bmatrix} 0.67 \\ 0.08 \\ 2.65 \end{Bmatrix} = \begin{Bmatrix} 0.66 \\ 0.07 \\ 2.65 \end{Bmatrix}$$

Illustrative Example 4.24.   Invert the following matrix using the Gauss-Jordan method.

$$\begin{bmatrix} 4 & 1 & 2 \\ 6 & 8 & 7 \\ 2 & 5 & 3 \end{bmatrix}$$

Solution.   The initial augmented matrix is

$$\begin{bmatrix} 4.0 & 1.0 & 2.0 & 1.0 & 0 & 0 \\ 6.0 & 8.0 & 7.0 & 0 & 1.0 & 0 \\ 2.0 & 5.0 & 3.0 & 0 & 0 & 1.0 \end{bmatrix}$$

As stated previously, for the kth step (i.e., for the $(k + 1)$th augmented matrix), the elements of the kth row are calculated by the equation

$$a'_{kj} = a_{kj}/a_{kk}$$

and the other elements are calculated by the equation

$$a'_{ij} = a_{ij} - a_{ik}a'_{kj}$$

Thus, for the first step, the equations are $a'_{1j} = a_{1j}/a_{11}$ for the first row and $a'_{ij} = a_{ij} - a_{i1}a'_{1j}$ for the other rows. Since $a_{11} = 4$, we have $a'_{1j} = a_{1j}/4$. Applying these equations, the second augmented matrix is

$$\begin{bmatrix} 1.00 & 0.25 & 0.50 & 0.25 & 0 & 0 \\ 0 & 6.50 & 4.00 & -1.50 & 1.00 & 0 \\ 0 & 4.50 & 2.00 & -0.50 & 0 & 1.00 \end{bmatrix}$$

For the second step, the equations are $a'_{2j} = a_{2j}/a_{22}$ for the second row and $a'_{ij} = a_{ij} - a_{i2}a'_{2j}$ for the other two rows. Applying these equations, the third augmented matrix is

$$\begin{bmatrix} 1.000 & 0 & 0.346 & 0.306 & -0.038 & 0 \\ 0 & 1.000 & 0.615 & -0.231 & 0.154 & 0 \\ 0 & 0 & -0.770 & 0.540 & -0.692 & 1.000 \end{bmatrix}$$

For the third step, the equations are $a'_{3j} = a_{3j}/a_{33}$ for the third row and $a'_{ij} = a_{ij} - a_{i3}a'_{3j}$ for the other two rows. Applying these equations, the fourth augmented matrix is

$$\begin{bmatrix} 1.000 & 0 & 0 & 0.550 & -0.350 & 0.450 \\ 0 & 1.000 & 0 & 0.200 & -0.400 & 0.800 \\ 0 & 0 & 1.000 & -0.700 & 0.900 & -1.300 \end{bmatrix}$$

Thus, the inverse of the given matrix was found to be the following matrix.

$$\begin{bmatrix} 0.550 & -0.350 & 0.450 \\ 0.200 & -0.400 & 0.800 \\ -0.700 & 0.900 & -1.300 \end{bmatrix}$$

The previous matrix is the inverse of the given matrix because matrix multiplication shows that

$$\begin{bmatrix} 4.00 & 1.00 & 2.00 \\ 6.00 & 8.00 & 7.00 \\ 2.00 & 5.00 & 3.00 \end{bmatrix} \begin{bmatrix} 0.550 & -0.350 & 0.450 \\ 0.200 & -0.400 & 0.800 \\ -0.700 & 0.900 & -1.300 \end{bmatrix} = \begin{bmatrix} 1.000 & 0 & 0 \\ 0 & 1.000 & 0 \\ 0 & 0 & 1.000 \end{bmatrix}$$

4.9   Plotting Tabulated Data

Very often the printed results of a digital computer calculation for an engineering problem are plotted, so that the engineer can better visualize the trends of these results. The interpretation of the computed results is an important step in the solution of an engineering problem. This plotting of the computer results is often done manually. If this plotting is performed by a non-professional subordinate who is unfamiliar with the problem, then the computer program should be designed to print the results in as clear a manner as possible in order to minimize the plotting errors. For example, the use of an Fw.d format will result in a clearer output for plotting purposes than an Ew.d format. The spacing and the titling of the output also affects its clarity. Many large computers have provisions for plotting data points on a cathode-ray tube, just after they are computed. These large computer installations usually also have Fortran subroutines, which are available for engineering usage, that construct the axes of the graph and plot a set of chosen data. A photograph of the cathode-ray tube during the computer computation will furnish the engineer with a plot of the computed results.

Some of the Fortran systems (of a more advanced type than that covered in this text) have provisions to allow alphabetic and logical variables and logical Boolean-type statements. These features permit the efficient programming of a Fortran subprogram that plots tabulated data. Some of these subprograms are available at computer installations for use in other programs. Many of these Fortran subprograms can plot several variables on one graph. Let us now consider how tabulated data may be plotted using the Fortran II system for the IBM 1620 computer. We shall discuss two rather crude means for doing this. We wish to plot computed values of y versus time t. The y-axis will be directed horizontally across the page, while the t-axis will be directed vertically and downward on the page. Thus, the user will have to turn the output sheet 90° to interpret this plot. We shall assume that the t_t and y_t values are stored in arrays T and Y (i.e., the program sets $T(I) = t_t$ and $Y(I) = y_t$) just before they are printed in the main program. If adequate storage is a problem, we would not need the T array since the t_t values can be recalculated in the plotting subprogram. This is because the interval for the t_t values is constant and equals $(\Delta t)_{\text{print}}$. As an example, we can plot the values of current i_t versus time t_t for the nonlinear circuit problem of Sec. 2.6 by storing the values of CUR in array Y just before they are printed and by calling for the use of a plotting subprogram at the end of each case.

One of the problems involved in writing a plotting subprogram is the scaling of the plot. This is not a big problem for the vertical t-direction if one does not mind using a lot of output paper. Most printers can print up to six vertical characters per inch. Scaling is a problem in the horizontal y-direction, because we are limited to the width of the output paper and by the number of print bars. Most printers can print ten horizontal characters per inch. We shall simplify this scaling problem by normalizing the value of y to be between zero and unity. A plot of these normalized values will still allow us to see the trends of the output variation and to visually interpret the results. Thus, this plotting subprogram will first normalize the values of y. This can be done by using a DO loop to find the maximum and minimum values of y, which we shall call y_{max} and y_{min}, and then by using another DO loop to calculate the normalized values and store them in array R, by utilizing the following equation

$$R(I) = \frac{Y(I) - y_{\text{min}}}{y_{\text{max}} - y_{\text{min}}}$$

If all of the y values are positive, we could also let $R(I) = Y(I)/y_{\text{max}}$. The last part of this subprogram must plot these normalized values. We shall also print the NP values of T(I), Y(I), and R(I) on the same horizontal line that we plot the T(I), R(I) data-point. This is done so that the user can determine the actual magnitudes of this plotted data. This part of the subprogram can be done by using one DO loop containing many IF and FORMAT statements to print an asterisk whose location denotes the size of quantity R(I) (and hence Y(I)) as follows

```
        DO 55 I = 1, NP
        IF (R(I) − 0.95)42, 42, 41
   41   PRINT 111, T(I), Y(I), R(I)
  111   FORMAT (2F10.4, F10.6, 2X1H *)
        GO TO 55
```

42   IF (R(I) − 0.90)44, 44, 43
43   PRINT 112, T(I), Y(I), R(I)
112   FORMAT (2F10.4, F10.6, 4X1H ∗)
      GO TO 55
44   IF (R(I) − 0.85)46, 46, 45

.

.

.

55   CONTINUE

Note in the previous program portion how the data-point asterisk is printed in a horizontal location according to the size of quantity R(I). That is, each FORMAT statement has a different coefficient for symbol X. We can also use slash marks in the FORMAT statements to obtain a wider vertical spacing if desired. Thus, the first portion of this printed and plotted output could be as follows, where the symbol b denotes a blank space and $y_{max} = 100$. Note how the asterisk location varies with the size of R. That is, two blanks are printed after the value of R if $1.0 \leq R < 0.95$, four blanks are printed after the value of R if $0.95 \leq R < 0.90$, etc.

```
      T              Y              R
.1000bbb96.4100bbb.964100bb∗
.2000bbb93.2080bbb.932080bbbb∗
.3000bbb88.7300bbb.887300bbbbbb∗
.4000bbb84.0000bbb.840000bbbbbbbb∗
```

The following DO loop is a much shorter means for plotting the normalized values in array R. The plot that results will be of a cruder form since the plot symbol will be the digit 1 and since this plot symbol will be followed horizontally by zeroes all the way to the right side of the page. This plot symbol is plotted by printing the value of the calculated term P, whose size varies with the value of R(I). For example, if R(I) = 0.130, V = 5.20, NV = 5, and P = 10^5. Thus, statement 55 will print the value of P as 100000. If R(I) = 0.082, V = 3.28, NV = 3, and statement 55 will print the value of P as 1000. This example well illustrates the usefulness of the truncation feature in fixed-point arithmetic.

```
      DO 55 I = 1, NP
      V = 40.0 ∗ R(I)
      NV = V
      P = 10.0 ∗∗ NV
55    PRINT 111, T(I), Y(I), R(I), P
111   FORMAT (2F10.4, F9.6, F43.0)
```

4.10 A Parameter Design Study

In many situations, an engineering designer must determine the combination of values for the parameters of a system that will cause a desired output for the system. Often many combinations of these parameter values will do the desired job for this system. As an elementary example, several combinations of inductors, capacitors, and resistors can usually be used in a multi-loop electrical circuit if it is desired to keep the loop currents, during a specified range of time, above a specified minimum value i_{min} and below a specified maximum value i_{max}. For a large-scale example, consider the design of an airplane or a missile to perform a specific military mission. There are many combinations of wing and body shapes, fuel tank locations and sizes, wing and body dimensions, etc., that will enable the aircraft or missile to perform its desired mission. Often the designs of the competing aircraft manufacturers are quite different, and the preferable design is based on such factors as initial cost, ease of maintenance, etc.

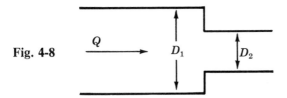

Fig. 4-8

Let us now consider the design of a rather elementary item in a fluid flow system. This rather simple example was chosen in order to minimize the complication of the resultant Fortran program. This fluid flow system could be a sub-system of a larger system. We wish to design a pipe contraction, which is illustrated in Fig. 4-8, that will cause a sudden drop in fluid pressure, and we wish this pressure drop to be within a specified range of values (i.e., above $(\Delta p)_{min}$ and below $(\Delta p)_{max}$). Pipe diameter D_1 is specified, but not the type of fluid, flow rate Q, or diameter D_2. From Sec. 2.12, we have the Bernoulli equation, which is

$$\frac{p_1}{\gamma} + \frac{V_1^2}{2g} + z_1 = \frac{p_2}{\gamma} + \frac{V_2^2}{2g} + z_2 + h_{L_{1-2}}$$

Since $z_1 = z_2$, we can solve this Bernoulli equation for pressure drop $\Delta p \equiv (p_1 - p_2)$ to obtain

$$\Delta p = \frac{\gamma}{2g}(V_2^2 - V_1^2) + \gamma h_{L_{1-2}}$$

where $h_{L_{1-2}}$ is the head loss across the contraction and equals $K_c V_2^2 / 2g$. From the continuity equation, which is also given in Sec. 2.12, we know that fluid velocities V_1 and V_2 equal Q/A_1 and Q/A_2 respectively. Thus, the pressure drop equation can be rewritten as follows:

$$\Delta p = \frac{\gamma Q^2}{2g} \left(\frac{K_c + 1}{A_2^2} - \frac{1}{A_1^2} \right)$$

The term K_c is called the *contraction loss coefficient*, and this term is often plotted, for a specific contraction shape, versus the diameter ratio D_2/D_1. As an example, for an abrupt contraction, which is the type illustrated in Fig. 4-8, $K_c = 0$ when D_2/D_1 equals unity, and K_c has a maximum value of 0.500 when D_2/D_1 approaches zero. The values of K_c, for specified values of D_2/D_1, decrease when a smoother type of contraction is used.

In this problem, we shall assume that we can use several types of fluids and several values for both pipe diameter D_2 and flow rate Q. Thus, we wish to find the combinations of values for D_2, Q, and specific gravity S that will cause a proper value of pressure drop Δp across this contraction. We could also have used differently shaped contraction devices in our design study if we wished to make this problem more general. We can obtain all combinations of the given D_2, Q, and S values by using three DO statements. A calculation sequence to do this is as follows:

1   Read and print the inputs: KODE, D_1, $(\Delta p)_{min}$, $(\Delta p)_{max}$, flow rate values
     $Q(1)$ to $Q(NQ)$, D_2 values $D(1)$ to $D(ND)$, specific gravity values
     $S(1)$ to $S(NS)$, and the $K_c = f(D_2/D_1)$ curve.
     $A_1 = \pi D_1^2 / 4$
     DO 8 K = 1, NS
     $\gamma = (62.4)S(K)$
     DO 8 J = 1, ND
     $A_2 = \pi D(J)^2 / 4$
     Use linear interpolation to find $K_c = f(D(J)/D_1)$.
     DO 8 I = 1, NQ

$$\Delta p = \frac{\gamma Q(I)^2}{2g} \left(\frac{K_c + 1}{A_2^2} - \frac{1}{A_1^2} \right)$$

     Test the KODE input: <0, print Δp, $Q(I)$, $D(J)$, and $S(K)$.
                          ≥ 0, print Δp, $Q(I)$, $D(J)$, and $S(K)$ only if
                          $(\Delta p)_{min} \leq \Delta p \leq (\Delta p)_{max}$.
8   CONTINUE
     Go to statement 1 for the next case.

The previous calculation sequence computes pressure drop Δp first for the combination $Q(1)$, $D(1)$, and $S(1)$; next for the combination $Q(2)$, $D(1)$, and $S(1)$; etc. If $NQ = 3$, $ND = 2$, and $NS > 1$, the three DO

statements would cause the order of the first eight parameter combinations
to be as follows

Q(1)	D(1)	S(1)
Q(2)	D(1)	S(1)
Q(3)	D(1)	S(1)
Q(1)	D(2)	S(1)
Q(2)	D(2)	S(1)
Q(3)	D(2)	S(1)
Q(1)	D(1)	S(2)
Q(2)	D(1)	S(2)

If the KODE input was positive or zero, the pressure drop Δp and the
values of the Q-D-S combination would be printed only if the value
of Δp was between the design values of $(\Delta p)_{min}$ and $(\Delta p)_{max}$. Thus, this
tells us the combination of parameters that will satisfy a specified design
criteria. If this KODE input is negative, for checkout purposes these four
terms are printed for all parameter-value combinations. The following
Fortran program was written from the previous calculation sequence, and
it utilizes both the curve-reading subprogram in Ill. Ex. 3.11 and the linear
interpolation subprogram in Sec. 4.2. Arrays CK and DRAT are used to
represent the $K_c = f(D_2/D_1)$ input curve. To summarize, this Fortran
program uses three DO loops to compute pressure drop Δp for every
possible combination of the Q(I), D(J), and S(K) inputs. If the KODE
term is not negative, the printout of this program tells us which of these
combinations result in a Δp value between $(\Delta p)_{min}$ and $(\Delta p)_{max}$ for the
designer's information. This program also prints the calculated terms
A_1, A_2, γ, and FAC for checkout purposes only. After the program is
checked out, the engineer might modify this program to not print these
four terms in order to have a neater printout. This program can also be
used to calculate Δp for contractions of different geometries by using a
different $K_c = f(D_2/D_1)$ curve for each successive case (i.e., set of inputs).

```
      DIMENSION CK(30), DRAT(30), D(20), Q(20), S(10)
    1 READ 11, KODE, D1, PMIN, PMAX
   11 FORMAT (I5, 3F8.3)
      PRINT 12, KODE, D1, PMIN, PMAX
   12 FORMAT (///6HINPUTS/I6, 3F11.3///16HPARAMETER
     X   VALUES)
      READ 13, NQ, (Q(I), I = 1, NQ)
      READ 13, ND, (D(J), J = 1, ND)
      READ 13, NS, (S(K), K = 1, NS)
   13 FORMAT (I5/(8F8.3))
      PRINT 14, NQ, (Q(I), I = 1, NQ)
```

```
        PRINT 14, ND, (D(J), J = 1, ND)
        PRINT 14, NS, (S(K), K = 1, NS)
14      FORMAT (//I5/(6F12.3))
        CALL CURVRD(DRAT, CK, NP)
        PRINT 15
15      FORMAT (///13HPRESSURE DROP)
        A1 = 0.7853982 * D1 ** 2
        DO 8 K = 1, NS
        GAM = 62.4 * S(K)
        DO 8 J = 1, ND
        A2 = 0.7853982 * D(J) ** 2
        RATIO = D(J)/D1
        CALL LINTRP(DRAT, CK, RATIO, NP, CKVAL)
        DO 8 I = 1, NQ
        FAC = (GAM * Q(I) ** 2)/64.4
        DP = FAC * ((CKVAL + 1.0)/A2 ** 2 - 1.0/A1 ** 2)
        IF (KODE)3, 4, 4
4       IF (DP - PMIN)8, 3, 5
5       IF (DP - PMAX)3, 3, 8
3       PRINT 16, DP, Q(I), D(J), S(K), GAM, FAC, A1, A2
16      FORMAT (F13.4, 5F11.3/F57.5, F14.5)
8       CONTINUE
        GO TO 1
        END
```

4.11   Curve-Fitting Tabulated Data

The reader has already learned, in a previous graphics or engineering orientation course, that the first step in determining an equation that fits tabulated data is to plot it, preferably on different types of graph paper. If the data plots as a straight line on regular rectangular graph paper, then the data fits an equation of the form $y = ax + b$. If the plotted data seems to be rather smooth and has no singular points or asymptotic regions, then the data might fit a higher degree polynomial. Methods for doing this shall be described later. If the plotted data is periodic, it should be fitted by the method of harmonic analysis, which shall be described later. If the tabulated data plots as a straight line on logarithmic graph paper, then this data fits an equation of the form $y = ax^b$. If the tabulated data plots as a straight line on semi-logarithmic graph paper, then the tabulated data fits an equation of the form $y = ar^x$. This data plotting may also achieve another purpose, because if this plotted data has a very irregular shape, we might check to see if some of these data points are bad or we might wish to smooth this data by using specific formulae for this purpose. As mentioned previously in Secs. 4.3 and 4.4, interpolated values and derivatives can be obtained from the equation that is used to approximate the fitted data.

The reader has already been shown how periodic functions and non-periodic functions over a finite interval may be represented by an infinite sum of sine and cosine terms, where this sum is called a *Fourier series*. In other words, this type of series will fit a periodic function $f(x)$, whose period is $2L$, by use of the following equation

$$f(x) = \frac{a_0}{2} + \sum_{n=1}^{\infty} \left(a_n \cos \frac{n\pi x}{L} + b_n \sin \frac{n\pi x}{L} \right) \tag{4-65}$$

where coefficients a_0, a_n, and b_n are given by

$$a_0 = \frac{1}{L} \int_{-L}^{L} f(x)\, dx$$

$$a_n = \frac{1}{L} \int_{-L}^{L} f(x) \cos \frac{n\pi x}{L}\, dx$$

$$b_n = \frac{1}{L} \int_{-L}^{L} f(x) \sin \frac{n\pi x}{L}\, dx$$

We can also use a finite Fourier series to represent tabulated or plotted data, and such a usage is called **harmonic analysis.** Suppose that the data is tabulated at N equally or unequally spaced points from $x = a$ to b, where this data represents one period if the data is periodic. Letting $2L = (b - a)$, the previous Fourier series equations become as follows

$$f(x) = \frac{a_0}{2} + \sum_{n=1}^{M} \left(a_n \cos \frac{2n\pi x}{b - a} + b_n \sin \frac{2n\pi x}{b - a} \right) \tag{4-66a}$$

$$a_0 = \frac{2}{b - a} \int_{a}^{b} f(x)\, dx \tag{4-66b}$$

$$a_n = \frac{2}{b - a} \int_{a}^{b} f(x) \cos \frac{2n\pi x}{b - a}\, dx \tag{4-66c}$$

$$b_n = \frac{2}{b - a} \int_{a}^{b} f(x) \sin \frac{2n\pi x}{b - a}\, dx \tag{4-66d}$$

where a finite number M (instead of an infinite number) of terms is now used to approximate $f(x)$. The integrals in the equations for a_0, a_n, and b_n must be approximated by numerical methods. Such methods are discussed in Sec. 4.5. Illustrative Example 4.25 furnishes the equations that approximate a_0, a_n, and b_n by use of the trapezoidal method. If $f(x)$ is an even function, we know that $b_n = 0$. If $f(x)$ is an odd function, we know that $a_n = 0$. There are Fortran SUBROUTINE subprograms available that will fit tabulated data by a finite Fourier series.

Now we shall discuss the fitting of tabulated data by polynomial equations. Like most of our discussions on previous numerical techniques, space does not permit us to go into much detail because this is quite an extensive subject. The polynomial interpolation equations furnished in Sec. 4.3 will fit a polynomial of degree n exactly through $(n + 1)$ successive points. As shown in Figs. 4-3 and 4-9, this polynomial fits the data but it may not fit the function that it represents. In Fig. 4-9, note that the dashed line, which represents the function $f(x)$ for the tabulated data, could be better approximated by a lower degree polynomial. A high degree polynomial can oscillate between the fitted points, since high degree polynomials have several maxima and minima along its range. Also, experimental data will often have some observational errors. Hence, such data can be smoothed and its general nature shown by using a polynomial of lower degree to fit its values. That is, we can use a polynomial of lower degree, which contains too few coefficients to allow it to pass through all of the points, but we can make it come as close as possible to these points by using the method of *least squares*.

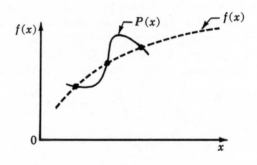

Fig. 4-9

Suppose we desired to fit m points (x_1, y_1) to (x_m, y_m) by a polynomial of degree n, where $n < (m - 1)$ and where the points may not be equally spaced. Since substitution of the values for these m points in this polynomial equation will give us m equations and $(n + 1)$ unknowns, we cannot get a solution and, hence, fit these points exactly, because there are more equations than unknowns. When the ith point (x_i, y_i) is substituted in this nth degree polynomial, the error E_i for this approximation will be

$$E_i = (a_0 x_i^n + a_1 x_i^{n-1} + \ldots + a_n - y_i)$$

Since this E_i error term can be positive or negative and since E_i^2 is always positive, the **least squares method** fits a polynomial so that the sum of the squares of these E_i error terms will be a minimum. That is, if we had used $\sum_{i=1}^{m} E_i$ for an error criterion, there would be a cancellation effect when some E_i error terms are positive and other E_i terms are negative. Let the term S equal $\sum_{i=1}^{m} E_i^2$ and, to simplify this discussion, let us consider the fitting of a polynomial of degree 2 through this tabulated data. Thus,

$$S = \sum_{i=1}^{m} E_i^2 = \sum_{i=1}^{m} (a_0 x_i^2 + a_1 x_i + a_2 - y_i)^2 \qquad \textbf{(4-67)}$$

and to obtain a minimum value for our error criterion term S, we want to determine the values of a_0, a_1, and a_2 such that $\partial S/\partial a_0 = 0$, $\partial S/\partial a_1 = 0$, and $\partial S/\partial a_2 = 0$. Since

$$\frac{\partial S}{\partial a_2} = (2) \sum_{i=1}^{m} (a_0 x_i^2 + a_1 x_i + a_2 - y_i)$$

$$\frac{\partial S}{\partial a_1} = (2) \sum_{i=1}^{m} x_i(a_0 x_i^2 + a_1 x_i + a_2 - y_i)$$

$$\frac{\partial S}{\partial a_0} = (2) \sum_{i=1}^{m} x_i^2(a_0 x_i^2 + a_1 x_i + a_2 - y_i)$$

setting the first of the previous three equations equal to zero and rearranging the summations, we obtain the following equation, where the indices for the summation signs were left off for convenience.

$$a_0(\sum x_i^2) + a_1(\sum x_i) + a_2(m) = \sum y_i \qquad \textbf{(4-68a)}$$

Upon setting the equations for $\partial S/\partial a_1$ and $\partial S/\partial a_0$ to both equal zero and rearranging the results, we obtain the following two equations in addition.

$$a_0(\sum x_i^3) + a_1(\sum x_i^2) + a_2(\sum x_i) = \sum (x_i y_i) \qquad \textbf{(4-68b)}$$

$$a_0(\sum x_i^4) + a_1(\sum x_i^3) + a_2(\sum x_i^2) = \sum (x_i^2 y_i) \qquad \textbf{(4-68c)}$$

Thus, we now have three linear algebraic equations from which we can solve for the three unknowns a_0, a_1, and a_2. The equation for the fitted, quadratic polynomial is now determined. If a polynomial of degree n is fitted through these m points by the method of least squares, then we would end up with $(n + 1)$ linear algebraic equations from which we can solve for the $(n + 1)$ coefficients a_0 to a_n. From the form of Eqs. (4-68a, b, c), the reader can determine the forms of these $(n + 1)$ equations. For example, the $(n + 1)$th and last equation is

$$a_0 \sum_{i=1}^{m} x_i^{2n} + a_1 \sum_{i=1}^{m} x_i^{2n-1} + \ldots + a_n \sum_{i=1}^{m} x_i^{n} = \sum_{i=1}^{m} (x_i^n y_i) \quad \textbf{(4-69)}$$

The application of the least squares method is exemplified in Ill. Ex. 4.26. It may be mentioned that the least squares method tries to approximate a function or data in a relatively uniform manner within an interval. A finite Taylor series, on the other hand, approximates a function $f(x)$ about a point, and the error of its approximation increases as x moves away from this point. It may be mentioned that the method of least squares is not limited to polynomial approximations. For example, it can be used to fit tabulated data by equations of the type $y = ae^{bx}$, because taking the natural logarithm of both sides of this equation gives $\log_e y = \log_e a + bx$. If we let $Y = \log_e y$ and $A = \log_e a$, then we can fit the data to the linear equation $Y = A + bx$, using the least-squares method. We can also fit tabulated data by equations of the type $y = kx^n$ because use of logarithms gives $\log y = n \log x + \log k$. If we let $Y = \log y$, $X = \log x$, and $K = \log k$, we can least squares fit the data by the linear form $Y = nX + K$. This least squares fit is applied to the logarithms of the tabulated data values. That is, the method minimizes the error criterion S, where $S = \sum (n \log x_i + \log k - \log y_i)^2$. Least-squares Fortran subprograms for data fitting are available to engineers who may wish to incorporate them in their computer programs. Since the solution of a set of linear algebraic equations is involved, many of these SUBROUTINE subprograms incorporate matrix arithmetic in their procedure. The linear algebraic equations can be solved by matrix inversion, after the elements of the matrices are computed.

When we wish to obtain a least-squares fit of a set of *equally spaced*, tabulated data by hand calculation, it may be desirable to approximate or fit this data by a linear combination of orthogonal polynomials. That is, we shall approximate $f(x)$ by $a_0 P_0(x) + a_1 P_1(x) + \ldots + a_n P_n(x)$, where $P_i(x)$ is a polynomial of degree i in x that possesses the orthogonality property $\sum_{r=0}^{n} P_i(x_r) P_j(x_r) = 0$ if $i \neq j$. This can be advantageous for hand calculation because the orthogonal properties of these polynomials allow the coefficients in the polynomial approximation to be fairly easily obtained by plugging in a formula. Thus, the solution of a set of linear algebraic equations is not required. That is, if the points are equally spaced, a least-squares application shows that the coefficients for an orthogonal polynomial approximation can be calculated from the equation $a_i = \sum_{r=0}^{n} P_i(x_r) f(x_r) / \sum_{r=0}^{n} P_i^2(x_r)$. For a least-squares fit of a set of $z = f(x, y)$ data, the coefficients of the orthogonal polynomials can be computed from the equation $a_{ij} = \sum P_i(x)f(x, y)P_j(y)/[\sum P_i^2(x) \sum P_j^2(y)]$. The forms of higher-degree orthogonal polynomials can be complex, but their values are tabulated in mathematics tables. Some examples of orthogonal polynomials are the Hermite, Legendre, Gram, and Laguerre polynomials. Another variation of the least squares method is to let $S = \sum w_i E_i^2$ (instead of $S = \sum E_i^2$) be the error criterion which is to be minimized. The w_i terms are positive weighting factor terms. A large value of w_i means that we want a good fit at that particular point, and a small value of w_i may be used to indicate a poor or questionable data point. This technique is sometimes called a *weighted least-squares method.*

Sometimes it is desired to fit a curve through exact, tabulated data which was obtained by calculation. Use of one high-degree polynomial to fit all of these points may not represent the overall function because of reasons mentioned previously. There are Fortran SUBROUTINE subprograms available that fit each set of three successive points by a quadratic polynomial, which has no oscillations as do high-degree polynomials. Thus, this type of subprogram fits the tabulated data by a set of connecting quadratic polynomials. The better subprograms also smooth the connections where two fitted quadratics intersect.

The *Chebyshev approximation method* rather accurately approximates functions that are represented by a set of tabulated data in the x-interval $(-1, 1)$ by a polynomial of degree n. This approximation is made in such a manner that the maximum value of the absolute deviation is a minimum, and it is given as a linear combination of Chebyshev polynomials of the form $b_0 C_0(x) + b_1 C_1(x) + \ldots + b_n C_n(x)$. The term $C_i(x)$ is a Chebyshev polynomial of degree i in x, and it is defined and discussed in more detail in Ill. Ex. 1.20. The $\sum_{i=0}^{n} b_i C_i(x)$ representation for $f(x)$ can be expressed in (i.e., converted to) a $\sum_{i=0}^{n} a_i x^i$ form, after the b_i coefficients have been evaluated, by substituting the b_i and $C_i(x)$ values in each term. This method produces an exact fit at the $(n + 1)$ zeroes or roots of the Chebyshev polynomial $C_{n+1}(x)$, and these roots are located between $x = -1$ and $x = 1$. Because this method fits a curve at specified values of x, the Chebyshev approximation method is usually applied to calculated, rather than experimental, data. As inferred previously, the Chebyshev type of polynomial approximation, for a smooth function within a specified interval, is the one for which the largest absolute value of the errors is a minimum. The Chebyshev approximation provides a uniform approximation to a smooth, continuous function (i.e., the deviations are relatively uniform and the maximum error is small); whereas the least-squares approximation, which minimizes the average of the squared errors, can have isolated points or regions where the approximation errors are relatively large. There are Fortran subprograms available that can calculate the Chebyshev polynomial approximations for tabulated data. This is not an easy calculation when applied to a set of arbitrarily spaced data, and a rather complex iterative procedure can be involved in such subprograms. As a very brief and incomplete summary, it may be stated that $b_0 = \sum_{r=0}^{n} f(x_r)/(n + 1)$ and that coefficients b_1 to b_n can be calculated from the equation $b_i = 2 \sum_{r=0}^{n} f(x_r)C_i(x_r)/(n + 1)$, where root $x_r = \cos [(2r + 1)\pi/(2r + 2)]$ (i.e., x_r is a root of $C_{m+1}(x)$). The reader is referred to numerical analysis references for more complete details on the theory and application of the Chebyshev approximation method.

Illustrative Example 4.25. Approximate the harmonic analysis integrals given by Eqs. (4-66b, c, d) using the trapezoidal method.

Solution. For a set of tabulated $g(x)$ data consisting of N equally spaced points from a to b, use of Eq. (4-34), which is the trapezoidal method, gives the approximation

$$\int_a^b g(x)\, dx = \left(\frac{b - a}{N - 1}\right)\left[\tfrac{1}{2}(g_1 + g_N) + \sum_{i=2}^{N-1} g_i\right]$$

where $g_i \equiv g(x_i)$. If the $g(x)$ data is periodic and if its period equals $(b - a)$, then $g_N = g_1$ and the previous approximation simplifies to

$$\int_a^b g(x)\, dx = \left(\frac{b - a}{N - 1}\right)\sum_{i=1}^{N-1} g(x_i)$$

Since $g(x) = f(x)$ in Eq. (4-66b), since $g(x) = f(x) \cos [2n\pi x/(b - a)]$ in Eq. (4-66c), and since $g(x) = f(x) \sin [2n\pi x/(b - a)]$ in Eq. (4-66d); these three approximations are

$$a_0 = \left(\frac{2}{N - 1}\right)\sum_{i=1}^{N-1} f(x_i)$$

$$a_n = \left(\frac{2}{N - 1}\right)\sum_{i=1}^{N-1} f(x_i) \cos \frac{2n\pi x_i}{b - a}$$

$$b_n = \left(\frac{2}{N - 1}\right)\sum_{i=1}^{N-1} f(x_i) \sin \frac{2n\pi x_i}{b - a}$$

If the tabulated data is not equally spaced, then we must apply Eq. (4-35) which states that

$$\int_a^b g(x)\, dx = \tfrac{1}{2} \sum_{i=1}^{N-1} [g(x_i) + g(x_{i+1})](x_{i+1} - x_i)$$

We apply the previous equation in the same manner as we did for equally spaced points, since the definitions for $g(x)$ are unchanged.

Illustrative Example 4.26. Suppose that we have a set of five tabulated (x, y) points, which are $(0, 0)$, $(1, 1)$, $(2, 1)$, $(3, -1)$, and $(4, -2)$. Approximate the function that is represented by these five points by a quadratic polynomial using the least-squares method.

Solution. Since we are fitting this tabulated data by a polynomial of degree 2, we wish to utilize Eqs. (4-68a, b, c). Since we have five points, $m = 5$, and since

$$\sum x_i = 0 + 1 + 2 + 3 + 4 = 10$$
$$\sum x_i^2 = 0^2 + 1^2 + 2^2 + 3^2 + 4^2 = 30$$
$$\sum x_i^3 = 0^3 + 1^3 + 2^3 + 3^3 + 4^3 = 100$$
$$\sum x_i^4 = 0^4 + 1^4 + 2^4 + 3^4 + 4^4 = 354$$
$$\sum y_i = 0 + 1 + 1 - 1 - 2 = -1$$
$$\sum x_i y_i = (0)(0) + (1)(1) + (2)(1) + (3)(-1) + (4)(-2) = -8$$
$$\sum x_i^2 y_i = (0)^2(0) + (1)^2(1) + (2)^2(1) + (3)^2(-1) + (4)^2(-2) = -36$$

Substitution of the previous results in Eqs. (4-68a, b, c) gives the following three linear algebraic equations in a_0, a_1, and a_2

$$30a_0 + 10a_1 + 5a_2 = -1$$
$$100a_0 + 30a_1 + 10a_2 = -8$$
$$354a_0 + 100a_1 + 30a_2 = -36$$

Solution of these previous three equations gives $a_0 = -0.429$, $a_1 = 1.11$, and $a_2 = 0.160$. Substitution of these values in the quadratic equation $f(x) = a_0x^2 + a_1x + a_2$ gives the least-squares approximation

$$f(x) = -0.429x^2 + 1.11x + 0.160$$

The error of this approximation at point (x_i, y_i) equals $y_i - f(x_i)$. Calculation shows that the errors are -0.16, 0.15, 0.34, -0.63, and 0.26, respectively, at $x = 0, 1, 2, 3$, and 4. It may be noted that the values of a_0, a_1, and a_2 can be calculated by algebra or by the following matrix calculations:

$$[D] = \begin{bmatrix} \sum x_i^2 & \sum x_i & m \\ \sum x_i^3 & \sum x_i^2 & \sum x_i \\ \sum x_i^4 & \sum x_i^3 & \sum x_i^2 \end{bmatrix} = \begin{bmatrix} 30 & 10 & 5 \\ 100 & 30 & 10 \\ 354 & 100 & 30 \end{bmatrix}$$

$$\begin{Bmatrix} a_0 \\ a_1 \\ a_2 \end{Bmatrix} = [D]^{-1} \begin{Bmatrix} \sum y_i \\ \sum x_i y_i \\ \sum x_i^2 y_i \end{Bmatrix} = [D]^{-1} \begin{Bmatrix} -1 \\ -8 \\ -36 \end{Bmatrix}$$

If we wanted to least-squares fit this data by the cubic polynomial, $a_0x^3 + a_1x^2 + a_2x + a_3$, then the four coefficients can be calculated from the following matrix equation. From this example, the reader can determine the matrix equation when a least-squares fit of tabulated data by a higher-degree polynomial is desired.

$$\begin{Bmatrix} a_0 \\ a_1 \\ a_2 \\ a_3 \end{Bmatrix} = \begin{bmatrix} \sum x_i^3 & \sum x_i^2 & \sum x_i & m \\ \sum x_i^4 & \sum x_i^3 & \sum x_i^2 & \sum x_i \\ \sum x_i^5 & \sum x_i^4 & \sum x_i^3 & \sum x_i^2 \\ \sum x_i^6 & \sum x_i^5 & \sum x_i^4 & \sum x_i^3 \end{bmatrix}^{-1} \begin{Bmatrix} \sum y_i \\ \sum x_i y_i \\ \sum x_i^2 y_i \\ \sum x_i^3 y_i \end{Bmatrix}$$

4.12 Introduction to Linear Programming

For some specific problems in industrial engineering, business management, and systems engineering, the technique of *linear programming* may be very usefully applied for their solution. One requirement for the problem is that the specified function and its constraints must be linearly related to its variables. Thus, any linearizing assumptions for such a problem must be physically valid. Linear programming is used to solve types of problems that require the determination of values that will make a specified function a maximum or a minimum, under a given set of constraints or conditions. For example, in industrial management it is desirable to maximize such items as profit, quantity, and quality and to minimize such items as cost and production time. Optimum production scheduling and optimum personnel assignment are two specific problem areas where linear programming might be applied. A brief production example is given in Ill. Ex. 4.27. We shall just introduce the reader to the general problem and to some of the mathematical concepts involved, since we shall not take the space to go into the details of any specific problem except for the briefly described one of Ill. Ex. 4.27.

To apply the technique of linear programming, the problem must be capable of being defined by a specific function f of the following *linear* form

$$f = b_1 x_1 + b_2 x_2 + \ldots + b_n x_n = \sum_{j=1}^{n} b_j x_j \qquad (4\text{-}70)$$

where the b_j constants are given and the x_j terms are variables whose values are to be determined in order to obtain an optimum value (either a maximum or a minimum) for function f. Further, these x_j variables are constrained by a set of m equations (i.e., $i = 1$ to m) which have one of the following *linear* forms:

$$\sum_{j=1}^{n} a_{ij} x_j \leq c_i \quad \text{or} \quad \sum_{j=1}^{n} a_{ij} x_j \geq c_i \quad \text{or} \quad \sum_{j=1}^{n} a_{ij} x_j = c_i \qquad (4\text{-}71)$$

For example, if we have a simple system consisting of only two variables, x_1 and x_2, the given problem may be mathematically expressible in the following linear form, where we wish to find the values of x_1 and x_2 that make function f a maximum (or minimum)

$$f = b_1 x_1 + b_2 x_2 \qquad (4\text{-}72)$$

and where the variables x_1 and x_2 can be constrained mathematically as follows

$$a_{11}x_1 + a_{12}x_2 \le c_1 \qquad \text{(4-73a)}$$

$$a_{21}x_1 + a_{22}x_2 \ge c_2 \qquad \text{(4-73b)}$$

$$a_{31}x_1 + a_{32}x_2 \ge c_3 \qquad \text{(4-73c)}$$

Note that the previous constraint equations are inequalities. Geometrically speaking, each of these inequalities defines a straight line that divides the x_1-x_2 plane into two portions, and the (x_1, x_2) points in one of these two portions are the points that satisfy the particular constraint equation. The equality part of each inequality defines the equation of the straight line. For example, the equation of the first straight line is $a_{11}x_1 + a_{12}x_2 = c_1$. Thus, the set of (x_1, x_2) points that satisfy all three inequalities can be determined from the intersections of these three lines. The intersection point for any pair of straight lines can be determined by solving the pair of straight-line equations algebraically for coordinates x_1 and x_2. If these three lines intersect at three different finite points to form a triangle, then the set of (x_1, x_2) points that satisfy the three inequalities may lie within and on the boundaries of this finite triangle. The vertices of this triangle are the three intersection points A, B, and C, as shown in Fig. 4-10. It can be derived mathematically that the maximum and minimum values for the two-variable function f, as defined by Eqs. (4-72) and (4-73a, b, c), will lie on the vertices of this finite-size triangle. Thus, once we have determined the values of x_1 and x_2 at the three intersection points, we only have to substitute these values into Eq. (4-72) to find the maximum (or minimum) value of f. That is, the largest of the three values is the maximum value of function f, and the smallest is the minimum value. It should be noted that the constraint equations do not always define a set of points which both satisfy the three inequalities and which lie within a finite area. For example, if a_{11} and a_{21} in the first two constraint equations were both equal to zero, we would have two parallel lines and only two intersection points A and B, as shown in Fig. 4-11. The equations for these two parallel lines are $x_2 = c_1/a_{12}$ and $x_2 = c_2/a_{22}$.

If we had only one linear constraint equation of the form $a_{11}x_1 + a_{12}x_2 \le c_1$, we would have another example of a set of points in an infinite area that satisfies the problem constraints. If the set of points that satisfies the system of linear constraint inequalities, for two variables, lies within a *finite* area, then this finite area is called a *convex polygon* (or a *convex polyhedron* if more than two variables are involved). If we have a linear programming problem with two variables and n linear constraint inequalities, we might obtain an n-sided convex polygon whose vertices are n different intersection points. That is, n linear constraints can form a

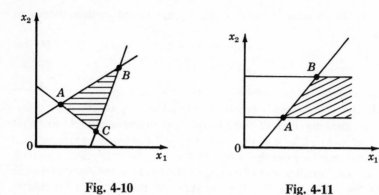

Fig. 4-10   Fig. 4-11

polygon with n sides. The maximum and minimum values for function f, where $f = b_1x_1 + b_2x_2$, will occur at two of the vertex points of this convex polygon. The x_1 and x_2 values at each of the n vertex points can be determined by algebra. Figure 4-12 illustrates a four-sided convex polygon for a linear programming problem consisting of two variables, x_1 and x_2, and four linear constraints.

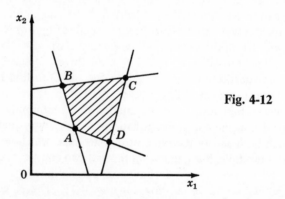

Fig. 4-12

This previous discussion of the two-variable problem was done to introduce the reader to the mathematical concepts of linear programming and to show the relative ease of its solution. Most situations, however, involve many variables, and the solution of such linear programming problems is quite a bit more involved. To standardize the mathematical form of the problem, it can be shown that Eqs. (4-70) and (4-71) may be transformed into the following form, where only equalities are now involved and where it is still desired to make function f a maximum or a minimum

$$f = \sum_{j=1}^{n+m} b_j x_j \tag{4-74}$$

$$\sum_{j=1}^{n} a_{ij} x_j \pm x_{n+i} = c_i \quad (i = 1, 2, \ldots, m) \tag{4-75}$$

The new variables x_{n+1} to x_{n+m} are not a part of the problem solution, and thus coefficients b_{j+1} to b_{j+m} must equal zero.

This many-variable linear programming problem may be solved by such techniques as the *distribution method, index method, ratio-analysis method, simplex method,* etc. The details and theory of these methods for solving this type of mathematical problem may be found in texts on linear programming. There are Fortran SUBROUTINE subprograms available that utilize these solution techniques. They will compute and furnish the optimum x_j values for a given set of input a_{ij}, b_j, and c_i values. Again it should be stated that the particular engineering or industrial management problem must first be expressed in the proper linear mathematical form before such a subprogram can be used to solve an optimization problem of this type. This may require detailed knowledge of the various facets of the problem in order to make the assumptions to do this.

Illustrative Example 4.27. Suppose that we wanted to determine the quantities to manufacture for products 1, 2, and 3 in order to maximize our profit. The profit on product 1 is 3 dollars, the profit on product 2 is 4 dollars, and the profit on product 3 is 8 dollars. Each product requires some or all of parts A, B, C, and D in its manufacture. Product 1 requires two B-parts and four C-parts in its manufacture, product 2 requires one of each part in its manufacture, and product 3 requires two of each part in its manufacture. As for supply, we have 120 A-parts, 250 B-parts, 500 C-parts, and 80 D-parts on hand. Express this production allocation problem as a linear programming problem to obtain the maximum profit.

Solution. Let x_1, x_2, and x_3 denote the number (i.e., the quantities) to manufacture for products 1, 2, and 3, respectively. Thus, our total profit may be defined by function f as follows

$$f = 3x_1 + 4x_2 + 8x_3$$

where the profit on product 1 is 3 dollars times x_1, the profit on product 2 is 4 dollars times x_2, and the profit on product 3 is 8 dollars times x_3. Thus, in this problem we wish to find the maximum value of function f that satisfies the problem constraints. Since the three quantities cannot be negative in value, one set of constraints is $x_1 \geq 0$, $x_2 \geq 0$, and $x_3 \geq 0$. The other set of constraints may be determined from our supply of parts. Since we have 120 A-parts and since we need one A-part for product 2 and two A-parts for product 3, one constraint inequality is

$$x_2 + 2x_3 \leq 120$$

From a similar reasoning, the other three constraint inequalities are

$$2x_1 + x_2 + 2x_3 \leq 250$$
$$4x_1 + x_2 + 2x_3 \leq 500$$
$$x_2 + 2x_3 \leq 80$$

Illustrative Example 4.28.   Write Eqs. (4-74) and (4-75) for the case where there are three variables and two constraints.

Solution.   Since $n = 3$ and $m = 2$, these equations are as follows, where $b_4 = b_5 = 0$ in the final solution

$$b_1x_1 + b_2x_2 + b_3x_3 + b_4x_4 + b_5x_5 = f$$
$$a_{11}x_1 + a_{12}x_2 + a_{13}x_3 \pm x_4 = c_1$$
$$a_{21}x_1 + a_{22}x_2 + a_{23}x_3 \pm x_5 = c_2$$

Illustrative Example 4.29.   Suppose that we wished to find the values of x_1, x_2, and x_3 that will give us the maximum value of function f, which is given by

$$f(x_i) = 5.61x_1 + 3.09x_2 + 4.74x_3$$

and which has the following two constraints:

$$5x_1 + 13x_2 + 9x_3 \leq 489$$
$$11x_1 + 8x_2 + 4x_3 \leq 604$$

Start the solution of this linear programming problem using the simplex method.

Solution.   The *simplex method* is an iterative technique that involves a matrix whose elements must be initially computed and continuously recomputed until a solution occurs. In theory, this method first computes a possible solution and then replaces this solution with a more optimum one, which for this problem is one that gives a higher value for function f. This process is repeated until the optimum solution (e.g., the one that gives the maximum value for function f) is obtained. The procedure is started by computing an initial matrix whose form is as follows for a problem involving three variables and two constraints.

$$
\begin{array}{ccccccc}
h_1 & d_1 & e_{11} & e_{12} & e_{13} & 1 & 0 \\
h_2 & d_2 & e_{21} & e_{22} & e_{23} & 0 & 1 \\
 & b_1 & b_2 & b_3 & b_4 & b_5 \\
g_0 & g_1 & g_2 & g_3 & g_4 & g_5
\end{array}
$$

As stated previously, $b_4 = b_5 = 0$. For the initial matrix, $h_1 = b_4$, $h_2 = b_5$, $d_i = c_i$, $e_{ij} = a_{ij}$, $g_0 = 0$, and $g_j = -b_j$. Thus, the initial values of these matrix elements can be obtained from the given equation for function f and its two constraint inequalities. Thus, for this problem, the initial matrix is as follows

0	489	5	13	9	1	0
0	604	11	8	4	0	1
		5.61	3.09	4.74	0	0
0	−5.61	−3.09	−4.74	0	0

The d_i and e_{ij} elements of this simplex matrix are recomputed by a set procedure whose details may be found in a linear programming text. It would take too much space to describe the details and theory of this procedure here. It involves the determination of a key row and a key column, where the key column is the column that contains the smallest (i.e., most negative) g_j value. The g_j elements are computed from the equation $g_j = \sum_{i=1}^{m} h_i e_{ij} - b_j$, where each h_i element equals one of the given b_j values. The matrix elements are recomputed during each iteration, and this iteration is continued until all values of g_j equal or exceed zero. The solutions for the x_j variables will appear in the d_i column (i.e., the column where the c_i values appeared in the initial simplex matrix). The maximum value of function f will appear where g_0 appeared in the initial matrix, and this result can be checked by substitution of x_1, x_2, and x_3 in the equation for function f.

In summary, this matrix iteration procedure is completed when all g_j values equal or exceed zero, the g_0 element at this time is the maximum value of function f, and the d_i elements at this time are the solutions for x_j. That is, since each h_i element equals one of the given b_j values, $h_i = b_j$ implies that $x_j = d_i$ in the final matrix. If a particular b_j value does not appear in the final h_i column, then that value of x_j is zero. Thus, a simplex method subprogram can be written without too much difficulty in Fortran, where the initial matrix is an input array, where the subprogram iteratively calculates the elements of new arrays until all g_j values equal or exceed zero, and where a printout of the final matrix will furnish the user with the desired x_j values along with the maximum value of function f.

PROBLEMS

4.1. Check out the Fortran program in Sec. 4.1 using the following inputs: $L = 15$ henries, $F = 20$, $a = 0$, $t_0 = 0$, $i_0 = 0$, and $t_{max} = 2.00$ sec. Let the output of the voltage source be given by the curve of Fig. 4-13, where E_t is the voltage output and t is the time in sec. Run this problem for $\Delta t = 0.050$ and 0.025 sec.

4.2. Check out the Fortran program in Sec. 4.2 using the following inputs: $t_0 = 0$, $i_0 = 0$, and $t_{max} = 2.00$ sec. Use the curve of Fig. 4-13 for the voltage source output, and let $R = 20$ ohms and $L = 15$ henries. Represent both the constant R and the constant L values by a curve, where each curve consists of two points. Run this problem, which is the same as that of Prob. 4.1, for $\Delta t = 0.050$ and 0.025 sec.

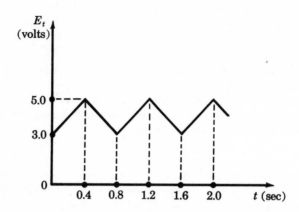

Fig. 4-13

4.3. Reprogram the heat transfer problem in Sec. 2.10 using $h = f(T_m)$ and $c = f(T_w)$ curves. Use curve-reading and linear-interpolation subprograms.

4.4. Reprogram the fluid flow problem in Sec. 2.12 using $Q = f(t)$, $p_1 = f(t)$, and $p_2 = f(t)$ curves. Use curve-reading and linear-interpolation subprograms.

4.5. Program the mechanical vibration problem of Sec. 2.9 using $c = f(\dot{x})$ and $k = f(x)$ curves. Use the curve-reading and Lagrange-interpolation subprograms.

4.6. Write a SUBROUTINE subprogram that will linearly interpolate a $z = f(x, y)$ curve by the method shown in Ill. Ex. 4.3.

4.7. Write a SUBROUTINE subprogram to perform a four-point Lagrange interpolation. For these four points, let there be two tabulated points about the interpolated point if $X(2) < XA < X(N - 1)$.

4.8. Write a SUBROUTINE subprogram that will quadratically interpolate a $z = f(x, y)$ curve. Use Lagrange's three-point formula for the four quadratic interpolations.

4.9. Write a Fortran program to numerically compute the derivative of $\sin x$ from 0 to π for 11 and 21 equally spaced points (i.e., 10 and 20 intervals) using the two SUBROUTINE subprograms of Ill. Exs. 4.9 and 4.10. Differentiate your results to obtain the second derivative of $\sin x$ by both methods. Calculate the error and the percent error of all numerical calculations.

4.10. Write a Fortran program to numerically calculate $\int \sin x \, dx$ from 0 to π for 11 and 21 equally spaced points (i.e., 10 and 20 intervals) using the trapezoidal, Simpson one-third, and Simpson three-eighths method subprograms given in Sec. 4.5. Integrate your results again to obtain $\int\!\!\int \sin x \, dx$ by all three methods. Calculate the error and the percent error of all numerical calculations (i.e., for all upper limits of the running integral).

4.11. Write five SUBROUTINE subprograms to integrate tabulated data that utilize Eqs. (4-24), (4-25), (4-30), (4-31), and (4-32), respectively. Redo Prob. 4.10 using these five subprograms.

4.12. Write a SUBROUTINE subprogram to integrate N equally spaced points as follows: use Eq. (4-26) over the first two and last two points, use Eq. (4-28) over the first three and last three points, use Eq. (4-29) over the first four and last four points, and use Eq. (4-30) for all other integrations. Redo Prob. 4.10 using this subprogram.

4.13. Write a Fortran program to numerically calculate $\int (\sin x/x) \, dx$ from 0.080 to 2π for 11, 21, and 33 equally spaced points (i.e., 10, 20, and 32 equal intervals) using the trapezoidal and Simpson one-third method subprograms given in Sec. 4.5. Calculate the error and the percent error of all numerical calculations (i.e., for all upper limits of the running integral). Modify your program to calculate $\int (\sin x/x^2) \, dx$ from 0.080 to 2π for the same points.

4.14. Keypunch the Fortran program in Sec. 4.6. Use this program to find the steady-state temperature distribution for a 5 ft by 4 ft rectangular plate. The temperatures (starting at the corners and using one ft intervals) across the top boundary (i.e., left-to-right) are 110 °F, 125 °F, 150 °F, 180 °F, 140 °F, and 120 °F. The temperatures across the bottom boundary are 80 °F, 60 °F, 70 °F, 75 °F, 90 °F, and 92 °F. The temperatures down the left-hand boundary are 110 °F, 104 °F, 95 °F, 88 °F, and 80 °F. The temperatures down the right-hand boundary are 120 °F, 111 °F, 108 °F, 99 °F, and 92 °F. Also run a second case using the boundary temperatures given in Ill. Ex. 4.14.

Fig. 4-14

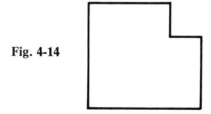

4.15. Suppose that we had to compute the electrostatic voltage potential distribution over the plate shown in Fig. 4-14. Modify the relaxation program in Sec. 4.6 so that it can solve this problem. Also modify the relaxation program in Sec. 4.6 so that it can handle a square plate with a square hole at its center.

4.16. Write a Fortran program that will solve for the steady-state temperature distribution (i.e., any problem that satisfies the three-dimensional Laplace equation) in a rectangular solid.

4.17. If there is a uniform heat generation of constant magnitude q_{gen} throughout a flat plate, it can be shown that the steady-state temperature distribution is a solution of the Poisson equation $T_{xx} + T_{yy} = q_{gen}$. Modify the Fortran program in Sec. 4.6 so that it can determine this temperature distribution within a rectangular flat plate by numerical means.

4.18. Write a Fortran program that will solve for the ϕ-values within a rectangular plate, where quantity ϕ satisfies the Poisson equation $\phi_{xx} + \phi_{yy} = x^2 y$. Locate the (0, 0) coordinate at the lower, left-hand corner of the plate. Let the ϕ-values at the boundary have an arbitrary variation, as was done in the relaxation program in Sec. 4.6.

4.19. Write a Fortran program that will numerically solve the wave-equation problem in Ill. Ex. 4.15. Solve this problem for $\Delta x = 2.0, 1.0, 0.50,$ and 0.25 ft and compare your results.

4.20. Write a Fortran program that will solve for the values of $\theta(x, t)$, the angle of twist for a torsionally vibrating rod. The rod is rigidly mounted at the left end and is unsupported at the other end. Assume that the initial twist distribution is maintained for a short period of time greater than Δt. To make this program general, let the initial twist distribution (i.e., the values of θ at $t = 0$ and at $t = -\Delta t$) be arbitrary, and use linear interpolation to calculate values from this arbitrarily tabulated distribution.

4.21. Write a Fortran program that will numerically solve the one-dimensional diffusion equation problem in Ill. Ex. 4.16 using Eq. (4-50). Solve this problem for $\Delta x = 0.250, 0.125,$ and 0.0625 ft and compare your results.

4.22. Same as Prob. 4.21, except use Eq. (4-49) instead of Eq. (4-50) to solve this problem.

4.23. Write a Fortran program to find the voltage variation $E(x, t)$ along a well-insulated, noninductive electric cable that is 20 ft long. The initial voltage varies linearly from 3.0 volts at the left end to 0.0 volts at the right end. At the left end, there is an applied voltage given by Fig. 4-13, and the right end is grounded. Let $a^2 = 25$, where $a^2 = 1/RC$; solve this problem for $\Delta x = 4.0, 2.0,$ and 1.0 ft using Eq. (4-50); and compare your results.

4.24. Same as Prob. 4.23, except use Eq. (4-49) instead of Eq. (4-50) to solve this problem.

4.25. Write a Fortran program that will numerically solve the two-dimensional diffusion equation problem in Ill. Ex. 4.17. Solve this problem for

$\Delta x = 0.250$, 0.125, and 0.0625 ft, and run each case up to the point where steady-state conditions are attained. Compare these steady-state results with those of Ill. Ex. 4.14.

4.26. Write a Fortran SUBROUTINE subprogram that will invert a matrix of arbitrary size N by use of the Gauss-Jordan method. Use Eq. (4-57) to iterate your result.

4.27. Modify your Fortran subprogram for Prob. 4.26 so that it would solve an arbitrary number of linear algebraic equations by the Gauss-Jordan method when an input KODE term is negative. Let this program invert a matrix when the KODE term is positive or zero. Note that the inputs and outputs are different for these two types of calculations.

4.28. Write a Fortran SUBROUTINE subprogram that will solve an arbitrary number of simultaneous, linear algebraic equations by use of the Gauss-Seidel method.

4.29. Write a Fortran SUBROUTINE subprogram that will solve an arbitrary number of simultaneous, linear algebraic equations using the conjugate-gradient method. Use the matrix arithmetic subprograms in Sec. 3.7.

4.30. Write a Fortran SUBROUTINE subprogram that will solve an arbitrary number of simultaneous, linear algebraic equations using Hotelling's method. Use the matrix arithmetic subprograms in Sec. 3.7.

4.31. Complete the two plotting subprograms that are described in Sec. 4.9. Use these subprograms to plot the current output in Prob. 4.1. Also use these two subprograms to plot $\cos x$ from 0 to π for 51 equally spaced values of x.

4.32. Consider the fluid-flow design problem in Sec. 4.10. Suppose that we intend to use equal-interval input data for the diameters, flow rates, and specific gravities. If there are many input diameters, then we would require less inputs if we just specified the diameter-interval, ΔD, and the minimum and maximum diameters, D_{min} and D_{max}. Rewrite the Fortran program in Sec. 4.10 to handle equal-interval data in this fashion for the diameters, flow rates, and specific gravities. Note in this new program that $D(1) = D_{min}$, $D(J + 1) = D(J) + \Delta D$, and $ND = 1 + (D_{max} - D_{min})/\Delta D$.

4.33. Incorporate another DO loop in the Fortran program in Sec. 4.10 so that several contraction devices may be considered in each case. Note that arrays CK and DRAT will now become two-dimensional arrays.

4.34. Write a SUBROUTINE subprogram that will perform a least-squares curve-fit for a set of N points, using a polynomial of an arbitrarily specified degree n.

4.35. Write a SUBROUTINE subprogram that will curve-fit periodic data using harmonic analysis. Evaluate the integrals by the trapezoidal method.

CHAPTER 5

Brief Introduction to Digital Machine-Language Programming and to Analog Computers

5.1 Introduction

This chapter contains brief introductions to both digital machine-language programming and to analog computers. The purpose of this chapter is to give the reader a better idea of how these two types of computers work, and to show why they are classified differently. Because the machine languages for different types of digital computers vary widely, we shall use a mythical machine language that is both typical and relatively simple. The author feels that it is easier to introduce a student to a simple, typical machine language than to an actual one, which is encumbered with many specific details. After the reader learns something about a typical digital-computer programming language, he should appreciate the amount of programming labor that is saved when user-oriented languages, such as Fortran, are utilized. The very brief treatment on analog computers shows that there are many different types and that their application or usage differ accordingly. Though this treatment on analog computers is rather brief, it should be adequate enough to show to the reader the difference in concepts when they are used to solve engineering and mathematical problems, as compared to digital computers.

As for the history of automatic digital computers, the first one was conceived and designed by Charles Babbage of England in 1833. Previous to this time, there were mechanical adding and calculating machines that had been conceived and built since 1642, and there was an automatic loom built in 1801 whose sequence of operations was controlled by punched cards. An endless series of punched cards was set to move past the loom needles, and only the needles which matched the punched holes were able to penetrate a specific card. Babbage's computer, which for financial and other reasons was never built, was designed to perform its calculations mechanically under the control of punched cards. From Babbage's death in 1871 until around 1942, little else of value had been done, except for a punched-card data processing machine that was built by Herman Hollerith, an American engineer, in 1890. In the United States, the Mark I computer, which could store 72 numbers and whose operations were controlled by punched tape, was built and completed in 1944. Improved computers that utilized punched cards and whose computations were performed electronically soon followed, and the first of these computers was the ENIAC which, except for its electronic operation, was similar to the Mark I. The proposal in 1945 by John von Neumann of the United States to store the sequence of operations (i.e., instructions) as numbers in the computer itself had greatly added to the effectiveness of digital computers. This concept of "stored programs" made it much easier to branch or skip to another instruction and to perform cyclic calculations. Because the potential of digital computers was not yet utilized, the early computers were specially-built and not mass-produced until the next decade. The first commercially available computers, which appeared in the early 1950's, were outgrowths of punched card calculators and were programmed by the very tedious and time-consuming method of wiring control-panel plugboards. The design and manufacture of digital computers in the middle 1950's that could be programmed without wiring plugboards had made digital computers much easier to utilize. Needless to say, the more that digital computers were utilized, the more future uses and larger needs were foreseen. The increasing complexity of the engineering problems in the aircraft and missile industries during the late 1950's created a need for large, mass-produced digital computers that could efficiently perform the required engineering calculations. The later development, during the late 1950's, of user-oriented programming languages, such as Fortran, and the inclusion of digital computer concepts and programming in college courses have greatly added to the number of potential users and also to the accelerating usage of digital computers.

An automatic digital computer, in actuality, is just a very fast machine that can add, shift, test signs, compare numbers, etc. As shown previously in Sec. 1.20, it calculates sines, square roots, logarithms, etc. by programmed approximation formulae. As shown in Secs. 4.3 and 4.4, it performs integrations and differentiations by programmed numerical techniques. To go further, a digital computer multiplies and divides by repeated additions and shiftings of numbers. Since

$$(328)(94) = (328)(90 + 4) = (3280)(9) + (328)(4)$$

a digital computer can obtain the product of the previous multiplication by adding the number 328 ninety-four times. It could obtain this product much faster, however, by adding 328 four times, shifting 328 to the left one place to obtain 3280, and then adding 3280 nine times. Thus, by 13 additions and one shift, a digital computer can obtain the product of a number multiplied by 94. Though digital computers perform multiplications and divisions by the process of repeated additions and shiftings of numbers, as do desk calculators, there are machine-language instructions that perform multiplications and divisions, just as there are multiply and divide buttons on a desk calculator.

5.2 The FAC Computer

Generally, a digital computer is composed of five components: input unit, output unit, arithmetic unit, control unit, and storage unit. Sometimes auxiliary storage units are also included. The *input unit* feeds numerical data and instructions into selected computer storages. This is usually done using the medium of punched cards, magnetic tape, or paper tape. The *output unit* takes selected data from the computer (usually computed data) so that the user can interpret the results of the computer calculations. This is usually done using the medium of printed pages or by storing this data on punched cards, paper tape, or magnetic tape and later feeding them to a printer. The *arithmetic unit* performs addition, subtraction, multiplication, and division operations in much the same manner as that done by a desk calculator. In addition, this unit can also shift and test numerical data. The *control unit*, which is usually in the same housing as the arithmetic unit, interprets the computer instructions so that the computer knows what operations to perform. The *storage unit* stores all of the numerical data and instructions inside the computer. The main storage unit is usually of the magnetic core type, but many small and medium computers use a magnetic drum. Auxiliary storage units, which are usually magnetic tape, magnetic disk, or magnetic drum, are usually cheaper, but slower, storage units that are used to increase the storage capacity of the computer. We shall not give a detailed description of these five components because a complete description would take up too much space.

Since the present digital computers vary so much in the details of their design and operation, we shall set up (i.e., program) problems on a mythical digital computer. We shall call this computer *FAC*, which is an abbreviation for "fictitious automatic computer." We shall assume that it is a relatively small computer that has only one storage unit of the magnetic core type whose capacity is 1000 words. A *word* is either an instruction or a number (i.e., a piece of numerical data). This computer will use punched cards for the input medium and a printer as the output unit. Each computer storage, and hence each word, will consist of eight decimal digits and a plus or minus sign. The arithmetic unit will consist of two registers: an *accumulator* which can hold sixteen decimal digits and a sign, and a *multiplier-quotient register*, also called the *MQ*, which can hold eight decimal digits and a sign. It is assumed that this computer can do both fixed-point and floating-point decimal arithmetic. The control unit contains three index registers and several special control registers. The FAC computer is functionally illustrated in Fig. 5-1.

A digital computer program breaks the given problem into a sequence of arithmetic (or special testing) steps and translates these steps into a language that is understood by the computer. The step-by-step organization is similar to that required when solving a problem on a desk calculator. For example, it has been stated before that a digital computer does not integrate or differentiate and that numerical techniques must be used. A *machine-language instruction* is a step in a computer program that is written in the computer's own language.

In order to identify each of the thousand words of storage, the storages will be numbered consecutively from 000 (i.e., 0) to 999. The input unit can feed data into any group of specified storages. The first instruction to be executed must be in storage 000, the next instruction in storage 001 (i.e., 1), and so on, unless the program tells the computer to skip to some other storage location for the execution of the next instruction. The loca-

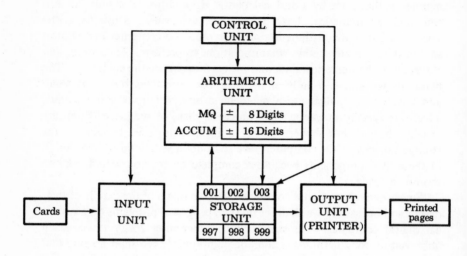

Fig. 5-1

tion identification number for a given storage is called its *address*. For this computer, as with most digital computers, when a number is read from a storage to a register, the given storage still contains that number. If a number is read into a storage, then any number in there previously will be destroyed before the given number is read in that storage.

Each *FAC instruction* consists of *eight digits and a sign*, which will always be positive. The first two (i.e., the two highest-order) digits define the computer *operation*. The next three digits usually *identify the computer storage* (by means of its address) to be used in conjunction with the computer operation. The last three digits, if used, are for *control of index registers*. We shall call these three parts of a FAC instruction the *operation*, *address*, and *index* portions of that instruction. We shall assume that 25 operations are possible for FAC. Though this is less than that for the average digital computer, these operations will still illustrate many of the fundamentals of machine-language programming. These 25 operations, which will be explained and illustrated in detail later in this text, are listed below. An abbreviated description for each of these operations is given within the parentheses, while the two-digit number is the identifying means by which the digital computer knows what arithmetic or other type of operation it is to perform.

0 1 (read input data)
0 2 (print output data)
0 3 (clear and add)

          0 4   (clear and subtract)
          0 5   (add)
          0 6   (subtract)
          0 7   (multiply)
          0 8   (divide)
          0 9   (floating add)
          1 0   (floating subtract)
          1 1   (floating multiply)
          1 2   (floating divide)
          1 3   (load MQ)
          1 4   (store MQ)
          1 5   (store accumulator)
          1 6   (clear storage)
          1 7   (accumulator left shift)
          1 8   (accumulator right shift)
          1 9   (transfer)
          2 0   (positive accumulator transfer)
          2 1   (zero accumulator transfer)
          2 2   (overflow transfer)
          2 3   (load index)
          2 4   (add index)
          2 5   (compare index)

5.3   *Fixed-Point Arithmetic Computations*

Let us suppose that the program instructions have already been loaded into the computer and that the executed program has also loaded the input data into the computer. Also suppose that two numbers, which we shall denote as A and B, are located in storages 651 and 992, respectively. The quantities A and B can be added by the three FAC instructions that follow. The sum (i.e., $A + B$) is stored in storage 846 (i.e., the storage whose address or addressed location is 846).

$$+03|651|000$$
$$+05|992|000$$
$$+15|846|000$$

Each of these three instructions consists of eight digits and a sign. That is, the first instruction is stored as the number $+03651000$ in the computer. We have used vertical separation marks so that the reader can more easily distinguish the operation, address, and index portions of these three FAC instructions. As mentioned previously, the first two digits of each instruction denote the operation, the next three digits is the address portion, and the last three digits is the index portion. The *addressed quantity* is the quantity that is located in the storage whose location or address is specified by the address portion of that instruction. The first of these three instructions performs operation 03, and Sec. 5.2 tells us that the abbreviated description for this operation is "clear and add." This operation first sets or clears the accumulator to equal zero, and then causes the first instruction to put quantity A (since the address portion for the first instruction is the address of the storage where A is located) from storage 651 into the accumulator. The second instruction performs operation 05 (i.e., add) by taking the addressed quantity B from storage 992 (since the address portion of the second instruction is 992) and then adding it to the quantity that is already in the accumulator. The third instruction performs operation 15 (i.e., store accumulator) by taking the quantity in the accumulator (which for this case is $A + B$) and storing it in storage 846 (since the address portion of this instruction is 846). The quantity $(A + B)$ will still remain in the accumulator. Note that the numbers in the index portion of the above three instructions were all 000, since no index registers were affected. To minimize the danger of *overflow* where non-zero digits may spill out the left end of the accumulator, quantities added to the accumulator are added in the eight lowest-order (i.e., right-most) digit positions of the sixteen-digit accumulator.

We had assumed here that both quantities A and B had the same decimal location. To symbolize the decimal location of a quantity, we will use the notation $c.d$ to denote c digits before the decimal point and d digits after the decimal point. If the decimal location of A is 2.6 and the decimal location of B is 4.4, we must line up the decimal points before we add A and B. This can be done by using a FAC instruction that contains a shifting operation. Let us now refer to the previous three FAC instructions that added quantities A and B. The first instruction puts quantity A in the right-half portion of the 16-digit accumulator. Since the decimal location for A is 2.6, quantity A is in the accumulator decimally as 10.6. The second instruction would put quantity B in the accumulator decimally as 12.4 (since the decimal location for B is 4.4) before it performs the addition. Thus, before we perform the addition, we want to have quantity A in the accumulator decimally as 12.4 so that the decimal points will be lined up. This can be done by putting the following instruction between the first and second of the previous three instructions.

$$+18|002|000$$

This instruction performs operation 18 (i.e., accumulator right shift) by shifting the quantity A in the accumulator two decimal places to the right, which will cause quantity A to lose its two right-most digits. Thus, A is now in the accumulator decimally as 12.4 and the decimal points are lined up when B is added to the accumulator. Note that the address portion of this instruction specifies the number of decimal places that the quantity in the accumulator should be shifted. Since we lose the right-most two digits for quantity A when we shift it two places to the right (which can be significant digits), we might wish to avoid this by using operation 17 (i.e., accumulator left shift) as shown in Ill. Ex. 5.1. Illustrative Example 5.2 exemplifies how fixed-point subtractions may be performed.

Next, let us consider the multiplication of two quantities. Again suppose that quantity A is located in storage 651 decimally as 2.6 and that quantity B is located in storage 992 decimally as 4.4. A program portion that would multiply A and B and store the result in storage 848, decimally as 5.3, could be as follows:

$$+13|651|000$$
$$+07|992|000$$
$$+18|007|000$$
$$+15|848|000$$

The first instruction uses operation 13 (i.e., load MQ) to destroy anything in the MQ register and then to place the quantity A, which will become the multiplier, in this MQ register. We know that the first instruction puts quantity A in the MQ register because its address portion is 651, which is the address for quantity A. The second instruction multiplies quantity A in the MQ register and the addressed quantity B, in storage 992, using operation 07 (i.e., multiply). That is, operation 07 multiplies the quantity denoted by the address portion of the instruction (in this case, B) by the quantity in the MQ register. The product A times B will appear in the accumulator decimally as 6.10. To generalize the decimal location of a product in the accumulator, let $a.b$ represent the decimal location of A and $c.d$ represent the decimal location of B. The decimal location $e.f$ of the product A times B in the accumulator is given by the equation

$$e.f = (a + c) . (b + d) \qquad (5\text{-}1)$$

That is, $e = a + c$ and $f = b + d$. The third instruction shifts the product to the right seven decimal places so that it appears decimally in the accumulator as 13.3 (i.e., the seven right-most digits of the product are lost). Since operation 15 stores the last or right-most eight decimal digits of the accumulator, the fourth and last instruction stores this product in storage 848 decimally as 5.3.

Next, let us consider the division of these same two quantities. A set of FAC instructions that would calculate B divided by A, could be as follows.

$$+03|992|000$$
$$+17|008|000$$
$$+08|651|000$$
$$+14|849|000$$

The first instruction puts B in the accumulator decimally as 12.4. The next instruction shifts the quantity to the left eight places so that dividend B is in the accumulator decimally as 4.12. The third instruction divides the quantity B in the accumulator by the addressed quantity A in storage 651, using operation 08 (i.e., divide). The result of the division appears in the MQ register decimally as 2.6. To generalize the decimal location after a division operation, let $a.b$ represent the decimal location of A and $c.d$ represent the decimal location of B. The decimal location $e.f$ for the result of B divided by A is given by the equation

$$e.f = (c - a) . (d - b) \qquad (5\text{-}2)$$

That is, $e = c - a$ and $f = d - b$. The fourth and last instruction uses operation 14 (i.e., store MQ) to put the result, B divided by A, from the MQ register into storage 849 decimally as 2.6. It might also be noted here that the left and right accumulator shift operations (i.e., 17 and 18) may be used to multiply or divide a quantity by a power of ten. A left shift results in multiplication, whereas a right shift results in division by a power of ten.

In this section, note that it takes three or four FAC instruction statements to perform a single addition, subtraction, multiplication, or division of two quantities. In the Fortran system, several arithmetic operations can be performed by one Fortran instruction statement. That is, one Fortran statement is usually equivalent to several machine-language instruction statements. Also note that for machine-language programming, we must keep track of the storage locations where the various quantities are stored, which is not required in Fortran programming. That is, the symbolic names for Fortran variables and the Fortran statement numbers both represent storage locations (i.e., addresses) in machine-language programming. This should help to illustrate to the reader the amount of programming labor that is saved when user-oriented programming languages, such as Fortran, are utilized.

Illustrative Example 5.1. Suppose that quantity A is in storage 651 decimally as 2.6 and that quantity B is in storage 992 decimally as 4.4. Write FAC instructions to add these two quantities in such a way that no significant digits of quantity A will be lost during the addition process. Store the result in storage 846.

Solution. This can be done by the following set of instructions. The first instruction puts quantity B in the accumulator decimally as 12.4. The second instruction performs operation 17 (i.e., accumulator left shift) with an addressed shift of 2 to put B in the accumulator as 10.6. Note that the address portion of the second instruction specified the number of decimal places to shift the quantity in the accumulator. Thus, the decimal points will be lined up when A is added to the accumulator by the third instruction, but digits may be lost when $(A + B)$ is stored in storage 846 by the fourth and last instruction, since only the right-most eight accumulator digits are stored. Thus, these instructions should not be used if the first two (i.e., the two high-order) digits of quantity B are significant.

$$+03|992|000$$
$$+17|002|000$$
$$+05|651|000$$
$$+15|846|000$$

Illustrative Example 5.2. Suppose that quantity A is in storage 651 decimally as 2.6, quantity B is in storage 992 decimally as 4.4, and that quantity C is in storage 458 decimally as 4.4. Write FAC instructions to compute $(-A - B + C)$ and to store the result in storage 847. Locate the first of these FAC instructions in storage 056.

Solution. A set of FAC instructions that will perform these calculations are given, along with some explanation, in Table 5-1. Two new operations are used. Operation 04 (i.e., clear and subtract) sets the accumulator to equal zero and then puts the negative of the quantity in the addressed storage (in this case, $-A$) in the accumulator. The operation 06 (i.e., subtract) performs a fixed-point subtraction in the accumulator. This program portion illustrates the algebraic feature of the accumulator. It may be noted that Ill. Exs. 5.1 and 5.2 utilize seven of the 25 types of FAC operations (i.e., 03, 04, 05, 06, 15, 17, and 18). In these examples, it should be noted how the sequence of operations is similar to that when using a desk calculator.

Table 5-1

Location	Operation	Address	Index	Accumulator Contents
056	+04	651	000	$-A$ as 10.6
057	+18	002	000	$-A$ as 12.4
058	+06	992	000	$(-A - B)$ as 12.4
059	+05	458	000	$(-A - B + C)$ as 12.4
060	+15	847	000	$(-A - B + C)$ as 12.4

5.4 Floating-Point Arithmetic Computations

In Sec. 5.3, we had discussed and utilized 11 of the 25 FAC operations (i.e., 03 to 08, 13 to 15, 17, and 18). In this section, we shall consider four more operations, which are 09, 10, 11, and 12. In a fixed-point arithmetic program, we must know the decimal location for each input, and we must keep track of the decimal point location after each arithmetic and shifting operation. We must do this if we wish to know where the decimal point is located on the output quantities when they are printed as digits without a decimal point. Fixed-point programming also requires careful planning in order to obtain adequate significance in the calculations without danger of overflow. In programming with floating-point arithmetic, however, no shifting operations are required and the programmer is relieved of the decimal point location problem. Besides being easier to program, floating-point arithmetic has less possibility of error. Some computers, however, do not have this feature.

We can represent any decimal number as a normalized decimal fraction (between 0.100 and unity in value) times the number ten raised to a nonfractional exponent. For example

$$2136.75 = (0.213675)(10^4)$$

The FAC computer does floating-point arithmetic by keeping the normalized decimal fraction and the ten's exponent together in the same eight-digit storage. The sign and first six digits represent the fraction F, while the last two digits represent T, which is the ten's exponent plus 49. This is done so that we can represent any number between 10^{-49} and 10^{50} without requiring a minus sign for the exponent representation in the storage. Thus, a number N is represented in floating point by

$$N = (F)(10^{T-49}) \tag{5-3}$$

When using floating-point arithmetic, the programmer must be sure that all data is read into the computer in floating-point form. This will be discussed in detail later. In floating-point addition or subtraction, one quantity is changed until both quantities have the same exponent before addition or subtraction takes place. In floating-point multiplication, the fractional parts are multiplied and the exponents are added. Actually, the resultant T value is the sum of the two previous T values minus 49. After each floating-point arithmetic operation, the result is normalized so that the fractional part is between 0.100 and one (i.e., has no leading zeroes).

As an example, suppose that we have quantities A, B, C, D, and E located successively in storages 601 to 605 and that the accumulator was cleared to equal zero. We wish to calculate both $(AB - C)$ and $(AB - C + D)/E$ and to store these two results in storages 606 and 607, respectively. A program portion (i.e., a set of FAC instructions) to perform these calculations is given in Table 5-2, which also contains some explanatory details. These instructions are located in storages 001 to 007.

Table 5-2

Location	Operation	Address	Index	Accumulator Contents
001	+13	601	000	0
002	+11	602	000	(A)(B)
003	+10	603	000	(AB − C)
004	+15	606	000	(AB − C)
005	+09	604	000	(AB − C + D)
006	+12	605	000	(AB − C + D)
007	+14	607	000	(AB − C + D)

Illustrative Example 5.3. Suppose that it were desired to find the average value of quantities A, B, C, D, and E, which are located in storages 601 to 605, respectively, in floating-point form. Let the numerical quantity 5.00 be located in storage 600 in floating-point form. Write a set of FAC instructions that will calculate this average value and store the result in storage 609.

Solution. The following set of seven FAC instructions will perform the desired calculations. The first instruction uses operation 03 to clear the accumulator to equal zero and to next store quantity A, from storage 601, in this accumulator. The next four instructions use operation 09 to successively perform floating-point additions. That is, quantities B, C, D, and E (from storages 602 to 605) are added to the contents of the accumulator. The last two instructions use operation 12 to perform a floating-point division by 5.00 (which is located in storage 600) and operation 14 to store the result of the division (which is located in the MQ register) in storage 609. That is, the floating-point-division operation, 12, divides the contents of the accumulator by the quantity in the addressed storage and puts the result in the MQ register.

$$+03601000$$
$$+09602000$$
$$+09603000$$
$$+09604000$$
$$+09605000$$
$$+12600000$$
$$+14609000$$

5.5 Program Control Operations

The usual sequence of calculations performed by a program is that corresponding to the sequence of instructions as they are located in that program. Thus, the instruction in storage 000 is followed by the instruction in storage 001, the instruction in storage 001 is followed by the instruction in storage 002, etc. The only exception to this in a FAC program is when operations 19 to 22 are used. Let the symbol N denote the number in the address portion of these instructions. Operation 19 causes the next executed instruction to be that located in storage N. Operations 20 to 22 cause a transfer to the instruction located in storage N if a certain condition occurs. If the specified condition does not occur, then the next instruction in sequence is executed. Operation 20 causes a transfer to instruction N if the accumulator contains a positive quantity; operation 21 causes a transfer to instruction N if the accumulator contains a zero quantity; and operation 22 causes a transfer to instruction N if an overflow has occurred in a computer calculation. The last operation is used to help indicate that there is an error in the results. The use of the control operations 19 to 21 is exemplified in Ill. Ex. 5.4.

Illustrative Example 5.4. Suppose that quantity A is in storage 601 and that quantity D is in storage 604. Locating the first instruction in storage 008, write FAC instructions that will calculate a quantity F in storage 608, where F is given by

$$F = 0 \qquad \text{if } A < D$$
$$F = A \qquad \text{if } A = D$$
$$F = A - D \quad \text{if } A > D$$

Solution. This quantity F can be computed by the FAC instructions in Table 5-3, which test the quantity $(A - D)$ in the accumulator for its sign in a manner analogous to a Fortran IF statement. Table 5-3 furnishes additional

Table 5-3

Location	Operation	Address	Index	Explanation
008	+03	601	000	A is in the accumulator
009	+10	604	000	(A − D) is in the accumulator
010	+20	015	000	If (A − D) > 0, go to 015
011	+21	014	000	If (A − D) = 0, go to 014
012	+16	608	000	F = 0
013	+19	016	000	Go to 016
014	+03	601	000	A is in the accumulator
015	+15	608	000	F = A or (A − D)
016				

details. Operation 16 causes the computer to store a zero quantity in the storage whose location is specified by the address portion of that instruction. Thus, if the quantity $(A - D)$ is negative, the program goes to instruction 012, which stores a zero quantity in storage 608 (i.e., instruction 012 calculates $F = 0$).

5.6   Use of Index Registers

If we had the problem of averaging one hundred quantities located in storages 601 to 700, programming by the method shown in Ill. Ex. 5.3 would be both time-consuming and monotonous, because this method would use the 09 operation 99 successive times. One method would be to make an addition loop, whereby the address of the instruction containing the addition operation is increased by 001 during each cycle of the loop. The easiest way to do this is by using index registers, since they can be used to modify an instruction without actually changing the contents of that instruction. When an instruction uses an index register, the contents of the specified index register are added to the address of the instruction before the instruction is executed. Thus, the *effective address* of an instruction is the sum of its address and the contents of the specified index register, but the actual number in the address portion of that instruction is never changed. Putting the number 001 in the index portion of an instruction will specify the first index register. The numbers 002 and 003 in the index portion will specify the second and third index registers, respectively.

Operations 23, 24, and 25 involve index register control. Index register operations, like the DO statement in Fortran, are very useful in performing cyclic calculations. Operation 23 stores the number located in the address portion of that instruction into the contents of the specified index register. This is a means for putting a number into an index register. Operation 24 is a means for modifying the contents of an index register. This operation adds the number located in the address portion of that instruction to the contents of the specified index register. Operation 25 is for program loop control. Assume that an instruction, located in storage L, uses operation 25 and contains quantity A in the address portion and contains quantity I in the index portion. If the contents of index register I do not equal the quantity A, the next executed instruction is located in storage $L + 1$. If the two quantities are equal, instruction $L + 1$ is ignored, and the next executed instruction is located in storage $L + 2$. The use of the index register operations 23 to 25, to perform a cyclic calculation, is exemplified in Ill. Ex. 5.5. This example should be compared with Ill. Ex. 5.3.

Illustrative Example 5.5.   Suppose that it were desired to find the average of 100 floating-point quantities that are located in storages 601 to 700. Let the numerical quantity 100.0 be located in storage 600 in floating-point form. Write a set of FAC instructions that will calculate this average value and store the result in storage 701. Locate the first instruction in storage 016.

Solution. This average value for 100 quantities can be computed by the FAC instructions in Table 5-4, which also explains some of the details. The first two instructions clear the accumulator to zero, while instruction 018 stores zero in the first index register. Instruction 019 does the addition with the help of the first index register. It is the first instruction in the addition loop. Instruction 020 adds the integral quantity one to the first index register during each executed cycle of the loop. Instruction 021 uses operation 25 to test whether 100 cycles of the loop have occurred. If so, then the program gets out of the loop by skipping to instruction 023 which calculates the average value. If the first index register contains a number less than 100, the program goes to instruction 022 which causes a transfer to instruction 019, and, thus, the program goes through another addition cycle. At the start of the second cycle, the first index register contains the quantity one. Instruction 019 (i.e., the instruction that is located in storage 019) adds to the accumulator the quantity that is located in the storage with the effective address 601*. That is, 601* denotes 601 plus the contents of the first index register. Thus, during the second cycle, instruction 019 adds to the accumulator the quantity in storage (601 + 1) or 602; and during the third cycle, instruction 019 adds to the accumulator the quantity in storage (601 + 2) or 603 since the first index register contains the quantity two at that time.

Table 5-4

Location	Operation	Address	Index	Explanation
016	+16	702	000	Set storage 702 to zero
017	+03	702	000	Set accumulator to zero
018	+23	000	001	Set Index Reg. 1 to zero
019	+09	601	001	Add 601* to accumulator
020	+24	001	001	Add 001 to Index Reg. 1
021	+25	100	001	If Index Reg. 1 = 100, go to 023
022	+19	019	000	Go to 019 for next cycle
023	+12	600	000	Divide by 100
024	+14	701	000	Store result in 701

5.7 Input and Output Operations

The program instructions are loaded into the computer either automatically or by the computer operator. The first FAC instruction must go into storage 000. The input data for the problem are loaded into the computer by the program itself when it is executed. Care must be taken that an input or calculated quantity is not stored in a storage containing an instruction. It is wise, when programming a problem in machine language, to make a list of where the input data, calculated quantities, and instructions are located in the computer storage unit.

Let us assume that the FAC input data are punched on cards and that these cards are run through a card reading device that electrically scans the punched holes and transmits the data into a selected group of locations in the computer storage unit. On this punched card, we will allow 72 columns of information to be punched, where in each column a plus or minus sign or a decimal digit may be punched. The FAC computer system is fixed such that up to eight data quantities, where each quantity contains a sign followed by eight decimal digits, may be read from a punched card. If the program uses fixed-point arithmetic, the input data must be put on the card in fixed-point form (i.e., no ten's exponent is used). If the program uses floating-point arithmetic, the input data must be put on the card in normalized floating-point form. That is, for the nine columns to specify a floating-point quantity, the first column contains a sign, the next six contain a decimal fraction between 0.100 and unity, and the last two columns contain the ten's exponent plus 49.

The operation 01 reads up to eight quantities from a card into successive storage locations in the computer. The address portion of that instruction specifies where the first quantity is to be stored, while the index portion specifies how many quantities are to be read from that card. The operation 02 causes a printing device to print the numbers from N successive computer storages, where N is specified in the index portion and where the location of the first storage is specified in the address portion. The number N must not exceed ten. If floating-point arithmetic is used, the last two digits of a printed quantity is its actual ten's exponent. Usually the printer will be fixed so that these two digits will be separated from the rest of the printed quantity.

Illustrative Example 5.6.   Write a complete FAC program that will load quantities A, B, C, D, and E from a punched card into storages 601 to 605; calculate and put $(AB - C)$ in storage 606; calculate and put $(AB - C + D)/E$ into storage 607; calculate F, where F is defined in Ill. Ex. 5.4, and store it in storage 608; print the five inputs and the three calculated terms; and then transfer control to the first instruction for the next case (i.e., to read in more data).

Solution.   The following instruction, which is located in storage 000 since it is the first instruction, uses operation 01 (i.e., read input data) to load the five quantities A, B, C, D, and E into storages 601 to 605.

$$+01|601|005$$

The instructions that calculate $(AB - C)$ and $(AB - C + D)/E$ are given in Table 5-2. Note that these instructions are located in storages 001 to 007 (i.e., the first of these instructions is located in storage 001, as desired). The instructions that calculate the term F are given in Table 5-3. Note that these instructions are located in storages 008 to 015, as desired. The details for these two sets of FAC instructions are explained in Sec. 5.4 and Ill. Ex. 5.4, respectively. The last two instructions, which are located in storages 016 and 017, are

$$+02|601|008$$
$$+19|000|000$$

The next to last instruction uses operation 02 (i.e., print output data) to print the eight quantities that are in storages 601 to 608 (i.e., the five input quantities and the three computed quantities). The last instruction uses operation 19 (i.e., transfer) to transfer control to the instruction in storage 000 (i.e., the first instruction) to read in more data and perform another set of calculations. The program stops when there are no more data cards to be read from the card reader. This is the only example of a complete computer machine-language program in this chapter. Using the three instructions in this section and the instructions in Tables 5-2 and 5-3, the complete set of FAC instructions are listed below. These 18 FAC instructions are stored as eight-digit numbers, as shown, in storages 000 to 017. The five input terms are in storages 601 to 605, and the three calculated terms are in storages 606 to 608.

$$+01601005$$
$$+13601000$$
$$+11602000$$
$$+10603000$$
$$+15606000$$
$$+09604000$$
$$+12605000$$
$$+14607000$$
$$+03601000$$
$$+10604000$$
$$+20015000$$
$$+21014000$$
$$+16608000$$
$$+19016000$$
$$+03601000$$
$$+15608000$$
$$+02601008$$
$$+19000000$$

5.8 Binary Arithmetic

The FAC computer is basically a binary computer electronically. It is programmed in decimal fashion because it utilizes additional electronic circuitry to internally convert decimal numbers to binary form before they are stored in the computer. It is economical for a computer to use a *binary number system* because only two digits are used, zero and one, and, thus, may be easily represented in a physical system by only two types of signals. Examples are a switch being on or off, an electron tube in the conducting or non-conducting state, holes punched or not punched on paper tape or cards, two types of magnetization on a magnetic tape or drum or disk, and a magnetic core which may be magnetized in one direction or the other. Because the resultant circuitry is less expensive, many computers have both the input data and instructions enter the computer in binary form. For this type of computer, the input is written usually in decimal form and a special program converts it to binary form. Another special program converts the binary output to decimal form before it is printed. Because such computers are completely binary in operation, it is useful to learn something about binary arithmetic. Because of the difficulty in locating binary points for fixed-point arithmetic, floating-point arithmetic operations are especially useful for this type of computer. To illustrate the relationship between binary and decimal numbers

$$123 = (1 \times 10^2) + (2 \times 10^1) + (3 \times 10^0)$$

Since $123 = 64 + 32 + 16 + 8 + 2 + 1$, we have the relationship

$$123 = (1 \times 2^6) + (1 \times 2^5) + (1 \times 2^4) + (1 \times 2^3)$$
$$+ (0 \times 2^2) + (1 \times 2^1) + (1 \times 2^0)$$

We may summarize the previous equations by the relationship $(123)_{10} = (1111011)_2$. That is, the binary number 1111011 equals the decimal number 123. Computers that are decimal or partially decimal in operation usually require a binary type of coding when storing a decimal digit. The following system, which is the binary representation of the corresponding decimal digit, may be used for this purpose.

$$(0)_{10} = (0000)_2 \qquad (5)_{10} = (0101)_2$$
$$(1)_{10} = (0001)_2 \qquad (6)_{10} = (0110)_2$$
$$(2)_{10} = (0010)_2 \qquad (7)_{10} = (0111)_2$$
$$(3)_{10} = (0011)_2 \qquad (8)_{10} = (1000)_2$$
$$(4)_{10} = (0100)_2 \qquad (9)_{10} = (1001)_2$$

In a similar manner, alphabetic letters may be stored in a computer by assigning a special binary code (i.e., a group of binary digits) for each alphabetic letter. These alphabetic letters may be used to print titles on top of the numerical output, in order to identify them.

If the base 8 is used to represent numbers, the representation is called the *octal number system*. For example,

$$(123)_{10} = (1 \times 8^2) + (7 \times 8^1) + (3 \times 8^0) = (173)_8$$

Because $2^3 = 8$, an octal digit represents exactly three binary digits. Thus, the octal notation is a convenient shorthand for representing large binary numbers. For example, $(123)_{10} = (173)_8 = (1\ 111\ 011)_2$. When performing binary arithmetic operations, the following rules hold

$$0 + 0 = \ 0$$
$$1 + 0 = \ 1$$
$$1 + 1 = \ 10 \quad \text{(i.e., 0 with 1 carried)}$$
$$0 \times 0 = \ 0$$
$$1 \times 0 = \ 0$$
$$1 \times 1 = \ 1$$

There are many ways by which we can convert numbers from one system to another. We shall discuss only a few of these methods. To convert a decimal integer to a binary integer, one method is to divide successively by 2. As an example for $(123)_{10}$

$$(1/2)(123) = 61 + 1/2 \quad \text{(i.e., remainder of 1)}$$
$$(1/2)(61) \ = 30 + 1/2$$
$$(1/2)(30) \ = 15 + 0 \quad \text{(i.e., remainder of 0)}$$
$$(1/2)(15) \ = \ 7 + 1/2$$
$$(1/2)(7) \ = \ 3 + 1/2$$
$$(1/2)(3) \ = \ 1 + 1/2$$
$$(1/2)(1) \ = \ 0 + 1/2$$

The binary representation of 123 consists of seven binary digits and is obtained by writing down, in succession from right to left, the previous remainders in the order in which they were calculated. Thus, $(123)_{10} = (1111011)_2$, which has been verified previously.

Conversely, we can convert a binary integer to a decimal integer by dividing successively by binary ten until a quotient zero is obtained. The remainders, when expressed in decimal notation and written in succession from right to left, give the desired decimal representation. This type of conversion is exemplified in Ill. Ex. 5.7. To obtain a decimal integer from an octal integer, the procedure is similar, except that division is done by octal ten, that is, 12. To convert a decimal integer to octal, the procedure is similar to that for conversion to binary, except that the division is by eight instead of by two.

To convert a proper decimal fraction to binary, we can multiply successively by decimal 2, where the integers in the results are the binary digits to the right of the binary point. It should be noted that terminating decimal fractions cannot always be represented as terminating binary fractions. For example,

$$2(0.42) = 0.84$$
$$2(0.84) = 1.68$$
$$2(0.68) = 1.36$$
$$2(0.36) = 0.72$$
$$2(0.72) = 1.44$$

Thus, $(0.42)_{10} = (0.01101XXX)_2$, where the integers obtained in the previous calculations represent the binary digits in the binary fraction. Improper decimal fractions may be converted to binary by converting the integral and fractional parts separately. To convert a binary fraction to decimal, multiply this fraction by binary ten. This latter type of conversion is exemplified in Ill. Ex. 5.8. Again it should be noted that there are other methods than those shown here that can be used to perform binary-decimal conversion operations.

Illustrative Example 5.7.   Convert the binary number 1111011 to a decimal number.

Solution.   As stated previously, this integer conversion can be performed by dividing successively by binary ten (i.e., 1010) until a quotient of zero is obtained. Use of this procedure gives

$$\frac{1111011}{1010} = 1100 + \text{remainder of } (11)_2 = (3)_{10}$$

$$\frac{1100}{1010} = 1 + \text{remainder of } (10)_2 = (2)_{10}$$

$$\frac{1}{1010} = 0 + \text{remainder of } (1)_2 = (1)_{10}$$

Thus, $(1111011)_2 = (123)_{10}$, which is a result that was previously obtained in this section.

Illustrative Example 5.8.   Convert the binary fraction 0.01101 to a decimal fraction.

Solution.   As stated previously, this conversion can be performed by successive multiplication by binary ten (i.e., 1010) as follows:

$$(0.01101)\,(1010) = 0.11010 + 11.01000 = 100.00010$$
$$(0.00010)\,(1010) = 0.10100$$
$$(0.1010)\,\,(1010) = 1.01000 + 101.00000 = 110.01000$$

Since $(100)_2 = 4$, $(0)_2 = 0$, and $(110)_2 = 6$, we obtain the result $(0.01101)_2 = (0.406XX)_{10}$. To give the reader an idea of what binary fractions represent, the binary fractions $(0.100)_2$ and $(0.010)_2$ represent $1/2$ and $1/2^2$, respectively, just as the decimal fractions $(0.100)_{10}$ and $(0.010)_{10}$ represent $1/10$ and $1/10^2$. Thus, $(0.100)_2 = (0.500)_{10}$ and $(0.010)_2 = (0.250)_{10}$.

5.9   Brief Comparison of Digital and Analog Computers

In general, computing devices may be classified as either analog or digital. A *digital computer* works with specific numerical quantities and performs its operations in a discrete, stepwise procedure. Examples are the abacus, adding machines, mechanical desk calculators, and the modern electronic digital computers. Most digital computers perform their operations by combinations of additions and subtractions (e.g., desk calculators and electronic digital computers perform a multiplication by successive additions). An *analog computer* performs its computing operations by manipulating *continuously-varying physical quantities* (e.g., voltage, electrical current, angular rotation of a shaft, position on a scale, etc.) which are used to represent numerical quantities. Some very simple analog computers are the slide rule, graphs, the automobile speedometer, and the planimeter. The accuracy of an analog computer is limited by the accuracy of its least-accurate components. Components of electronic analog computers that have an accuracy of one-tenth of one per cent are rather expensive, since they require careful design. Their accuracies usually vary between one-half and five per cent. Thus, digital computers are more general in purpose and more accurate, but are less economical than analog computers. An analog computer has components that can generate such functions as e^{at}, sin bt, etc., while a digital computer must employ formulas that approximate these functions. This has been shown in Sec. 1.14. As shown in Sec. 4.5, a digital computer performs an integration by using an approximate numerical technique, while certain types of analog computers have components that can perform an integration. By the use of analog-to-digital converters and digital-to-analog converters, digital and analog computers have been combined into one computational system. Because of the timing problems involved, this combination is uneconomical and is used only for special purposes. The *digital differential analyzer*, whose chief purpose is to solve ordinary differential equations, works with digital quantities and performs its operations on a discrete, digital basis. This special-purpose type of computer has a built-in numerical integration scheme and imitates an analog computer with regard to problem setup, but still has digital computer accuracy.

There are no absolute criteria that specify which types of problems should be solved on which types of computers. This depends upon too many factors, some of which could be the allotted time, number of parameters, accuracy required, type of input, most desirable output form for a clear interpretation of the results, availability, economic considerations, and especially the problem type. The digital computer can handle a much wider range of problems. For example, an analog computer would not, in general, be used for matrix arithmetic calculations or to find the roots of equations. The D.C. electronic differential analyzer, which is by far the most widely used type of analog computer, is very useful for solving linear and nonlinear differential equations whose coefficients are not overly complex. This type of computer provides an economical means for obtaining plotted results of fair accuracy; and it allows the user an easy means for changing the input parameters, after a glance at the plotted results, for successive cases. For problems where an oscillation is involved (e.g., a vibration or an A.C. circuit), there is no big problem with integration, while a digital computer should employ an accurate type of numerical integration technique to solve this type of problem. This type of analog computer can also employ a human input, one example being the use of a human being to manipulate (i.e., operate) the controls during an analog solution of an aircraft piloting problem. As another specific example, the D.C. differential analyzer has also been combined with an elastic membrane, which is the analog of Laplace's equation, to solve a problem involving ordinary differential equations, whose coefficients were computed from a steady-state temperature distribution.

5.10 Classification of Analog Computers

Analog computers have been classified according to the type of physical quantity employed (e.g., mechanical, electrical, electronic, electromechanical, etc.), but are more generally classified as either *direct analog computers* or *differential analyzers*. The *direct analog computer* is a model of the physical system to be analyzed and, thus, does not directly perform mathematical operations (i.e., addition, multiplication, integration, etc.). The particular direct analog computer should, of course, be easier to build and modify than the physical system to be analyzed. Thus, an aerodynamic wind tunnel and other scale models are direct analog computers. Two other types are the field plotter, which measures the electrostatic potential distribution across a thin sheet of conducting paper, and a soap film membrane of uniform tension, whose shape is to be measured and whose boundary is a bent wire. Both of these systems are used to represent physical systems that may be represented by Laplace's partial differential equation (e.g., steady-state temperature distributions, fluid flow streamlines, magnetic potential distributions, etc.) which is discussed in Sec. 4.6 of this text. The most popular direct analog computer is the network analyzer which will be discussed next. There are many other examples of direct analog computers, but they are designed only for specialized applications.

The *network analyzer* consists of combinations of passive electrical components (i.e., resistors, inductors, and capacitors) whose magnitudes are both variable and wide in range and which may be flexibly interconnected. It is natural to use a direct analog computer consisting of passive electrical components because they are much easier to build and modify than their physical counterparts and because they may be used to represent many types of physical systems (e.g., mechanical vibrations, heat flow, fluid flow, acoustic vibrations, etc.). This latter point has probably been shown in other courses. To set up and solve such problems on a network analyzer, we must first obtain the electrical network analogy of the physical system to be studied, connect the proper electrical components, and then adjust these components to the proper values. The *thermal analyzer* is a special network analyzer, consisting of variable resistors and capacitors, for studying heat flow problems; whereas the *transient analyzer* is a special type of network analyzer for studying transient phenomena. The more general type of network analyzers will have output recording devices and provisions for generating various forcing functions. The network analyzer is an economical device, but is limited in application mainly to system analogies that may be expressed as ordinary differential equations with constant coefficients. If an analogy exists between two physical quantities, they are linearly related. As an example, consider voltage E and an analogous quantity Q, both of which vary with time. Then, $E(T) = aQ(kt)$, where a and k are proportionality constants, and a fast timewise simulation can be obtained by setting the time scale factor k to a value less than one. Scaling will be discussed later in more detail. As a rather simple example, if the spring-mass system in Fig. 2-6 is linear, then it could be solved on a network analyzer by connecting a voltage source of output $E_0 \cos \omega t$, an inductor, a resistor, and a capacitor in series as a one-loop circuit. This is a solution circuit because the loop equation for this circuit is

$$E_0 \cos \omega t = L \frac{di}{dt} + Ri + \frac{1}{C} \int_0 i \, dt$$

which can be rewritten as follows, since current $i = dq/dt$

$$E_0 \cos \omega t = L\ddot{q} + R\dot{q} + \frac{q}{C}$$

This circuit equation is mathematically analogous to the equation of motion for the linear spring-mass system, which is

$$F_0 \cos \omega t = \frac{W}{g} \ddot{x} + c\dot{x} + kx$$

That is, charge q is analogous to displacement x, inductance L is analogous to mass W/g, resistance R is analogous to damping coefficient c, capacitance C is analogous to $1/k$, and voltage E_0 is analogous to force F_0. The initial displacement and initial velocity for this spring-mass system can be simulated on the network analyzer by an initial charge on the capacitor and by an initial loop current. The network analyzer circuit that would be used to solve the two-degree-of-freedom spring-mass system in Fig. 2-14 would consist of two loops and would include a voltage source to simulate the applied force, two inductors to simulate the two masses, and two capacitors to simulate the two linear springs.

The *differential analyzer*, which is designed mainly to solve ordinary differential equations, performs mathematical operations on the varying, physical quantities that are employed. It consists of a combination of different components, each of which performs a specific mathematical operation (e.g., addition, multiplication, integration, etc.), and when the components are properly interconnected they represent the mathematical equations to be solved (instead of a physical system). Analog differential analyzers may be physically classified as to being of the *mechanical, D.C. electronic,* or *A.C. electromechanical type.* By far the most popular type of analog computer is the *D.C. electronic differential analyzer,* so much so, that analog computers are often mistakenly considered to be synonymous with D.C. electronic differential analyzers. The *A.C. electromechanical types* have been used primarily for special purpose applications (e.g., aircraft navigation and military fire control systems). D.C. voltages may be integrated by purely electronic devices, but integration of A.C. voltages requires a mechanical or electromechanical device.

Because of their historical importance, mechanical differential analyzers shall be discussed briefly in this text, even though their usage was never widespread. The variable quantities are represented on this type of computer by the angular positions of shafts from a referenced zero position. These shafts and other computer components (i.e., mechanical adders, multipliers, integrators, etc.) are connected in such a manner that a mathematical equation is represented. Addition of two quantities (i.e., angular displacements) is performed mechanically by differential gearing similar to that in the rear axle of an automobile. Subtraction is performed in similar fashion, where the negative input is obtained by reversing the direction of its shaft rotation. Quantities are positive or negative in this computer according to the direction of its shaft rotation. If the gear ratio of two meshed gears is R (where R is the ratio of the number of driver teeth to the driven teeth), then the driven or output gear will move R times as fast as the driver or input gear. Thus, multiplication by a constant is obtained by setting the proper gear ratios between the shafts whose angular positions represent the physical variables. Arbitrary functions can be generated by using special cams. The output is plotted on an output table. Input tables may be used to provide input data in graphical form. Initial values are obtained by initially rotating the proper shafts.

Integration is obtained by means of a *Kelvin wheel-and-disk integrator,* which is illustrated in Fig. 5-2. In principle, the Kelvin integrator consists of a friction wheel that rotates without slipping on a disk, where the axes of the wheel and disk are normal to each other as shown in Fig. 5-2. If

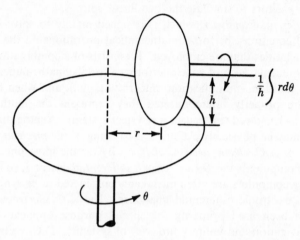

Fig. 5-2

the disk moves an angle $d\theta$ when the wheel is at a distance r from the center of the disk, then the rim of the wheel moves a distance $r\,d\theta$, and the wheel itself has turned an angular distance $r\,d\theta/h$. By letting the distance r be a variable input quantity over a finite period when rotating the disk, the output shaft of the wheel rotates an angular displacement which is given by the integral $\int r\,d\theta/h$. The Kelvin wheel integrator is schematically represented in Fig. 5-3. It might be noted that, in spite of its rather good accuracy, the use of the mechanical differential analyzer was never widespread because of its slowness of operation and because of the awkward paths that the represented variables must travel. The principles for setting up problems on the mechanical and electronic differential analyzers are similar, and this will be discussed in more detail in Sec. 5.11. The mechanical differential analyzer generates some of its functions in a rather interesting manner. For example, since $e^x = \int e^x\,dx$, the function e^x can be generated using one integrator as shown in Fig. 5-4. The output is connected to an input for this case because the output integral equals the integrand e^x. Since $x^2 = \int 2x\,dx$, the function x^2 can be generated using one integrator. Since $\log_e x = \int (1/x)\,dx$ and since $1/x = -\int (1/x)d(\log_e x)$, the functions $\log_e x$ and $1/x$ can be generated by using two integrators. Since $\tan x = \int (1 + \tan^2 x)\,dx$ and since

$\tan^2 x = \int 2 \tan x \, d(\tan x)$, we can generate the functions $\tan x$ and $\tan^2 x$ using two integrators, an adder, and a constant-multiplier of value 2. Since $\int \sin ax \, d(ax) = -\cos ax$ and since $\int \cos ax \, d(ax) = \sin ax$, the functions $\sin ax$ and $\cos ax$ can be generated using two integrators and two constant-multipliers of values -1 and a. Since

$$\int uvw \, dx = \int u \, d \int v \, d \int w \, dx$$

we can generate this integral using three integrators. We can obtain the product xy by using two integrators and an adder, as shown in Ill. Ex. 5.9.

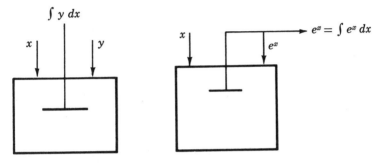

Fig. 5-3   Fig. 5-4

Illustrative Example 5.9. Show how the product xy may be computed on a mechanical differential analyzer.

Solution. Since $d(xy) = x \, dy + y \, dx$, then $xy = \int x \, dy + \int y \, dx$, and we can obtain the product of the two variables x and y by using two integrators and an adder A as shown in Fig. 5-5.

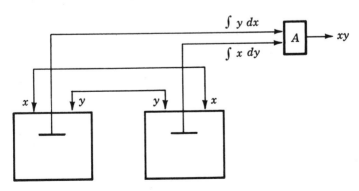

Fig. 5-5

5.11 The D.C. Electronic Differential Analyzer

As mentioned previously in Sec. 5.10, a differential analyzer has components that perform specific mathematical operations (e.g., addition, multiplication, integration, etc.), and it uses a combination of these components to solve the mathematical equations for a given problem. Because a problem is solved on any differential analyzer type of analog computer by connecting components that perform specific mathematical operations, a simple schematic symbol to denote a specific component is very helpful. That is, if the diagram that shows the connections of the differential analyzer components for solving a specific problem is both simple and clear and also shows enough detail so that it is complete, then there is a smaller chance that the components will be connected improperly during computer operation. Thus, we shall employ simple schematics to represent the different types of components for a D.C. electronic differential analyzer. We shall not discuss how to manually connect these components, nor shall we discuss the detection and correction of component malfunctions (e.g., amplifier drift) since this requires a rather good electrical background.

For *D.C. electronic differential analyzers*, the variable quantities are represented by D.C. voltages that may vary with time. This type of computer can solve both linear and nonlinear ordinary differential equations. The solutions can be recorded by special output devices (e.g., pen recorder or oscilloscope) that plot the timewise variations of the voltage-represented physical quantities. Thus, time is usually the independent variable, but we can solve problems where a displacement is the independent variable by letting the computer time represent this displacement. Just as the Kelvin wheel-and-disk integrator is the heart of the mechanical differential analyzer, the heart of the D.C. electronic differential analyzer is the *operational amplifier*. These are D.C. electronic amplifiers of extremely high gain and large impedance. Basically, it accepts a D.C. input voltage and generates a much larger voltage of opposite polarity. Output voltage E_0 is approximately equal to $-KE_i$, where gain $K \gg 1$ (e.g., gain K varies from 10^5 to 10^8 for modern transistorized electronic differential analyzers). The operational amplifier is schematically represented in Fig. 5-6.

$$E_i \longrightarrow \boxed{K} \longrightarrow E_0 = -KE_i$$

Fig. 5-6

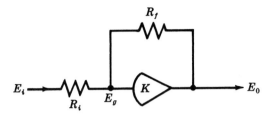

Fig. 5-7

Now let us consider an operational amplifier having an input resistor R_i and a feedback resistor R_f, as shown in Fig. 5-7, where all voltages are referenced to ground. Since the input voltage to the amplifier is E_g, $E_0 = -KE_g$. Since the amplifier input impedance is so high, most of the input current goes through the feedback resistor R_f. Thus, we have the approximation.

$$\frac{E_i - E_g}{R_i} = \frac{E_g - E_0}{R_f}$$

Substitution of $E_0 = -KE_g$ in the previous equation gives

$$\frac{1}{R_i}\left(E_i + \frac{E_0}{K}\right) = -\frac{1}{R_f}\left(\frac{E_0}{K} + E_0\right)$$

which can be rewritten as

$$E_0\left[\frac{1}{KR_i} + \frac{1}{R_f}\left(1 + \frac{1}{K}\right)\right] = -\frac{E_i}{R_i}$$

Thus, the ratio of the output voltage E_0 to the input voltage E_i is given by

$$\frac{E_0}{E_i} = -\frac{R_f}{R_i}\left[\frac{1}{1 + \frac{1}{K}\left(1 + \frac{R_f}{R_i}\right)}\right] \tag{5-4}$$

Since the amplifier gain K is extremely large, we may use the approximation

$$\frac{E_0}{E_i} = -\frac{R_f}{R_i} \tag{5-5}$$

so that this operational amplifier circuit just changes the sign and magnitude of the input voltage. If we modified the operational amplifier circuit so that there are two input resistors R_1 and R_2, as shown in Fig. 5-8, it can be shown in an analogous manner that

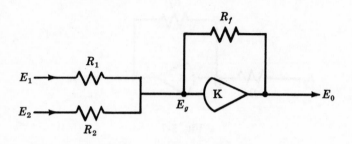

Fig. 5-8

$$E_0 = -\frac{R_f}{R_1} E_1 - \frac{R_f}{R_2} E_2$$

Thus, if we have n input resistances and a feedback resistance of value R_f, then

$$E_0 = -\sum_{k=1}^{n} \frac{R_f}{R_k} E_k \qquad (5\text{-}6)$$

Such an amplifier circuit is called a *summer*. For many analog computers, the resistance ratios are controlled to be either 1, 4, or 10. Schematically the summer can be represented by the diagram shown in Fig. 5-9. By paralleling the input resistors, values other than 1, 4, or 10 can be obtained.

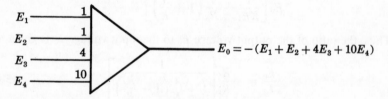

Fig. 5-9

If in Fig. 5-7, we replaced the feedback resistor R_f by a capacitor of capacitance C, then because of the high amplifier input impedance, the feedback capacitor current almost equals the input current, as before. Since the feedback loop has a capacitor, this gives

$$\frac{E_i - E_g}{R_i} = C \frac{d(E_g - E_0)}{dt}$$

Substitution of $E_g = -E_0/K$ and rearranging gives

$$R_iC \frac{dE_0}{dt} = -E_i - \frac{1}{K}\left(E_0 + R_iC \frac{dE_0}{dt}\right)$$

Since the amplifier gain K is very large, we may use the approximation

$$\frac{dE_0}{dt} = -\frac{1}{R_iC} E_i$$

Thus, we have

$$E_0 = -\frac{1}{R_iC} \int_0^t E_i \, dt + E_0(0) \qquad (5\text{-}7)$$

where $E_0(0)$ is the initial voltage on the capacitor. This is how operational amplifier circuits are used to perform integrations in a D.C. differential analyzer. Initial values for a problem are set in a D.C. differential analyzer by charging the feedback capacitor in each *integrator* (which has just been described) to the required voltage value, before the switch to start computer computation is thrown. By using an input capacitance of value C and a feedback resistance of value R, an operational amplifier can be made to perform differentiations. The resulting equation is $E_0 = -RC(dE_i/dt)$. Because differentiation amplifies the unavoidable input noise signals, which might cause amplifier saturation, the problem equations should be rearranged so that differentiation is avoided.

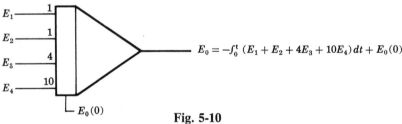

$$E_0 = -\int_0^t (E_1 + E_2 + 4E_3 + 10E_4)\, dt + E_0(0)$$

Fig. 5-10

An *integrator* is an amplifier circuit that contains one feedback capacitor and one or more input resistors. For many large analog computer installations, the input resistors and the feedback capacitor are internally connected and fixed in value. The schematic in Fig. 5-10 can be used to represent such an integrator, where multiplication of an input voltage by 1 or 4 or 10 can be obtained by connecting a patchboard cord to the proper input jack. This fixed-value type of analog computer uses standard resistors of 10.0×10^5, 2.5×10^5, and 1.0×10^5 ohms and a standard capacitor of 1.0×10^{-6} farad to achieve these $1/RC$ gains of 1, 4, and 10. These values can be changed by putting two resistors in parallel or series by jack connections, if desired. Other types of analog computers, however, have plug-in resistors and capacitors. Thus, for this type of analog computer, which is not uncommon at colleges, the schematics in Figs. 5-9 and 5-10 for a summer and an integrator should be modified to contain input resistors and a feedback resistor or capacitor of specified magnitudes. This should be done because these resistors and capacitors must be physically inserted before the computer is run to solve a specific problem. We shall use the fixed-value type of summer and integrator in this text; the reader should be able to convert to the plug-in type if needed, since the gains for a summer or an integrator are specified by its R_f/R_i or $1/R_iC$ values.

Multiplication of voltages by constants less than unity are generally done by using *potentiometers*. That is, if the total resistance of the potentiometer is R_p and if the total resistance from the point of contact by the potentiometer arm to the ground is R_a, then the output voltage E_0 equals $(R_a/R_p)E_i$, where E_i is the input voltage. Since the divided resistance R_a is less than the total resistance R_p, then we can use simple potentiometers to multiply voltage quantities by constants, whose values are positive and less than one. The coefficient setting P (i.e., R_a/R_p) is usually read on a potentiometer dial whose scale is often linear. Thus, multiplication by a constant may be represented schematically as shown in Fig. 5-11, where the constant P, which equals R_a/R_p, must be less than one. The schematic in Fig. 5-12 illustrates the use of a summer and a potentiometer to multiply voltages by constants whose values are greater than unity.

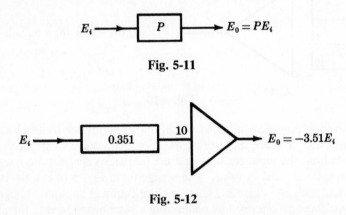

$$E_i \longrightarrow \boxed{P} \longrightarrow E_0 = PE_i$$

Fig. 5-11

$$E_i \longrightarrow \boxed{0.351} \xrightarrow{10} \longrightarrow E_0 = -3.51E_i$$

Fig. 5-12

Since we have mentioned output recorders, summers, integrators, and potentiometers in this section, we have covered the components that are necessary to solve homogeneous, linear differential equations with constant coefficients, using a D.C. differential analyzer. It might be mentioned that these components can be used to solve some nonhomogeneous differential equations because they can be used to generate certain time-varying functions, in a manner somewhat similar to that shown in Sec. 5.10 for a mechanical differential analyzer. To furnish some examples, the generation of the functions e^{-at}, sin at, and cos at is shown in Ill. Ex. 5.10. The *first step* in solving an engineering problem on a differential analyzer type of analog computer is, of course, to determine the mathematical equations that describe this physical problem and to write them in a proper form. Assuming that these equations contain one or more differential equations, each differential equation should be written in a form that solves for its highest derivative. That is, we want a set of equations that solve for the highest derivative for each variable. The equations for the lower-order derivatives and the algebraic equations should be written after the particular differential equation that they affect. This step of the setup procedure is exemplified in Ill. Exs. 5.10 and 5.11. The *second step* is to scale the problem, and this is described in the next paragraph. The *third step* is to draw a diagram which shows the component magnitudes and settings, where each component is represented by a simple schematic, and which shows how these components are connected. This block diagram represents the problem equations in scaled form. The *fourth step* is to connect these components in proper fashion and to run the problem. The potentiometers, initial values, and function generators must be set before the problem is run. At some computer installations, the setting of these devices is done automatically instead of manually. The *fifth and last step* is to interpret the results, where scale factors must be taken into account.

In a D.C. electronic differential analyzer, physical quantities are represented by voltages. *Magnitude scale factors* indicate the specific relations between voltages and these physical quantities. Thus, if $\dot{x}$ is velocity and x is displacement, they are represented by $X = S_1 x$ and $\dot{X} = S_2 \dot{x}$, where X and $\dot{X}$ are voltages and constants S_1 and S_2, which linearly relate the terms, are magnitude scale factors. The allowed output voltage-range for the operational amplifiers in most electronic differential analyzers is usually ± 100 volts (which will be assumed in this text), ± 50 volts, or ± 10 volts. When outside its allowed voltage-range, the amplifier becomes nonlinear and saturation occurs. For accuracy considerations to obtain as much significance as possible in the results, the scale factors should be as large as possible. That is, if the maximum displacement for a vibration problem was 6 inches, we would not want to have one volt represent a one-inch displacement in such a problem, since the plotted results would be relatively insignificant (i.e., a six-volt maximum output is only six per cent of the allowable voltage). Also, if the voltage is low for a long interval of time, drift, noise, and other effects would decrease the per cent accuracy of the solution. Thus, since the problem variables will have many different values, the magnitude of a scale factor S is set to equal 100 volts divided by the estimated maximum value for the particular physical quantity. If we allow a margin of safety for our estimates of the maximum values by letting the maximum voltage value be 90 volts, then our scale factor S_2 for $\dot{x}$ is $90/\dot{x}_{max}$ volt/(in./sec) and scale factor S_1 for x is $90/x_{max}$ volt/in.

It may not be desirable to solve our problems on this type of computer with a one-to-one time scale. Too fast a time can cause amplifier instability and servo unreliability problems; but fast running-times are desirable in order to minimize amplifier drift, capacitor leakage, and other accumulative errors, and to obtain results more quickly. Time scale is also affected by the type and capabilities of the recording device (e.g., pen recorder or oscilloscope). For example, pen inertia and friction limit the velocity range for using a pen recorder. For the physical equation that is transformed to a voltage, computer-time equation, we let computer time T be related to physical time t by the equation $T = kt$, where k is the *time scale factor* and where the physical problem is slowed down by the computer if $k > 1$. It can be shown that the nth order derivative $d^n x/dt^n$ can be time-scaled by the equation $d^n x/dt^n = k^n d^n x/dT^n$, where k is the time scale factor. After the magnitude and the time scaling is completed, we then draw a computer block diagram, using schematic representations, to show how the computer components must be connected in order to solve these transformed voltage equations. Time scaling should precede magnitude scaling if they are done separately, because the derivatives with respect to computer time T, instead of physical time t, are the terms that should be magnitude scaled. The scaling of a physical problem is exemplified in Ill. Ex. 5.12.

Illustrative Example 5.10. Show how we may generate the functions e^{-at}, $\sin at$, and $\cos at$ on a D.C. electronic differential analyzer, where $a < 1$.

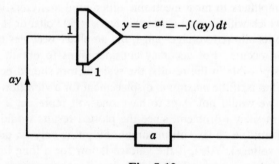

$$y = e^{-at} = -\int(ay)\,dt$$

Fig. 5-13

Solution. We know that e^{-at} is the solution of the differential equation $\dot{y} + ay = 0$ when $y(0) = 1$. Thus, the function e^{-at} can be generated by the method shown in Fig. 5-13, which simulates the equations

$$\dot{y} = -ay$$
$$y = -\int (ay)\, dt$$

We know that $\sin at$ is the solution of the differential equation $\ddot{y} + a^2 y = 0$ when $y(0) = 0$ and $\dot{y}(0) = a$, and that $\cos at$ is the solution of the same differential equation when $y(0) = 1$ and $\dot{y}(0) = 0$. Thus, we can generate either function using the same circuit but different initial values. The function $\sin at$ can be generated by the method shown in Fig. 5-14, which simulates the following equations.

$$\ddot{y} = -a^2 y$$
$$\dot{y} = -\int (a^2 y)\, dt$$
$$y = \int \dot{y}\, dt$$

It may be noted that this method also generates $-a \cos at$, since $\dot{y} = a \cos at$. The generation of functions of the dependent variable (e.g., $\sin x$ and $\cos x$) are somewhat more involved, as shown in Sec. 5.12, because this type of computer integrates with respect to time.

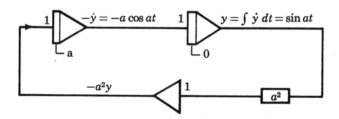

Fig. 5-14

Illustrative Example 5.11. Consider a one-degree-of-freedom, spring-mass-damper system consisting of a mass that weighs 77.2 lb, a linear spring whose spring constant k equals 1.60 lb/in., and a linear damper whose damping coefficient c equals 0.140 lb-sec/in. That is, this spring-mass system looks like the one illustrated in Fig. 2-6, except that this system has no applied force. Draw the block diagram that will show how to solve on a D.C. electronic differential analyzer for the timewise displacement and velocity variations for this linear spring-mass system. Use unit scale factors throughout.

Solution. As stated previously, the first step is to obtain the system equation. The equation of motion for this spring-mass-damper system is the following linear, homogeneous differential equation with constant coefficients

$$\frac{W}{g}\ddot{x} + c\dot{x} + kx = 0$$

Substitution of the given numerical values for W, c, and k, along with $g = 386$ in./sec^2, gives

$$0.200\ddot{x} + 0.140\dot{x} + 1.60x = 0$$

Solving this equation for its highest derivative $\ddot{x}$ gives

$$\ddot{x} = -0.700\dot{x} - 8.00x$$

Since $\dot{x} = \int \ddot{x}\, dt$, we want the computer to simulate the following equations

$$\dot{x} = \int (-0.700\dot{x} - 8.00x)\, dt$$

$$x = \int \dot{x}\, dt$$

as is done by the block diagram in Fig. 5-15. The first step in drawing this block diagram is to draw the integrator that integrates the highest derivative $\ddot{x}$, where the input $-(0.700\dot{x} + 8.00x)$ and the output $-\dot{x}$ are both shown. This represents our first equation. Then we draw our second integrator which integrates $-\dot{x}$ to give us x. Now we can draw the summer and the two recorders that measure $\dot{x}$ and x. The last step is to draw the connections and the potentiometers that will furnish the inputs for the first integrator (i.e., the one that integrates $\ddot{x}$ to obtain $-\dot{x}$).

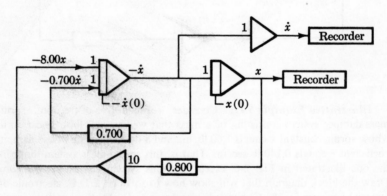

Fig. 5-15

Illustrative Example 5.12.   Scale the problem in Ill. Ex. 5.11 if the estimates for maximum displacement, velocity, and acceleration are 9 inches, 45 in./sec, and 90 in./sec^2, respectively. We also want the computer to run at the same speed as the physical or real time.

Solution. To allow a tolerance or safety margin in case we miscalculated the maximum values, we shall let the maximum voltages that represent the velocity, displacement, and acceleration all equal 90 volts. Thus, the scale factor for displacement x is (90 volts)/(9 in.) or 10 volts/in., and $X = 10x$, where X is the measured voltage that represents displacement x. The scale factor for velocity $\dot{x}$ is 90 volts/(45 in./sec) or 2 volt-sec/in., and $\dot{X} = 2\dot{x}$, where $\dot{X}$ is the measured voltage that represents velocity $\dot{x}$. Since the scale factor for acceleration $\ddot{x}$ is 90/90 or 1.00 volt-sec²/in., $\ddot{X} = \ddot{x}$. The problem equation that was to be solved in Ill. Ex. 5.11 was

$$\ddot{x} = -0.700\dot{x} - 8.00x$$

Since that example had unit scale factors, it had the relationships $\ddot{X} = \ddot{x}$, $\dot{X} = \dot{x}$, and $X = x$, so that the previous equation could be used to represent a voltage-time equation for that problem. Substitution of $\ddot{x} = \ddot{X}$, $\dot{x} = 0.500\dot{X}$, and $x = 0.100X$ in the previous equation gives

$$\ddot{X} = -0.350\dot{X} - 0.800X$$

Since $\dot{X} = \int \ddot{X}\,dt$, we want the computer to simulate the following voltage-time equations:

$$\dot{X} = \int (-0.350\dot{X} - 0.800X)\,dt$$

$$X = \int \dot{X}\,dt$$

Thus, we now draw a block diagram for a D.C. electronic differential analyzer solution of the variation of voltages $\dot{X}$ and X with time t. The procedure for doing this is given in Ill. Ex. 5.11, and the diagram will be similar to that in Fig. 5-15, except for the potentiometer settings. That is, we want the input for the first integrator to be $-(0.350\dot{X} + 0.800X)$ and the input for the second integrator to be $-\dot{X}$. The initial values for the two integrators would equal $2\dot{x}(0)$ and $10x(0)$ volts. The scale factors must be used to convert the measured voltages $\dot{X}$ and X to the physical quantities $\dot{x}$ and x, when the output data is interpreted. That is, 1.00 volt for X equals 0.100 inch for displacement x, and 1.00 volt for $\dot{X}$ equals 0.500 in./sec for velocity $\dot{x}$.

To show how magnitude and time scaling might be done together in a more general fashion, let us scale a second-order linear, homogeneous differential equation, with constant coefficients, that is written in general form as follows

$$\ddot{x} + a\dot{x} + bx = 0$$

Substitution of $\ddot{x} = k^2 d^2x/dT^2$ and $\dot{x} = k\,dx/dT$, where k is the time scale factor, in the previous equation gives

$$k^2 \frac{d^2x}{dT^2} + ak\frac{dx}{dT} + bx = 0$$

The next step is to calculate the three magnitude scale factors S_1, S_2, and S_3 from x_{max}, dx_{max}/dT, and d^2x_{max}/dT^2, so that X_{max}, dX_{max}/dT, and d^2X_{max}/dT^2 all equal about 90 volts. Substitution of $x = X/S_1$, $dx/dT = (dX/dT)/S_2$, and $d^2x/dT^2 = (d^2X/dT^2)/S_3$ in the previous equation gives

$$\frac{k^2}{S_3}\frac{d^2X}{dT^2} + \frac{ka}{S_2}\frac{dX}{dT} + \frac{b}{S_1}X = 0$$

Solving the previous equation for its highest derivative gives

$$\frac{d^2X}{dT^2} = -\frac{aS_3}{kS_2}\frac{dX}{dT} - \frac{bS_3}{k^2S_1}X$$

For this problem, $k = 1$, $S_1 = 10$, $S_2 = 2$, $S_3 = 1$, $a = 0.700$, and $b = 8.00$. Substitution of these values in the previous equation gives

$$\frac{d^2X}{dT^2} = -0.350\frac{dX}{dT} - 0.800X$$

which agrees with our previous result, since computer time T equals physical time t. It should be noted that there are many scaling shortcuts, whose details may be found in textbooks on analog computers.

5.12   Other Components for the D.C. Electronic Differential Analyzer

In order to solve nonlinear differential equations, linear differential equations with variable coefficients, and nonhomogeneous differential equations, other components than those mentioned in the previous section are necessary. The discussion on the components in this section will be very brief and sketchy because complete descriptions in an understandable form would take up much space. The reader is referred to analog computer texts which give much more detail on these components. These components are specialized, and if one expects to use the D.C. electronic differential analyzer frequently, then he should also gain a thorough understanding of the equipment, including the electronic components, that are involved. Methods for multiplying two variable quantities (i.e., two voltages) are of two types. A *servo-multiplier* performs such a multiplication by electromechanical means. The *electronic multiplier* uses electronic means. A *servo-multiplier* consists of a servo system, whose output shaft drives the arms of two (or more) potentiometers. The ends of the first potentiometer are connected to $+100$ and -100 volts, while the ends of the second potentiometer are connected to $+E_2$ and $-E_2$ volts. The servo system is used to cause the output of the first potentiometer to equal the input voltage to the servo system, which we shall call E_1. Thus, the servo system moves the arm of the first (and also the second) potentiometer so that the potentiometer setting P for the first (and the second) potentiometer equals $E_1/100$. Since the input for the second potentiometer is E_2, its output equals PE_2 or $E_1E_2/100$. Thus, we have achieved a means for multiplying voltages E_1 and E_2. The division of E_1E_2 by 100 helps to keep the output of this multiplier from exceeding 100 volts in absolute value.

The servo system portion consists of an amplifier connected to a motor whose output shaft turns the potentiometer arms. The output voltage of the motor is fed back and subtracted from the input voltage. This differential voltage is fed into the amplifier, which amplifies this magnitude so that it can operate the motor. When this differential voltage is non-zero, the motor is driven, thus turning the potentiometer arms, and will stop when the system is balanced so that the output voltage of the motor equals the input voltage for the servo system. The frequency-response characteristics of a servo-multiplier are limited, so that *electronic multipliers*, which are the other type of multiplier, have a wider range of usefulness and must be used for high frequency applications. The *time-division multiplier* and the *quarter-square multiplier* are two commonly used kinds of electronic multipliers. Some electronic multipliers reverse the sign (i.e., their output is $-E_1E_2/100$). The schematic in Fig. 5-16 will be used to represent a multiplier (i.e., either a servo-multiplier or an electronic multiplier). As is shown in Ill. Ex. 5.14, either type of multiplier may be combined with an amplifier in different ways to perform a division, a square root, or a cube root operation.

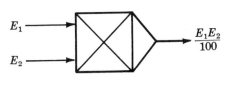

$$E_1 \qquad E_2 \qquad \frac{E_1E_2}{100}$$

Fig. 5-16

A special device or component that is devised to calculate sines and cosines is called a *resolver*, and such a device can calculate $E_1 \sin \theta$ and $E_1 \cos \theta$, when E_1 is an input voltage and θ is an input angle. A *polar resolver*, whose voltage inputs are E_1 and E_2, can be used to compute angle θ, where $\theta = \tan^{-1}(E_2/E_1)$, and magnitude R, where $R = \sqrt{E_1^2 + E_2^2}$. Vacuum tube and transistor *diodes* are convenient components for use in a D.C. differential analyzer. They basically conduct only when plate voltage E_1 exceeds cathode voltage E_2 and hence acts like a one-way check valve. That is, the output voltage E_0 equals E_1 if $E_1 > E_2$, and E_0 equals zero if $E_1 < E_2$. A *relay*, which is an electrical switch that can go to one of two positions depending upon whether a coil is energized or unenergized, can be used to simulate physical discontinuities. One example is a rectangular pulse, whose voltage equals E_g for $t < T$ and whose voltage equals zero for $t > T$, so that there is a sudden voltage discontinuity when time t equals T.

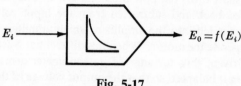

$$E_i \longrightarrow \boxed{} \longrightarrow E_0 = f(E_i)$$

Fig. 5-17

A very important class of components are *function generators*, which can be represented by the schematic diagram shown in Fig. 5-17. Two kinds of function generators are of the curve-follower type. The *x-y plotter* uses a magnetic coil which follows a curve that is drawn with an ink of high electrical conductivity. An alternating current is passed through this line to produce a magnetic field, which can be sensed by this coil so that it follows the curve in the y direction as the coil is driven in the x direction. The *photoelectric curve-follower* consists of a cathode-ray tube, upon which the curve is drawn and where the portion above this curve is transparent and the portion below is opaque. This can be done by placing an opaque mask over the lower portion of the cathode-ray tube, where the upper boundary of the mask, which can be followed by an electron beam from an electron gun, is the shape of the given function.

Other kinds of function generators approximate a curve by a series of straight-line segments, as shown in Fig. 4-1 in Sec. 4.1. This type of approximation can be done electromechanically by a *tapped potentiometer* in which a servo system moves the potentiometer arm to various positions according to the input voltage E_i. The various portions of the potentiometer have different resistances according to the slope of the given straight-line segment. Another means is to use a *group of relays*, which can be used to approximate both continuous and discontinuous functions by a series of straight-line segments, where each relay would switch on at a different end point for a straight-line segment. A rectangular wave function, which has many discontinuities, can be easily handled by such a device. The most widely used function generator is the *biased-diode function generator*, which is flexible and can be run on a rather fast time scale. It is an electronic device which consists of several diode bridge circuits, where each circuit corresponds to a straight-line segment. Each diode bridge circuit also has controls by which the length and slope of the corresponding straight-line segment can be set. As mentioned before, when the applied voltage exceeds the cathode voltage, a diode tube conducts, thus effectively closing this electronic switch. Thus, the voltage at which a specific diode tube begins to conduct is set to correspond to the x-value for which its simulated straight-line segment begins.

The generation of certain specific time-varying functions was discussed in Sec. 5.11. By use of multipliers, integrators, etc., we can also generate functions of dependent variables. For example, since $d(e^x)/dt = (e^x)(\dot{x})$, we can use the equation $e^x = \int \dot{x}e^x \, dt$ to generate the function e^x. That is, the circuit would have a multiplier, whose inputs are $\dot{x}$ and e^x and whose output is $\dot{x}e^x/100$, and an integrator, whose input is $-\dot{x}e^x$ and whose output e^x is also a multiplier input. We can also generate the functions $\cos x$ and $\sin x$ by a circuit consisting of two multipliers and two integrators. Since $d(\cos x)/dt = -\dot{x}\sin x$ and $d(\sin x)/dt = \dot{x}\cos x$, we can apply the equations $\cos x = -\int \dot{x}\sin x \, dt$ and $\sin x = \int \dot{x}\cos x \, dt$, so that the two integrators can generate $\cos x$ and $\sin x$ by these integral formulae. The integrands can be obtained from the multiplier outputs, where the inputs for each multiplier are $\dot{x}$ and an integrator output. We can also generate the function $\log_e x$ by applying the equation $\log_e x = \int \dot{x}(1/x) \, dt$ and by use of a division circuit to generate $1/x$.

Illustrative Example 5.13. Draw the block diagram that will show how to solve, on a D.C. electronic differential analyzer, for the variables x and y in the following two differential equations. Use unit scale factors throughout. Function $F(t)$ can be approximated by a series of straight-line segments.

$$\dot{x} - 0.402xy = 0$$
$$\dot{y} - 0.581x = F(t)$$

Solution. These two differential equations can be solved by a circuit consisting of two integrators, two potentiometers, two summers, a function generator, and a multiplier, as shown in Fig. 5-18. The first integrator calculates x

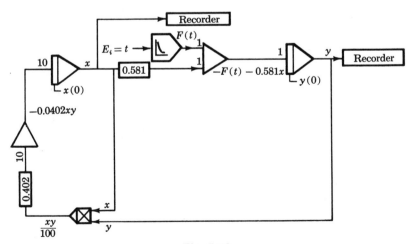

Fig. 5-18

from the equation $x = \int (0.402xy)\, dt$, while the second integrator calculates y from the equation $y = \int [F(t) + 0.581x]\, dt$.

Illustrative Example 5.14.   Show how a multiplier and an amplifier may be connected to perform a division operation and how they may be connected to perform a square root computation.

Solution.   The schematic in Fig. 5-19, which has a multiplier in the feedback loop, can be used to perform a division operation. The voltage output of the multiplier, E_f, equals $E_0E_2/100$. The feedback current, i_f, equals $(E_f - E_g)/R_f$. Because of the high impedance of the amplifier, this feedback current almost equals the negative of the input current, i_i, which is $(E_1 - E_g)/R_i$. Thus, we have

$$-i_i = \frac{E_g - E_1}{R_i} = \frac{E_f - E_g}{R_f} = \frac{E_0E_2 - 100E_g}{100R_f}$$

Solving the previous equation for output voltage E_0 for the case when voltage E_g equals zero and when resistance R_f equals resistance R_i, we obtain $E_0 = -100E_1/E_2$, so that a division operation is achieved. To obtain a square root, we use the same circuit as that shown in Fig. 5-19, except that we let both

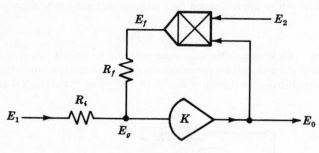

Fig. 5-19

inputs to the multiplier be E_0. Thus, the output, E_f, of the multiplier equals $E_0^2/100$. Since the feedback current equals the negative of the input current, we obtain the following equation:

$$-i_i = \frac{E_g - E_1}{R_i} = \frac{E_f - E_g}{R_f} = \frac{E_0^2 - 100E_g}{100R_f}$$

Solving the previous equation for output voltage E_0, for the case when $100R_f = R_i$ and when $E_g = 0$ (i.e., E_g equals the ground voltage), we obtain $E_0^2 = -E_1$. If we used a sign-reversing type of electronic multiplier, the multiplier output would now be $-E_0^2/100$, instead of $E_0^2/100$, so that $E_0^2 = E_1$ or $E_0 = \sqrt{E_1}$. A cube root circuit uses two feedback multipliers with an amplifier.

PROBLEMS

5.1. Reprogram the three example Fortran programs in Secs. 1.2 and 1.13 using FAC machine-language instructions.

5.2. Using FAC machine-language instructions, write programs to calculate the functions e^x, sin x, cos x, $\sqrt{x}$, and $|x|$. Use the approximation formulae given in Sec. 1.14.

5.3. Reprogram the linear electrical circuit problem in Sec. 2.2 using FAC machine-language instructions.

5.4. Reprogram the four Fortran program portions in Ill. Exs. 3.5 to 3.8 using FAC machine-language instructions.

5.5. Using FAC machine-language instructions, write a program that will read in a set of equally spaced, tabulated data; compute the derivatives of this data using Eqs. (4-19) to (4-23); and print the computed results.

5.6. Using FAC machine-language instructions, write a program that will read in a set of equally spaced, tabulated data; compute the running integrals of this data by both the trapezoidal and the Simpson one-third methods; and then print the computed results.

5.7. Using FAC machine-language instructions, write a program portion that will add two matrices and a program portion that will multiply two matrices. Assume that the two matrices and all other necessary inputs are already loaded in the computer.

5.8. Convert the following decimal numbers to binary and octal numbers.

(a) $3\frac{7}{16}$ (b) 8.071 (c) 320.75 (d) 0.1492

5.9. Write the decimal number equivalent of the following binary numbers.

(a) 11101011.0111 (b) 10001100.11101

5.10. Perform the following binary arithmetic and check the results decimally.

(a) (1111)(1101) (b) (100011000)/(1110)

5.11. Draw the two network-analyzer circuit diagrams that will solve for the timewise displacement and velocity variations for the two-degree-of-freedom, spring-mass systems that are illustrated in Figs. 2-14 and 2-16.

5.12. Draw the four schematic diagrams for generating the functions $1/x$ and $\log_e x$, tan x and $\tan^2 x$, sin ax and cos ax, and $\int u\, v\, w\, dx$ on a mechanical differential analyzer.

5.13. Draw the three schematic diagrams that will solve, on a mechanical differential analyzer, for the timewise displacement and velocity variations for the three spring-mass systems that are illustrated in Figs. 2-6, 2-14, and 2-16. Use unit scale factors throughout.

5.14. Using only integrators, summers, and potentiometers, show how we may generate the functions t^3, e^{at}, sinh at, cosh at, and $\log_e t$ on a D.C. electronic differential analyzer. To generate sinh at and cosh at, use the fact that the solution of the differential equation $\ddot{y} - a^2 y = 0$ is $A \cosh at + B \sinh at$.

5.15. Draw the schematic block diagram for Ill. Ex. 5.12. Draw another schematic block diagram for the case when we desire to slow down the computer solution of the problem by a factor of 3.20. Show your scaling details first.

5.16. Same as Prob. 5.13, except draw the three diagrams for a D.C. electronic differential analyzer solution.

5.17. Scale Ill. Ex. 5.13 and redraw the block diagram circuit for the case where the maximum values of x, $\dot{x}$, y, $\dot{y}$, and $F(t)$ are 20, 180, 12, 80, and 45, respectively, and where we want to slow down the computer solution of the problem by a factor of 2.50.

5.18. Draw the block diagrams which show how a D.C. electronic differential analyzer can generate the functions e^x, sin x, cos x, and $\log_e x$. Use the methods suggested in Sec. 5.12.

5.19. Draw the block diagram schematics that will show how to solve, on a D.C. electronic differential analyzer, the following two sets of simultaneous differential equations. Function $F(t)$ can be approximated by a series of straight-line segments. Use unit amplitude scale factors for $F(t)$, z and $\dot{z}$. The maximum values of x, $\dot{x}$, y, and $\dot{y}$ are 34, 285, 61, and 408 in both (a) and (b). The computer is to run at the same speed as physical or real time.

a) $\ddot{x} + 7\ddot{x}y - 0.4\dot{x}^2 + 3.2xy = 0$
$\ddot{y} + 0.5\dot{x}^2\dot{y} + 1.8\dot{x}y - 0.3xy^2 = F(t)$

b) $\ddot{x} + 9\dot{x}\dot{z} + 14x = F(t)$
$\ddot{y} + 6\dot{x}\dot{y} - 17y = 0$
$\ddot{z} + 4\dot{x}\dot{z} - 8yz = 0$

Bibliography

1. Digital and Analog Computers and Computer Programming

Arden, B. W., *An Introduction to Digital Computing*. Reading, Massachusetts: Addison-Wesley Publishing Co., Inc., 1963.

Bartree, T. C., *Digital Computer Fundamentals*. New York: McGraw-Hill Book Co., Inc., 1960.

Berkeley, E. C., *Giant Brains: or Machines That Think*. New York: John Wiley and Sons, Inc., 1949.

Booth, K. H. V., *Programming for an Automatic Digital Calculator*. New York: Academic Press, Inc., 1958.

Calingaert, Peter, *Principles of Computation*. Reading, Massachusetts: Addison-Wesley Publishing Co., Inc., 1965.

Flores, Ivan, *Computer Logic*. Englewood Cliffs, New Jersey: Prentice-Hall, Inc., 1960.

Gruenberger, F. J. and D. D. McCracken, *Introduction to Electronic Computers*. New York: John Wiley and Sons, Inc., 1963.

James, M. L., G. M. Smith, and J. C. Wolford, *Analog and Digital Computer Methods in Engineering Analysis*. Scranton, Pennsylvania: International Textbook Co., 1964.

Jenness, R. R., *Analog Computation and Simulation: Laboratory Approach*. Boston, Massachusetts: Allyn and Bacon, Inc., 1965.

Johnson, C. L., *Analog Computer Techniques*. New York: McGraw-Hill Book Co., Inc., 1956.

Karplus, W. J. and W. J. Soroka, *Analog Methods in Computation and Simulation.* New York: McGraw-Hill Book Co., Inc., 1959.

Korn, G. A. and T. M. Korn, *Electronic Analog Computers.* New York: McGraw-Hill Book Co., Inc., 1956.

Levine, Leon, *Methods for Solving Engineering Problems Using Analog Computers.* New York: McGraw-Hill Book Co., Inc., 1964.

McCracken, D. D., *Digital Computer Programming.* New York: John Wiley and Sons, Inc., 1957.

McCracken, D. D., *A Guide to ALGOL Programming.* New York: John Wiley and Sons, Inc., 1962.

Organick, E. I., *A Fortran Primer.* Reading, Massachusetts: Addison-Wesley Publishing Co., Inc., 1963.

Richards, R. K., *Digital Computer Components and Circuits.* Princeton, New Jersey: D. Van Nostrand Co., Inc., 1957.

Siegel, Paul, *Understanding Digital Computers.* New York: John Wiley and Sons, Inc., 1961.

Smith, R. E. and D. E. Johnson, *Fortran Autotester.* New York: John Wiley and Sons, Inc., 1962.

Ware, W. H., *Digital Computer Technology and Design,* vols. 1 and 2. New York: John Wiley and Sons, Inc., 1963.

Weiss, E. A., *Programming the IBM 1620.* New York: McGraw-Hill Book Co., Inc., 1965.

2. Numerical Analysis

Chung, An-min, *Linear Programming.* Columbus, Ohio: Charles E. Merrill Books, Inc., 1963.

Conte, S. P., *Elementary Numerical Analysis.* New York: McGraw-Hill Book Co., Inc., 1965.

Forsythe, G. E. and W. R. Wasow, *Finite-Difference Methods for Partial Differential Equations.* New York: John Wiley and Sons, Inc., 1960.

Hamming, R. W., *Numerical Methods for Scientists and Engineers.* New York: McGraw-Hill Book Co., Inc., 1962.

Hartree, D. R., *Numerical Analysis.* Oxford: The Clarendon Press, 1958.

Hastings, C., J. T. Hayward, and J. P. Wong, *Approximations for Digital Computers.* Princeton, New Jersey: Princeton University Press, 1955.

Henrici, Peter, *Elements of Numerical Analysis.* New York: John Wiley and Sons, Inc., 1964.

Herriott, J. G., *Methods of Mathematical Analysis and Computation.* New York: John Wiley and Sons, Inc., 1963.

Hildebrand, F. B., *Introduction to Numerical Analysis.* New York: McGraw-Hill Book Co., Inc., 1956.

Householder, A. S., *Principles of Numerical Analysis.* New York: McGraw-Hill Book Co., Inc., 1953.

Jennings, Walter, *First Course in Numerical Methods*. New York: The Macmillan Co., 1964.

Kunz, K. S., *Numerical Analysis*. New York: McGraw-Hill Book Co., Inc.. 1957.

Macon, Nathaniel, *Numerical Analysis*. New York: John Wiley and Sons, Inc., 1963.

Milne, W. E., *Numerical Solution of Differential Equations*. New York: John Wiley and Sons, Inc., 1953.

Nielsen, K. L., *Methods in Numerical Analysis*. New York: The Macmillan Co., 1964.

Ralston, A., *A First Course in Numerical Analysis*. New York: McGraw-Hill Book Co., Inc., 1965.

Ralston, A. and H. S. Wilf, *Mathematical Methods for Digital Computers*. New York: John Wiley and Sons, Inc., 1960.

Scarborough, J. B., *Numerical Mathematical Analysis*. Baltimore: The Johns Hopkins Press, 1962.

Stanton, R. G., *Numerical Methods for Science and Engineering*. Englewood Cliffs, New Jersey: Prentice-Hall, Inc., 1961.

Todd, J. (ed.), *Survey of Numerical Analysis*. New York: McGraw-Hill Book Co., Inc., 1962.

3. Numerical Methods with Fortran and Setup of Engineering Problems

Cheng, D. K., *Analysis of Linear Systems*. Reading, Massachusetts: Addison-Wesley Publishing Co., Inc., 1959.

Haberman, C. M., *Engineering Systems Analysis*. Columbus, Ohio: Charles E. Merrill Books, Inc., 1965.

Haberman, C. M., *Application of Ordinary and Partial Differential Equations to Engineering Analysis*. Alhambra, California: M. C. Webster Multicopy Service, 1962.

Harris, L. D., *Numerical Methods Using Fortran*. Columbus, Ohio: Charles E. Merrill Books, Inc., 1964.

James, M. L., G. M. Smith, and J. C. Wolford, *Analog and Digital Computer Methods in Engineering Analysis*. Scranton, Pennsylvania: International Textbook Co., 1964.

Johnson, W. C., *Mathematical and Physical Principles of Engineering Analysis*. New York: McGraw-Hill Book Co., Inc., 1944.

Kuo, S. S., *Numerical Methods and Computers*. Reading, Massachusetts: Addison-Wesley Publishing Co., Inc., 1965.

McCormick, J. M. and M. G. Salvadori, *Numerical Methods in Fortran*. Englewood Cliffs, New Jersey: Prentice-Hall, Inc., 1964.

McCracken, D. D. and W. S. Dorn, *Numerical Methods and Fortran Programming*. New York: John Wiley and Sons, Inc., 1964.

Pennington, R. H., *Introductory Computer Methods and Numerical Analysis.* New York: The Macmillan Co., 1965.

Pipes, L. A., *Matrix Methods for Engineering.* Englewood Cliffs, New Jersey: Prentice-Hall, Inc., 1963.

Southworth, R. W. and S. L. Deleeuw, *Digital and Numerical Methods.* New York: McGraw-Hill Book Co., Inc., 1965.

Ver Planck, D. W. and B. R. Teare, *Engineering Analysis.* New York: John Wiley and Sons, Inc., 1954.

Answers for
Specific Problems

1.2 The first, third, and fifth quantities need a decimal point; the second should not have a comma; and the fourth quantity is too large.

1.4 The symbols IB, KN2, N, and K4A6 can represent fixed-point variables; the symbols A4 and D can represent floating-point variables; and the other symbols cannot represent either type of variable.

1.5 (a) $C/D - 4.0 * A/R$

    (b) $7.8 * (X + Y ** 3) ** 1.81$

    (d) $7.0 * X + (13.0 * Y/(Z - 9.81))$

1.6 (d) $X - 8.71R^{I+7}$

    The sequence is: $I + 7$, R^{I+7}, $8.71R^{I+7}$, and $X - 8.71R^{I+7}$.

    (e) Improper, since the expression contains fixed- and floating-point variables.

    (g) Improper, since a fixed-point quantity cannot have a floating-point exponent.

    (h) $S(P - T + R)$

    The sequence is: $T - R$, $P - (T - R)$, and $S(P - T + R)$.

1.8 (a) Fixed-point quantity with a floating-point exponent.

    (c) The left-hand side should be a Fortran variable, instead of 7.

    (d) The right-hand side contains fixed- and floating-point quantities.

1.9 (a) $Y = 2 - 5 = 3.0$

    (c) $Y = (8 + 5)/3 = 4.0$

    (f) $M = 8 + 5(1) = 13$

1.10   READ 12, A, B, C, D
        12 FORMAT (4F8.3)
            PUNCH 13, A, B, C, D
        13 FORMAT (4F12.3)
1.11   READ 87, A, B, C, X, Y, Z
        87 FORMAT (3F7.2)
1.13 -814.7183; -814.718300; -814.718; -814.71; 814.7183; 14.7183; 4.718; and -814
1.14 Only $3.458 + 01$ does not represent 348.5
1.15   PRINT 17, K, L, X, Y, Z
        17 FORMAT (2I6///2F9.2,E14.3)
1.16   PRINT 31, MA, MB, IA, IB, A, B, C, D, E, F, G, H
        31 FORMAT (2I6/2I6/(2F11.3))
1.20   PRINT 32
        32 FORMAT (24H1QUANTITY A IS TOO LARGE)
1.22 IF $(A**2-D-R**1.8)47, 51, 54$

2.4 (a) For $\Delta t = 0.050$ sec and $(\Delta t)_p = 0.100$ sec, the output is

TIME	CURRENT
.00000	6.00000
.10000	5.10628
.20000	5.03723
.30000	5.32815
.	.
.	.
.	.
1.00000	.95294
1.10000	$-.14424$
1.20000	$-.87086$
1.30000	-1.04645
1.40000	$-.63462$
1.50000	.25573

(b) For $\Delta t = 0.025$ sec and $(\Delta t)_p = 0.100$ sec, the output is

TIME	CURRENT
.00000	6.00000
.10000	5.21556
.20000	5.16435
.30000	5.42338
.	.
.	.
.	.
1.00000	.89198
1.10000	$-.16835$
1.20000	$-.83252$

TIME	CURRENT
1.30000	−.93522
1.40000	−.45984
1.50000	.47469

2.16 For $\Delta t = 0.00100$ hr, the output is

TIME	TA	TB
.00000	640.00000	580.00000
.00100	630.81674	576.27843
.00200	622.30444	572.76560
.00300	614.41245	569.45288
.00400	607.09422	566.32930
.	.	.
.	.	.
.	.	.
.02800	528.41109	528.19828
.02900	527.26763	527.53577
.03000	526.20531	526.91405

3.3
```
      SUM = 0.0
      DO 5 I = 1, N
   5  SUM = SUM+A(I)−B(I)**2
      R = SUM ** 0.282
```
3.6
```
      SUM = 0.0
      DO 5 J = 1, 30
      DO 5 I = 1, 40
   5  SUM = SUM+Y(I,J)*SINF(X(I))+R(I,J)
```
3.8 The following program first assumes that A(1) is both the largest and smallest element in array A. The DO loop picks out the largest element BIGA and the smallest element SMALLA.

```
      DIMENSION A(200)
   1  READ 10, (A(I), I = 1, 200)
  10  FORMAT (5F8.2)
      BIGA = A(1)
      SMALLA = A(1)
      DO 5 I = 2,200
      IF (A(I)−BIGA)4, 5, 6
   6  BIGA = A(I)
      GO TO 5
   4  IF (A(I)−SMALLA)7, 5, 5
   7  SMALLA = A(I)
   5  CONTINUE
      PRINT 10, BIGA, SMALLA
      GO TO 1
      END
```

3.9 (a) LOGTF(X) = LOGF(X)/2.3026
     (b) SINHF(X) = 0.5*(EXPF(X)−EXPF(−X))
     (c) COSHF(X) = 0.5*(EXPF(X)+EXPF(−X))
     (d) TANHF(X) = (EXPF(X)−EXPF(−X))/(EXPF(X)+EXPF(−X))
     (e) COSF(X) = SQRTF(1.0−SINF(X)**2)
     (f) ASINF(X) = ATANF(X/SQRTF(1.0−X**2))

4.1 For $(\Delta t)_p$ = 0.1000 sec and Δt = 0.0500 sec, the output is given in the
     first two columns. The third column gives the computed current values
     for Δt = 0.0250 sec.

TIME	CURRENT	CURRENT
.0000	.0000	.0000
.1000	.0201	.0202
.2000	.0409	.0410
.3000	.0622	.0624
.4000	.0840	.0843
.	.	.
.	.	.
.	.	.
1.7000	.1755	.1746
1.8000	.1763	.1759
1.9000	.1802	.1801
2.0000	.1868	.1871

4.2 The results are the same as those for Prob. 4.1.

4.9 The following table contains the results for calculating $d(\sin x)/dx$ from 0
     to 2π for eleven equally spaced points. Column 4 contains the results
     when the more accurate formulae are applied.

X	DSINDX	ERROR	DSINDX	ERROR
.00000	.98363	.01636	1.03177	.03177
.31415	.93548	.01556	.94996	.00109
.62831	.79577	.01324	.80875	.00026
.94247	.57816	.00962	.58759	.00019
1.25663	.30396	.00505	.30891	.00010
1.57079	.00000	.00000	.00000	.00000
1.88495	−.30395	−.00505	−.30891	−.00010
2.19911	−.57816	−.00962	−.58759	−.00019
2.51327	−.79577	−.01324	−.80875	−.00026
2.82743	−.93548	−.01556	−.94996	−.00109
3.14159	−.98368	−.01636	−1.03177	.03177

4.10 The following table contains the results for calculating $\int_0^x \sin x \, dx$ from
      0 to 2π for eleven equally spaced points. Column 2 contains the results
      for the trapezoidal method; columns 3 and 4 contain the results and the
      errors for the Simpson one-third method; and column 4 contains the
      results for the Simpson three-eighths method.

X	TRAP	SIMPSON1	ERROR	SIMPSON2
.00000	.00000	.00000	.00000	.00000
.31415	.04854			
.62831	.18940	.19099	−.00001	
.94247	.40881			.41226
1.25663	.68528	.69101	−.00004	
1.57079	.99176			
1.88495	1.29823	1.30908	−.00007	1.30917
2.19911	1.57470			
2.51327	1.79411	1.80911	−.00010	
2.82743	1.93498			1.95129
3.14159	1.98352	2.00010	−.00011	

4.14   The results will vary slightly depending upon the values that were assumed initially. For the following input array, which is printed as follows,

BOUNDARY AND INITIAL VALUES

110.00	125.00	150.00	180.00	140.00	120.00
104.00	110.00	102.00	125.00	115.00	111.00
95.00	100.00	90.00	98.00	105.00	108.00
88.00	75.00	80.00	85.00	100.00	99.00
80.00	60.00	70.00	75.00	90.00	92.00

the rest of the output will be as follows, where 11 iterations were required and the largest residual is 0.95, if $R_{max} = 1.00$.

ITERATIONS

   11

RELAXED VALUES

110.00	125.00	150.00	180.00	140.00	120.00
104.00	113.45	125.85	134.93	123.86	111.00
95.00	99.32	105.70	110.57	109.94	108.00
88.00	83.70	87.85	92.66	97.79	99.00
80.00	60.00	70.00	75.00	90.00	92.00

RESIDUALS

.34	.67	.54	.41
.58	.78	.95	.47
.34	.66	.55	.41

5.8   (a) $(3 \frac{7}{16})_{10} = (11.0111)_2 = (3.34)_8$

   (c) $(320.75)_{10} = (101000000.11)_2 = (500.6)_8$

Index

Accumulator, 227
Adams method, 64, 67, 81
Address, 228
Aitken method, 157
Analog computer, 244, 245
Arithmetic statement, 11
Arithmetic statement function, 125
Arithmetic unit, 226
Array, 116, 123
Average-value iteration, 91, 94

Babbage, Charles, 225
Backward difference, 155
Backward-slope equation, 162
Bairstow method, 103, 105
Bender-Schmitt method, 182
Bernoulli equation, 86, 203
Bernoulli method, 104, 105
Bessel method, 154, 156
Biased-diode function generator, 262
Binary arithmetic, 240
Birge-Vieta method, 103, 105
Bisection method, 95
Block diagram, 32
Boole's formula, 169
Brute-force iteration, 89, 91, 93

Calculation sequence, 23, 31
CALL statement, 128

Card reader, 14
Central-difference equation, 163
Characteristic equation, 100, 135
Characteristic values, 134
Chebyshev approximation, 211
Chebyshev polynomial, 41
Choleski method, 189, 192
Column matrix, 132
Comment card, 25
COMMON statement, 129
Computed GO TO statement, 24
Conduction, 173, 181
Conjugate-gradient method, 191
CONTINUE statement, 121
Continued statement, 4
Continuity equation, 86, 204
Contraction loss coefficient, 204
Control statements, 23
Control unit, 227
Convection, 77
Convex polygon, 215
Convex polyhedron, 215
Corrector method, 81
Cramer's rule, 186
Crout method, 189, 192
Curve-fitting, 206

D.C. electronic differential analyzer, 244, 247, 250

276